AASHTO 1914–2014

A Century of Achievement for a Better Tomorrow

Author's Acknowledgements

The author acknowledges the following people who shared their transportation knowledge, experience, and wisdom to shape the book's overall direction and content: Allen Biehler, Carlos Braceras, Jennifer Brickett, Sean Connaughton, Tony Dorsey, Malcolm Dougherty, Thomas M. Downs, Shannon Eggleston, Dan Flowers, Frank Francois, King Gee, Arthur Guzzetti, Mike Hancock, Kelly Hardy, John Horsley, Michael Lewis, Grant Levi, Susan Martinovich, Alan Pisarski, Ananth Prasad, Pete Rahn, Kirk Steudle, Paul Trombino, Richard Weingroff, Leslie Wollack, and Bud Wright. Special thanks to Lloyd Brown and Bob Cullen who provided constant support, direction, input, feedback, advice, and encouragement.

Introduction

A century is a long time in the life of an association, and the American Association of State Highway and Transportation Officials is proud to share with you a glimpse of its history in this commemorative centennial book.

This is actually the fourth anniversary book produced by AASHTO. Similar books were published to commemorate its 25th, 50th, and 75th anniversaries. Each uniquely captures the highlights of that era and the main issues facing transportation.

Our goal in starting this project was to tell the overarching story of America's transportation system—how it has grown and shifted and changed throughout the last 100 years—and weave into that story the role AASHTO and its members played in that national legacy. I think we have done that, and along the way I think we also came across some of the delightful nuggets that make books like this so important.

A major theme of this 100-year story is how much AASHTO depends on the participation of its members for their knowledge and inspiration—the vision to innovate and anticipate the future. As we embark on AASHTO's next 100 years, you can be assured that the achievements ahead will be equally dependent on the collaboration and commitment of AASHTO's members and the broader transportation community.

$\sim$ Bud Wright
AASHTO Executive Director

"In large measure, America's history is a history of her transportation."
~ President Lyndon B. Johnson

Foreword by the Author

Transportation is at the core of American life.

It has influenced the geography and economy of the country. The availability of transportation from waterways to railroads to highways and airports has defined where and how population centers grew, business and industry developed, and people stayed connected with each other.

From its earliest days, America has always been a country on the go. Early settlers and immigrants explored and developed the new world using horses, Conestoga wagons, keelboats, barges, ferries, steamships, streetc ars, interurbans, railroads, bicycles, and eventually automobiles to expand their horizons. As the country grew, America's transportation system evolved to meet the expanding mobility needs of an increasingly widespread population—buses, trains, airplanes, rapid transit, highways, higher-speed railroads, and more. Slowly, roads began to catch up with the itch to keep moving.

On the occasion of the 100th anniversary of the founding of the American Association of Highway and Transportation Officials (AASHTO), this book attempts to capture the essence of America's transportation history since 1914. It provides snapshots, milestones, stories, and photographs that catalogue the events, advancements, decisions, people, and partnerships that shaped and influenced this century of transportation achievement. It is a pretty amazing story.

The biggest challenge in writing a book about 100 years of transportation history is to make choices about what to include in order to capture the breadth of achievement without overwhelming the reader. If the stories included here increase appreciation for transportation's powerful role in shaping America's past, present, and future; rekindle personal transportation memories of going on family road trips, getting a driver's license, or taking that first airplane ride; or stimulate a desire to dive deeper into our country's remarkable transportation story, then we will have succeeded in our endeavor.

America's history is indeed a history of her transportation. We hope you enjoy the journey in the pages that follow.

~ Chris Becker

"America's transportation system is the finest in the world. The web of streets, highways, bridges, and railroads that crisscross our Nation and our complex network of shipping lanes and air routes keep us connected to one another and the world. They enable us to move people and goods swiftly and efficiently across the country and around the globe and fuel the engine of our robust economy."

~ President William Jefferson Clinton

In his proclamation for National Defense Transportation Day and National Transportation Week, May 8, 1998

The Illinois Central Railroad freight yard at South Water Street in Chicago in 1943.
Courtesy of Library of Congress

Table of Contents

INTERSTATE FREEWAY

UNDER CONSTRUCTION

"Our unity as a nation is sustained by free communication of thought and by easy transportation of goods and people."

~ President Dwight D. Eisenhower

A construction sign on I-70 in Missouri sometime during the early years of building that highway network.
Courtesy of Missouri DOT

Executive Summary
A Century of Transportation Achievement: 1914–2014

It was 1914. World War I had erupted in Europe. In the United States, more than 1.7 million cars and trucks were lumbering along 71,000 miles of largely unpaved, unconnected, muddy roads. More than 4,400 people would die in accidents on those narrow, bumpy, unmarked, unregulated, and dangerous roads. And the automakers in Detroit, the nation's Motor City, were revving up their assembly lines to meet the demand for cars to fulfill the country's growing passion for driving. Railroads, freighters, ferries, trolleys, streetcars, and subways, which dominated personal and freight mobility for most of the previous century, were on the cusp of ceding dominance to automobiles and trucks.

Into that disjointed, decentralized, and inadequate transportation environment came the American Association of Highway Officials (AASHO), a newly constituted organization of state highway engineers that believed it could lead the development of a national highway system to improve mobility for both people and goods.

America's transportation system was on the verge of a transformation.

100 Years of Transportation Transformation

It is 2014. America's transportation system has evolved from a series of scattered pieces into an interconnected network of highways, railroads, airports, public transit systems, waterways, and pipelines that support personal mobility, freight movement, and economic growth. Today, America's transportation assets are valued at more than $7 trillion and include:

- 4.1 million miles of roads
- 605,000 bridges
- 3,155 transit stations
- 408,000 directional transit route-miles[1]
- 139,000 miles of railroad lines
- 25,000 navigable waterways for commercial shipping
- 5,100 public-use airports
- 8,000 commercial waterways and lock facilities
- 2.6 million miles of oil and gas pipelines
- 517 Amtrak stations and thousands of regional and local rail terminals[2]

How that system evolved from a hodgepodge of disconnected pieces to a multi-trillion dollar national asset over the past 100 years is a story as vast as the country itself, interwoven into every aspect of daily life. It is, in fact, a story about the growth of the country, the leadership of individuals who recognized the importance of transportation to the country's future, and the role the American Association of State Highway and Transportation Officials (AASHTO) played in that transportation transformation since its 1914 founding.

Here are a few highlights of the story.

Chicago's Galewood freight yard for the Chicago, Milwaukee, St. Paul & Pacific Railroad in 1943.
Courtesy of Library of Congress

Transportation is about quality of life and economic growth. It is the connection among people, ideas, goods, and services. "Our economy, our lifestyle, the design of our urban and rural areas, and indeed our survival as a modern nation are all dependent upon our having a good transportation system," wrote then-AASHTO Executive Director Frank Francois in 1998.

1914 Snapshot
By the Numbers

U.S. POPULATION **99,111,000**

FEDERAL SPENDING **$0.73 billion**

UNEMPLOYMENT RATE **7.9 percent**

AVERAGE ANNUAL INCOME **$627**

COST OF A GALLON OF MILK **32 cents**

MILES OF ROADS **71,376**

REGISTERED MOTOR VEHICLES **1.9 million**

AVERAGE COST OF A CAR **$550**

Sources:
U.S. Census Bureau—
Historical National
Population Estimates;
www.infoplease.com;
Historical Statistics
of the United States,
1789–1945; University
of Florida Agricultural
Experiment Station;
Report for the Fiscal
Year Ending June 30,
1914; Federal Highway
Administration
Highway Statistics:
Summary to 1975;
TheCostofLiving.com;
web.bryant.edu

1914 Snapshot
Events

- World War I begins.

- Congress establishes the Federal Trade Commission.

- Ford Motor Company raises daily wages from $2.40 for a nine-hour workday to $5.00 for an eight-hour workday.

- The Panama Canal opens.

- The last known passenger pigeon dies in the Cincinnati Zoo.

- The world's first commercially successful red and green traffic light is installed at Euclid and East 10th Streets in Cleveland.

- Babe Ruth makes his major league debut as a pitcher for the Boston Red Sox.

- President Wilson signs a proclamation officially establishing the second Sunday in May as Mother's Day.

Sources:
Wikipedia;
TheCostofLiving.com;
www.historyorb.com

The vision that led to the creation of AASHTO in 1914 has had a lasting impact on America's transportation system. The federal–state partnership that grew out of AASHTO's creation made the country's transportation achievement possible. Before 1914, responsibility for highways was as disjointed as the roads themselves. AASHTO's establishment brought state highway leaders together and provided a framework for a productive federal–state partnership that built a transcontinental highway system and made much of the country's transportation achievements possible.

The Interstate system profoundly changed the face of America. Construction of the 46,931-mile Dwight D. Eisenhower National System of Interstate and Defense Highways, beginning in 1956, was both an incredible infrastructure achievement and a turning point in America's economic and social growth. It was the seminal achievement in a century of transportation milestones. The Interstate system stimulated the nation's economy by forever changing how people and freight moved, expanded the connection between home and jobs, redefined the relationship between urban and rural America, facilitated the evolution of metropolitan areas with central business districts and suburban communities, and united and connected the country.

The need to deliver mail and get farm crops to market helped build the nation's freight system. A strong, reliable, integrated transportation system is vital to ensure efficient, cost-effective freight movement to expand the nation's economy. America's freight system grew up with the country—starting on the waterways, moving to the railroads, and gradually incorporating the new Interstate system before all the pieces came together. The U.S. Post Office Department often led the way in testing new transportation systems because mail was so essential to connecting and informing the expanding country.

Railway mail being unloaded from a train in Washington, D.C., in 1938.
Courtesy of Library of Congress

A rapid and sustained rise in traffic fatalities early in the century shocked the country into focusing on highway safety. The dramatic increase of cars on poor roads in the 1920s brought with it a steep rise in traffic fatalities. It would take more than 50 years to begin to slow the annual fatality rate. A series of national highway safety conferences from 1924 through 1955 raised the spotlight on highway safety. AASHTO played a critical role in improving and standardizing signs, highway design, traffic control systems, and driver training and licensing to make America's roads safer. Every feature of the Interstate system was built with safety in mind–and those features have had a major impact on highway safety.

While highway construction dominated much of the century, America's transportation system has become increasingly multi-modal. At various points in history, different modes of transportation dominated before being replaced by an emerging mode—bicycles and public transit gave way to railroads, personal motor vehicles, and eventually jets. Choices were limited to whatever was available at the moment. Completion of the Interstate system provided a foundation for an interconnected transportation system that builds on the successes of the past and draws together diverse modes to meet changing mobility needs.

San Francisco Municipal Railway (Muni) light rail cars near the Bay Bridge.
Courtesy of Library of Congress

Collaboration is essential to transportation success. AASHTO was founded on the belief that collaboration among the states in partnership with the federal government was essential to building and sustaining a comprehensive, connected, consistent, and safe highway system. Successful construction of the Interstate highway system confirmed the validity of that belief and provided a continuing framework for a federally-assisted, state-led national transportation system that allows people and goods to flow smoothly throughout the country. That commitment to collaboration extended to a model for transportation research using pooled state and federal funds that has produced significant advancements during the past 100 years.

U.S. DOT Secretary Rodney Slater at the 2000 AASHTO Annual Meeting in Indianapolis, Indiana.

The transportation ride ahead offers both great promise and significant challenges. With America's population projected to grow to 400 million by 2040, the transportation infrastructure that exists today will be stretched to meet emerging mobility needs, continue to strengthen the economy, and support environmental goals including reducing carbon emissions. On the immediate horizon are the needs for new collaboration models, new approaches to funding the nation's transportation infrastructure, new technological approaches to ensure seamless transportation across modes, and renewed investment in the public-sector transportation workforce.

"In a nation that spans a continent, transportation is the web of Union."

~ President Lyndon B. Johnson

A Bay Area Rapid Transit (BART) station in Oakland, California.

America's transportation achievements over the past 100 years go hand-in-hand with the story of AASHTO's evolution as a leader in helping to build the country's transportation system, as a laboratory of innovation, and as the voice of transportation at the national and state levels. The following chapters tell that story.

STATE ROAD OFFICIALS FORM AN ASSOCIATION

WASHINGTON, D.C., December 12—State highway commissioners and engineers from twenty-seven states were represented here today when the organization of the American Association of State Highway Officials was perfected. All states are expected to be represented in the organization, ultimately.

These officers were elected: President, Henry G. Shirley of Maryland; vice president, Austin B. Fletcher, of California; secretary, Joseph Hyde Pratt, of North Carolina; treasurer, F.F. Rodgers, of Michigan.

At today's meeting seventeen states were represented by their highway commissioners or engineers, while ten states were represented by proxy. None but state highway commissioners or engineers will constitute the voting power of the association.

The purpose of the organization is to centralize the work of good roads organizations as far as possible and to secure the holding of one good roads convention annually. It also was decided to co-operate with federal organizations in the consideration of road problems.

During the day the delegates called on President Wilson.

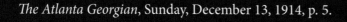

The Atlanta Georgian, Sunday, December 13, 1914, p. 5.

AASHTO's founders at the organizational meeting on December 12, 1914.

The AASHO logo, which was adopted in 1930 and remained in effect until the association changed its name in 1973.

The Founders

(Pictured above with Federal roads officials.)

S.E. Bradt, *Illinois*

John Craft, *Alabama*

Lamar Cobb, *Arizona*

George P. Coleman, *Virginia*

S. Percy Hooker, *New Hampshire*

W.S. Keller, *Alabama*

F.M. Kerr, *Louisiana*

James H. MacDonald, *Connecticut*

James R. Marker, *Ohio*

Joseph Hyde Pratt, *North Carolina*

George A. Ricker, *New York*

Paul D. Sargent, *Maine*

Henry G. Shirley, *Maryland*

W.D. Sohier, *Massachusetts*

E.A. Stevens, *New Jersey*

Sidney Suggs, *Oklahoma*

R.C. Terrell, *Kentucky*

A.D. Williams, *West Virginia*

Chapter 1
AASHO: An Institution Is Born

The idea for an organization made up of the public officials who were responsible for planning and administering state highway programs emerged from a meeting at the Georgian Terrace Hotel in Atlanta, Georgia, on November 11, 1914. While there were several highway groups at the time, most represented diverse road interests and perspectives including contractors, good-roads activists, equipment and materials producers, local elected officials, and interested individuals, in addition to state highway officials. This new organization was to be exclusive to state highway officials to leverage their engineering expertise.

Following the Atlanta meeting, 17 state highway leaders met at the Raleigh Hotel in Washington, D.C., on December 12, 1914, to establish the organization that would help bring America out of the transportation mud. Ten other states were represented by proxy. After finishing their first business meeting, the participating highway leaders walked up Pennsylvania Avenue to meet with President Woodrow Wilson to launch what they hoped would become a powerful federal–state partnership.

And the rest, as they say, is history.

One hundred years later, the organization that emerged from that meeting in the Raleigh Hotel—the American Association of State Highway Officials (AASHO) and later the American Association of State Highway and Transportation Officials (AASHTO)—has had a significant and lasting impact on America's transportation system. From AASHTO's advocacy for the 1916 Federal-Aid Road Act that became law less than two years after the association's founding, to development of engineering standards that are viewed collectively as a bible for highway and bridge construction worldwide, to pivotal support for collaborative construction of the Interstate system, to the creation of a strong and unified voice for transportation among the 52 member departments, AASHTO has helped shape the direction of America's transportation history.

Rhode Island
DOT Director
Michael P. Lewis

AASHTO's creation was driven partly by an urgent need for better roads and partly by a vision of what America's highway and transportation system could become. "The vision that those men had 100 years ago—to be so forward-thinking about the importance of collaboration among the states—is quite remarkable," said Michael P. Lewis, Director of the Rhode Island Department of Transportation and 2012–2013 AASHTO President.

Broadening the Focus: The Big T

In 1973, the American Association of Highway Officials (AASHO) became the American Association of Highway and *Transportation* Officials (AASHTO) to reflect the connection among transportation modes and embrace a broader organizational focus. It was more than a name change. AASHTO expanded its mission to include all modes of transportation including air, public transit, rail, and water, broadened its membership to encompass a wide array of state transportation officials, and deepened its ties to other transportation organizations.

Creation of a unified U.S. Department of Transportation in 1966 laid the foundation for a dramatic change in how government approached transportation. States followed suit over the next 10 years by consolidating their scattered transportation functions into single agencies. New Jersey, which in 1894 became the second state to establish a highway department after Massachusetts, was the first to create a department of transportation in 1967.

Former AASHTO Executive Director Frank Francois

Frank Francois, the first Executive Director to lead AASHTO with a "T" during his entire tenure, said the transition from a highway-centric organization to a transportation-system focus was a "long and continuing process" involving both structural changes such as new committees and new thinking about how to build a "balanced transportation system." Francois, who was the first AASHTO Executive Director who did not come from a state highway department, acknowledged in his 1980 application that he was not a highway man, a public transportation man, or an airport man despite having knowledge of all three from his many years as a county official. "I believe that all forms of transportation need our support, and that they must fit together and function in a complementary manner if we are to properly serve the American public," he wrote to the selection committee. He got the job and led AASHTO for nearly 19 years.

Transportation Turning Point
The 1914 AASHO Constitution

PURPOSE. The purpose for which the Association is organized and for which it shall be perpetuated is to study the various materials, methods of construction, maintenance, and other highway problems of the United States; to exchange ideas; to promote a closer relationship between state highway departments with a view of establishing a uniform system of administration, construction and maintenance, and legislation for the purpose of conserving the capital invested in highway construction and maintenance by producing the highest possible efficiency; and to cooperate in every way possible with the United States Office of Public Roads or similar Federal organization in the consideration of road problems.

An Institution More Than an Association

While AASHTO's foundation is the member departments that pay dues to support core operations, its work over the past 100 years and the purpose for which it was created go far beyond traditional association activities. Former Executive Director John Horsley said AASHTO's standard-setting role led to "the best highway system in the world" and sets AASHTO apart as an institution more than an association.

"AASHTO is an institution without which America's transportation system would not be as good as it is," Horsley said. "An institution has a substantive impact on society over a long period of time, and AASHTO has certainly done that."

Former AASHTO Executive Director John Horsley

AASHTO Outlasts the Raleigh Hotel

While AASHTO has thrived since December 12, 1914, the Raleigh Hotel where AASHTO was born lasted only 50 more years with many ups and downs. Dating back to 1893, the hotel flourished through the 1920s and 1930s before undergoing several renovations and ownership changes, achieving a brief renaissance in the 1940s and early 1950s. It closed permanently in 1963, and all of its furnishings, including its famous mahogany bar, were sold at a three-day auction. Once one of the largest and grandest hotels in Washington, D.C., the building at the corner of 12th Street and Pennsylvania Avenue was torn down in 1964—the same year that AASHTO celebrated its first 50 years and looked ahead to the next 50.

In contrast, the Georgian Terrace Hotel in Atlanta where the concept for the organization that would become AASHTO was developed in November 1914 has thrived over the past 100 years and still stands today in Atlanta's Fox Theater Historic District.

The one-time Raleigh Hotel in Washington, D.C., the site of AASHO's official establishment on December 12, 1914.
Photo by Herbert A. French

The current site in the nation's capital where the longtime Raleigh Hotel once stood.
Photo courtesy of Tim1965, 2010

An ad for the Georgian Terrace Hotel where plans were made for AASHO's organizational meeting in Washington, D.C.

Women in AASHTO

The role of women in AASHTO grew slowly over this century of transportation achievement. The election of Susan Martinovich, then-director of the Nevada Department of Transportation, as AASHTO president in 2012 was a significant turning point for women in AASHTO. Martinovich, who worked for the Nevada Department of Transportation for more than 28 years, recalled her first AASHTO meeting in 1997 when she was chief engineer and represented her state on the AASHTO Standing Committee on Highways. At that time, there was one other woman on the 52-member committee-Carol Murray who was chief engineer for the New Hampshire Department of Transportation. Both later became directors of their state DOTs.

Much earlier in AASHTO's history, Helen Whitaker played a pivotal leadership role in an association transition in the 1940s. Whitaker served as assistant to long-time AASHO Executive Secretary William Markham who led the association for 22 years. When Markham stepped down as AASHO leader in 1942, Whitaker took over the day-to day administrative operations serving as acting executive secretary until Hal H. Hale became the new executive secretary in January 1944. Whitaker continued to serve as assistant executive secretary through 1944.

Susan Martinovich, AASHTO President (2011) was Director of Nevada DOT and the first woman President of AASHTO.

Helen Whitaker (above) served as acting executive secretary between the administrations of William Markham and Hal H. Hale (1942–1944).

Adriana Gianturco became the first woman to lead a state department of transportation when Governor Jerry Brown appointed her Director of the California Department of Transportation in 1976. She led Caltrans until 1982. Since Gianturco's appointment, approximately 40 women have led state DOTs. In 2014, there are six women DOT directors.

Adriana Gianturco was Director of Caltrans (1976–1983) and was the first woman to hold the position.
Photo courtesy of Caltrans.

Delegates at the 1942
AASHO Annual Meeting
in St. Louis, Missouri.

Transportation Turning Point
AASHTO Committees Maximize Collaboration and Standard Setting

From its earliest days, AASHTO has relied on a committee structure to engage officials from state member departments, study emerging transportation issues, and develop technical standards that are used both nationally and worldwide because of their proven status. The work of the committees also forms the basis for the policy and standards manuals that AASHTO publishes. AASHTO's founders saw state member departments as "fifty-two experimental stations where new ideas for the improvement of highway construction and management should be encouraged and tested with the greatest possible latitude permissible within acceptable engineering standards."[4] That view has continued through AASHTO's 100 years of achievement. Early committees included those focused on administration, design, construction, maintenance, and bridge design and construction. As the work of state highway departments became more complex, AASHTO's committees expanded to cover emerging areas. In 1976, in conjunction with broadening its mission from highways only to all modes, AASHTO overhauled its committee structure by adding a series of "modal" committees—public transportation, water transportation, aviation, and railways—to reflect the breadth of modern transportation and AASHTO's role in it.

The committees are also the entry point for many state DOT employees to AASHTO's work. Serving on committees brings together expertise to develop standards and connects state transportation employees with others from throughout the country. "AASHTO is us," said Susan Martinovich, former Director of the Nevada Department of Transportation and 2011–2012 AASHTO President. "It is state people coming together to provide all these valuable documents that are used not only nationally but are also recognized internationally."

U.S. DOT Secretary
Rodney Slater at
the 2000 AASHTO
Annual Meeting in
Indianapolis, Indiana.

A meeting of the Next
Generation Corridor
Equipment Committee
(NGEC).

100 Years of Growth, Impact, and Influence

Today, AASHTO is THE voice of transportation, working to educate the public and key decision makers about the critical role transportation plays in securing a good quality of life and a sound national economy. It has grown from a small organization with a big vision to a large, influential, and financially strong institution.

For many member directors, AASHTO's greatest impact has been its ability to foster collaborative thinking, information sharing, and mutual support among states with diverse needs, interests, challenges, and resources.

"In large part, AASHTO's 100-year legacy is the development of technical standards that are used worldwide and the ability to shape critical federal legislation that has helped develop our national transportation system," said Utah Transportation Director Carlos Braceras. "But for me, it is the people. The time we spend together is where I gain the most value by finding out things that are happening in one state that I can use in Utah or the people I call on a moment's notice for advice. 'We the people' is AASHTO's biggest legacy."

Wyoming DOT Director and AASHTO Vice President John Cox (left), former Washington State DOT Secretary Paula Hammond (center), and Kentucky Transportation Cabinet and AASHTO President Mike Hancock (right) at the AASHTO Centennial shadowbox display unveiling, Washington Briefing 2014.

John Cox, Bud Wright, and Mike Hancock during a panel discussion on the AASHTO Centennial; 2014 Washington Briefing.

AASHTO's Centennial Legacy

Today's state transportation leaders say the vision of the highway commissioners and engineers who met at the Raleigh hotel 100 years ago has had a major impact on America's transportation system and still resonates today. They point to five key achievements—AASHTO's centennial legacy—that have made America's and state transportation systems better.

1. **VOICE FOR THE STATES.** The 50 states, the District of Columbia, and Puerto Rico have a strong and clear voice in public policy, advocacy, standard setting, and research through AASHTO. Working together, they are better able to shape and define transportation policy that works for all states, advocate for continued investment in infrastructure, and propel transportation and the state's role in it to the forefront of national discourse.

2. **FEDERAL–STATE PARTNERSHIP.** The partnership began when AASHTO shepherded the first federal-aid bill through Congress less than two years after its founding. That bill and AASHTO's role in it has shaped and sustained a federal–state partnership for America's surface transportation system over the past 100 years and offers promise for the future. The partnership goes far beyond national legislation to include research on every dimension of transportation and its impact on American life and continued economic growth.

3. **RESEARCH, INNOVATION, AND BEST PRACTICES.** Since its founding AASHTO has promoted, supported, and coordinated key research initiatives and technical services—often in partnership with the federal government and private sector as well as the states—to develop and share innovations on a scale that no single state could create and sustain on its own.

4. **STANDARDS AND TECHNICAL PUBLICATIONS.** AASHTO is the leader in developing design and engineering standards for transportation infrastructure that provide consistency, uniformity, and reliability. AASHTO's standards support creation of a world-class transportation system.

5. **STATE COLLABORATION.** AASHTO brings the states together to develop standards, share ideas, identify best practices, develop well-informed policies, and work together for the greater good. The power of states working together within AASHTO was a hallmark of the Interstate era. It remains the cornerstone of AASHTO's centennial legacy.[3]

TransportationTV logo.

President George H.W. Bush signs ISTEA.
Courtesy of FHWA

A materials laboratory technician in Missouri.

Cover for AASHTO's "Green Book."

Connecticut DOT Commissioner James P. Redeker.

Transportation is cars, trucks, bicycles, buses, trains, ships, and airplanes. It's people. It's goods and services. Transportation is the movement, the infrastructure, and the people and technology who build it and keep it working.

～ Bud Wright, AASHTO Executive Director

The Charlotte Area Transit System's Linx light rail service in North Carolina.

Photo by Katy Warner, North Carolina DOT, 2013

Chapter 2
A Ride Through Time

This century of transportation achievement is marked by innovation, progress, and major turning points that shaped the country's growth and development. AASHTO's history is interwoven with many of those transportation turning points. The following sections provide a rapid ride through some of the key events that shaped the country's transportation history.

1880–1913: Public Transportation, Bicycles, and the Model T

Throughout the 19th century, public transportation, from ferryboats to horse-drawn street railway lines, to railroads, buses, and subways, met most mobility needs. The popularity of bicycles at the turn of the century and introduction of affordable cars gave a hint of the dramatic change in personal mobility that was just around the corner. At the same time, establishment of highway departments in 30 states, the District of Columbia, and Puerto Rico began to provide a framework for an increasingly influential state role in road building.

Key turning points during these early transportation years include:

1880 ◎ The League of American Wheelmen is founded representing 100,000 bicyclists in the country and becoming a strong voice for good roads through publications such as *The Gospel of Good Roads: A Letter to the American Farmer*.[5]

1882 ◎ The American Street Railway Association, predecessor to the American Public Transportation Association, is established.

1888 ◎ The world's first successful electric street railway system, which was developed by Frank J. Sprague, begins operating in Richmond, Virginia.

1893 ◎ The Office of Road Inquiry is created in the U.S. Department of Agriculture to support government action on improving America's roads; in present-day Chicopee, Massachusetts, Charles and Frank Duryea road-test what is widely regarded as the first functioning gasoline-powered automobile in the United States.

1895 ◎ The first electric elevated rail line opens in Chicago.

Logo for the American Street Railway Association (now the American Public Transportation Association [APTA]).

Wabash Avenue, Chicago, Illinois, 1907.
Copyright by Detroit Publishing Co.; Library of Congress, Prints & Photographs Division, Detroit Publishing Company Collection

1896 The U.S. Post Office Department initiates Rural Free Delivery on experimental basis, promising home-mail service in rural areas wherever sufficiently passable roads are available. (The service becomes permanent in 1902.)

1897 The first subway in the United States opens in Boston.

1903 The Wright brothers make the first powered, heavier-than-air flight at Kitty Hawk, North Carolina.

1904 The first state-operated street railway opens in Bismarck, North Dakota; the New York City Subway, which was to grow into the most extensive public transportation system in the world, opens its first underground line.

1905 The Office of Public Roads is established, replacing the Office of Road Inquiry, with Logan Waller Page as the first director. Page was a partner in the establishment of AASHTO.

1907 The Supreme Court rules in *Wilson v. Shaw* that Congress has the power to construct interstate highways under its interstate commerce authority, establishing a legal foundation for a federal role in supporting construction of good roads.

1908 Henry Ford introduces the Model T; one tube of the McAdoo rapid transit tunnel system under the Hudson River between New York City and New Jersey—the first transportation tunnel beneath a major river—opens.

1912 The San Francisco Municipal Railway, the first publicly operated street railway in a large city, opens, and the Cleveland Railway becomes the first street-railway system to operate buses; the Post Office Appropriations Act of 1913, in authorizing an experimental post-road program, helps spur renewed national interest in federal funding to build and improve roads; and Salt Lake City Utah Policeman Lester F. Wire invents the first interconnected, manually operated traffic signal in the United States.

1913 The Lincoln Highway, the first cross-county road for motorized vehicles, is dedicated; Grand Central Terminal opens in New York City connecting three commuter railroads and spurring significant economic development in the surrounding area; and the U.S. Post Office launches parcel post for delivery of small packages.

1914–1955: The Good Roads Era

While public transportation continued to meet mobility needs during this period, the focus on improving the nation's roads took off beginning with AASHTO's establishment and creation of a new federal–state partnership. Combined, those actions changed the face of American transportation.

Key turning points during the good roads era include:

1914 ◎ **The American Association of State Highway Officials is created in Washington, D.C.**

◎ The Panama Canal opens, connecting the Atlantic and Pacific Oceans through Central America.

1916 ◎ President Woodrow Wilson signs into law the Federal-Aid Road Act of 1916, which was largely crafted by AASHTO leaders, launching the federal-aid highway program.

◎ William Boeing tests his first airplane in Seattle.

U.S.S. Arizona in lock, Panama Canal, 1921.
Courtesy of Library of Congress; Photo by C.F. Rottmann

1918 ◎ The Post Office begins scheduled airmail service between New York and Washington, D.C., first using Army pilots and training planes and three months later introducing newly hired civilian pilots and six specially built mail planes.

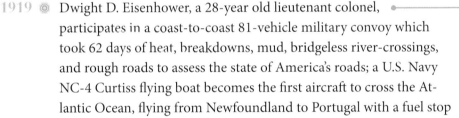

1919 ◎ Dwight D. Eisenhower, a 28-year old lieutenant colonel, participates in a coast-to-coast 81-vehicle military convoy which took 62 days of heat, breakdowns, mud, bridgeless river-crossings, and rough roads to assess the state of America's roads; a U.S. Navy NC-4 Curtiss flying boat becomes the first aircraft to cross the Atlantic Ocean, flying from Newfoundland to Portugal with a fuel stop in the Azores.

1920 ◎ **AASHTO, the state highway departments, and the U.S. Bureau of Public Roads collaborate to create the Highway Research Board of the National Research Council to provide a clearing house and a forum for improving highway engineering.**

◎ Detroit police officer Williams Potts invents the electric, three-color traffic signal; Chicago's Michigan Avenue Bridge across the Chicago River, the first double-deck bridge built with roadway on both levels, opens.

1921 ◎ Mail is flown both day and night for the first time from San Francisco to New York.

1922 ◎ More than 10,000 miles of paved roads—three times the work of the previous five years— are completed with a combination of state funds and federal aid.

1923 ◎ **AASHTO leads development of a uniform system of highway signs to improve highway safety.**

1924 ◎ Secretary of Commerce Herbert Hoover convenes the First National Conference on Street and Highway Safety bringing together a wide range of public, civic, and private organizations to deal with the sharp increase in highway fatalities.

1925 ◎ The Central Railroad of New Jersey operates the first commercially successful diesel-electric locomotive in the United States.

◎ **AASHTO leads the development of a numbering system for U.S. highways to replace named highways.**

1926 ◎ The first commercial airmail flight occurs, and the Post Office begins transferring its lights, airways, and radio service to the Department of Commerce and its airport terminals to the municipalities in which they are located.

1927 ◎ Charles Lindbergh completes the first solo, non-stop trans-Atlantic flight; the Model T ceases production after total sales of 15 million at a final cost of $290 per car.

◎ **AASHTO releases the first national guidebook on the manufacture, display, and erection of standard road markers.**

1928 ◎ The first U.S.-based commercial use of a rail detector car, which proves to be a major breakthrough in railroad maintenance and safety, is introduced along the Wabash Railway to help prevent derailments and service failures.

1930 ◎ The first air-traffic control tower is built in Cleveland.

1931 ◎ **AASHTO publishes first editions of key engineering guidebooks, establishing its role as the source of specifications and standards for highways, bridges, and road materials.**

1932 ◎ A 20-mile segment of Germany's autobahn, regarded as the world's first superhighway and an influence on General Eisenhower's vision of the Interstate system, opens between Cologne and Bonn.

1933 ◎ The Boeing 247, considered the first modern airplane with a capacity of 10 passengers and a cruising speed of 150 miles per hour, makes its maiden voyage.

1935 ◎ **The Joint Committee on Uniform Traffic Control Devices, formed in 1932 by AASHTO and the National Conference on Street and Highway Safety, publishes the first edition of the *Manual on Uniform Traffic Control Devices for Streets and Highways* to support improved highway safety.**

1936 ◎ The Douglas Aircraft DC-3, called the plane that changed the world, makes its debut with more powerful engines and room for 20 passengers.

1937 ◎ Route 66, sometimes called "the Mother Road" is completed linking Chicago and Santa Monica, California, running 2,448 miles through eight states and three time zones; the Golden Gate Bridge opens connecting San Francisco and Marin County with two towers rising 746 feet above the water and strung with 80,000 miles of cable.

1938 ◎ The Civil Aeronautics Act establishes the Civil Aeronautics Board to determine airline routes of travel and prices for passenger fares.

1939 ◎ The U.S. Bureau of Public Roads becomes the Public Roads Administration and is moved from the Department of Agriculture to the Federal Works Agency, reflecting a shift in the focus of and approach to highway construction.

1940 ◎ The Pennsylvania Turnpike, the "granddaddy of the pikes" and the first limited-access highway in the United States, opens; in California, the Arroyo Seco Parkway between Los Angeles and Pasadena, the first freeway in the western United States, opens.

Pennsylvania Turnpike, Paying Toll, 1942.

Courtesy of Library of Congress, Prints & Photographs Division, FSA/OWI Collection

1941 ◎ The Highway Post Office, consisting of buses equipped for mail sorting and town-to-town delivery, begins service with three routes that eventually grow to 200 routes in the 1950s.

Bell 9-59B Airacomet at the National Museum of the United States Air Force.

Courtesy of U.S. Air Force. Location: National Museum of the U.S. Air Force, 2007

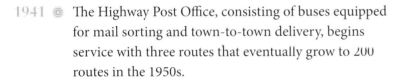

1942 ◎ The Bell P-59, America's first jet plane, is built based on a prototype designed by British pilot Frank Whittle.

1944 ◎ President Franklin D. Roosevelt signs the bill designating a future Interstate system.

1946 ◎ Public transportation ridership reaches its highest level ever at 23.4 billion; the Bell 47 becomes the first helicopter certified for commercial use.

1951 ◎ The SS United States, the largest ocean liner constructed entirely in the United States and the fastest vessel of its kind to cross the Atlantic Ocean in either direction, is launched.

1952 ◎ The 4.35-mile Chesapeake Bay Bridge linking Maryland's eastern and western shores, then-the world's largest continuous over-water steel structure, opens.

The S.S. United States.
Courtesy of John Oxley Library, State Library of Queensland

1955 ◎ The big three automakers in Detroit—General Motors, Ford, and Chrysler—claim 94 percent of all auto sales in the United States and 48 percent of world sales.

1956–1970: The Interstate Years

The idea of a comprehensive system of highways to connect America had been on the minds of American presidents from the country's earliest days. President George Washington saw the value of a national road to unite the young country and connect the population centers in the east with the wide open expanses of the west. While some progress was made over the years, the hopes and dreams about the potential power of a national highway system were realized during Dwight Eisenhower's two terms as President.

Key turning points during the Interstate years include:

1956 ◎ President Eisenhower signs the Federal-Aid Highway Act of 1956 authorizing $25 billion in federal support to build the Interstate system and establishing the Highway Trust Fund. Over the next 10 years, more than $1 billion of Interstate system funding provided 48,000 workers with a full year's pay during this peak building period.[6]

◎ Malcom McLean invents the shipping container which revolutionizes the freight industry by reducing labor and dock servicing times for moving cargo between trucks and ships.

1957 ◎ **AASHTO develops the numbering system for naming Interstate highways, building on the framework for the U.S. routes, and selects the shield that would identify all Interstate highways.**

1958 ◎ The Federal Aviation Agency is established to oversee airline safety; the Chevrolet Impala is the first automobile equipped with cruise control, known as "auto-pilot."

◎ **The AASHTO Road Test begins along a seven-mile track in Ottawa, Illinois, to study how traffic contributes to pavement deterioration on highways and bridges.**

1959 ◎ The 2,342-mile Saint Lawrence Seaway opens providing passage for ships from the Atlantic Ocean to the Great Lakes, creating a "fourth seacoast."

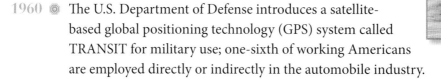

1960 ◎ The U.S. Department of Defense introduces a satellite-based global positioning technology (GPS) system called TRANSIT for military use; one-sixth of working Americans are employed directly or indirectly in the automobile industry.

1962 ◎ **The National Cooperative Highway Research Program, which conducts research on critical highway design and construction issues nationwide, is created, with sustained financing provided by pooled-state funds and federal aid.**

1964 ◎ President Lyndon B. Johnson signs the Urban Mass Transportation Act which for the first time committed federal funds to support local transit investments and led to the creation of the Federal Transit Administration.

1965 ◎ **Launch of the AASHTO Materials Reference Laboratory (AMRL)**  **provides the framework for standardizing construction materials nationwide.**

1967 ◎ The U.S. Department of Transportation begins operation, bringing together multiple federal agencies with a shared mission of shaping and administering policies and programs to protect and enhance the safety, adequacy, and efficiency of the nation's transportation system and services.

1969 ◎ Congress passes the National Environmental Policy Act (NEPA) requiring federal agencies to consider the environmental effects of proposed federal agency actions, including transportation projects.

1970–1990: The Post-Interstate Era

By 1970, more than 30,000 miles of Interstate highway were built, finally achieving the vision of a comprehensive transcontinental road system. Traffic on those superhighways, bridges and tunnels continued to grow—and so did fatalities—while public transportation ridership dropped to its lowest point. Growing concern about the impact on the environment and on health and quality of life began to influence the transition from a highway- and car-dominated culture to an era of transportation choice.

Southern California's Santa Monica Freeway (a segment of I-10) in 1964.
Courtesy of Caltrans

Amtrak Logo.
Courtesy of Amtrak

Important milestones that shaped the post-Interstate era include:

1970 ◎ President Richard Nixon signs the Clean Air Act to control air pollution on a national level and protect the public from airborne contaminants known to be hazardous to human health.

1971 ◎ Amtrak, the first federally-subsidized intercity passenger railroad, is created; the Boeing 747, a wide-body jet with a capacity of 450 passengers, makes it first commercial flight from New York to London

1972 ◎ Public transportation ridership falls to its lowest point in the 20th century at 6.6 billion while traffic fatalities reach their highest point at 54,589.

1973 ◎ **AASHO is renamed the American Association of State Highway and Transportation Officials (AASHTO) reflecting the association's shift from focus on highways only to one that embraces all modes of transportation.**

1974 ◎ The National Mass Transportation Assistance Act of 1974 not only helps cover capital expenses for transit systems but also provides the first federal funding assistance towards the operating costs of those networks; the Highway Post Office makes its final run from Cincinnati to Cleveland after 33 years of mail delivery by bus.

1975 ◎ For the first time, more Americans live in suburbs than in cities.

1976 ◎ The Railroad Revitalization Regulatory Reform Act of 1976 reduces federal regulation of railroads and authorizes funding and implementation procedures for the newly created northeastern railroad system, Conrail.

1977 ◎ The Railway Post Office service, which had been officially inaugurated in 1869 to deliver mail via trains, made its final run between New York City and Washington, D.C.

1978 ◎ The Airline Deregulation Act sets the stage for several key changes in U.S. aviation by allowing new airlines into the market, permitting airlines to set their own fares and phasing out the Civil Aeronautics Board.

1980 ◎ The Staggers Rail Act of 1980 introduces further major regulatory changes for U.S. railroads and replaces the regulatory structure for that industry that had been in existence since the Interstate Commerce Act of 1887.

◎ The Motor Carrier Act of 1980 deregulates the trucking industry in such ways as reducing the Interstate Commerce Commissions control over that transportation mode and providing more latitude for that industry to set rates.

◎ Japan becomes the world's leading auto maker.

1983 ◎ The St. Lawrence Seaway carries its billionth ton of cargo.

◎ A public transportation trust fund for capital projects is created through dedication of one cent of the federal gas tax.

1990 ◎ AASHTO and the Highway Users' Foundation for Safety and Mobility (HUFSAM) team up to create the Intelligent Vehicle/Highway Society of America (IVHS America and later ITS America), to foster the development and deployment of intelligent transportation systems (ITS).

1991–2014: The Era of Transportation Choice

The Interstate era was a reflection of what the country wanted at that time," said Kirk Steudle, Director of the Michigan Department of Transportation. "We want something different now—more options, more choices, more flexibility, and greater access." Those changing expectations, combined with growing concerns about environmental health and climate change, led to today's era of multi-modal transportation.

Key turning points during this era of transportation choice include:

1991 ◎ The Intermodal Surface Transportation Efficiency Act of 1991 initiates the framework for a national inter-modal transportation system that is economically efficient and environmentally sound.[7]

1993 ◎ The 46,931-mile Interstate system is officially designated the Dwight D. Eisenhower System of Interstate and Defense Highways.

1994 ◎ Washington state's first state-funded passenger train departs Seattle's King Street Station, and rail passenger service between Seattle and Vancouver B.C. resumes after a 14-year hiatus.

1998 ◎ The *Thinking Beyond the Pavement* **National Workshop, sponsored by AASHTO, FHWA, and the Maryland Department of Transportation, launches a national focus on integrating highways with communities and the environment while maintaining safety and performance.**

2000 ◎ President Bill Clinton signs legislation to open the U.S. Defense Department satellite GPS system for use by civilians worldwide.

2001 ◎ **AASHTO creates the Center for Environmental Excellence to encourage innovative ways to streamline the transportation delivery process and assist transportation agencies in incorporating environmental compliance, sustainability, and stewardship into transportation planning, project development, construction, maintenance, and operations.**

2004 ◎ **AASHTO publishes** *A Guide for Achieving Flexibility in Highway Design*, **which shows highway designers how to think flexibly, how to recognize the many choices and options they have, and how to arrive at the best solution for the particular situation or context.**

2006 ◎ **AASHTO creates the Center for Excellence in Project Finance to support state departments of transportation in using state-of-the-art finance methods to advance transportation projects and leverage funding.**

2008 ◎ The Passenger Rail Investment and Improvement Act is enacted to strengthen the United States passenger rail network through expansion of Amtrak, establishment of state-sponsored rail corridors, and development of high-speed rail corridors.

2009 ◎ President Barack Obama signs the American Recovery and Investment Act which leads to major investments in highways, bridges, and transit to strengthen transportation infrastructure, create jobs, and stimulate the nation's economy.

2010 ◎ Google unveils and begins publicly testing a driverless car.

2011 ◎ Highway fatalities drop to 32,310—the lowest level since 1949.

Google Car.
Reproduced by permission from Steve Jurvetson.

2012 ◎ Public transit ridership grows to a record 10.5 billion trips despite the loss of 74 million trips on transit systems from Washington, D.C., to Boston because of Hurricane Sandy and the blizzard that follows the next week.

2014 ◎ **AASHTO celebrates the 100th anniversary of its founding.**

"The Interstate System is a wonder of engineering and construction. But the partnership that built it might be even more impressive than the concrete-and-steel highways that stretch across our nation"

~ *The Roads that Built America*, Dan McNichol

Inset Photo: President Woodrow Wilson signs into law the Federal Aid Road Act of 1916 (also known as the Bankhead-Shackleford Act).
Courtesy of FHWA

Chapter 3
The Federal–State Partnership

AASHTO was created to forge a strong federal–state partnership to build a road system that would be the envy of the world. Less than two years after AASHTO's founding, Congress passed and President Woodrow Wilson signed the Federal-Aid Road Act of 1916 which created a framework for the long-imagined national system of roads that would be built and maintained by the states with federal financial support.

The 1916 federal-aid law led to the gradual development of better roads in the United States over the next four decades. It became the basis for the partnership that eventually built the 46,931-mile Interstate system. That partnership was designed to blend engineering expertise and politics to produce good decisions that benefitted the country as a whole. "It rested on the idea that engineers were the central figures not only in shaping and administering the road system, but also in defining the policy behind it," said Bruce Seely of the Michigan Technological Institute.

Federal Aid to Build Good Roads

The idea of federal investment in road construction in the late 19th and early 20th centuries faced multiple obstacles despite a growing call for good roads. Many in Congress questioned whether the federal government had the constitutional authority to support road construction. Others worried about the wisdom of a long-term federal financial commitment to building roads. In the early 1900s, five factors converged to produce action:

1. The growing involvement of initially reluctant farmers in the demand for good roads which highlighted the importance of better roads to everyday life;
2. The rise of the affordable automobile which added another good-roads voice—motorists and their advocacy group, the American Automobile Association (AAA);
3. The 1905 appointment of Logan Waller Page—a progressive who believed in a leadership role for engineers and scientists, more than politicians, in road building—as director of the U.S. Office of Public Roads;

4. The 1907 Supreme Court decision in *Wilson v. Shaw* that confirmed Congressional authority to construct interstate highways under its constitutional right to regulate interstate commerce; and

5. AASHTO's establishment in 1914 with Logan Waller Page as a strong proponent for and participant in the association's inaugural meeting.[8]

Science and Engineering vs. Politics and Tradition

Public Roads Director Page strongly supported creation of a national organization made up of state highway commissioners and their immediate staffs who were experts in the technical aspects of road building. As a scientist himself, Page felt that road building was better left to engineers, whom he believed would apply nonpartisan judgment based on data, training, and expertise that was free of "political taint and corrupt influence."[9] He also believed in the benefits of standardization of roadbuilding—an approach that became a hallmark of AASHTO's highway influence.

Logan Waller Page.
Courtesy of FHWA

Engineers working in a drafting room in 1950s Missouri.
Courtesy of Missouri DOT

Pioneering engineer Marilyn J. Reece, who designed the San Diego–Santa Monica Freeway interchange.
Courtesy of Caltrans

AASHTO, with its membership of people who both knew how to build roads and were responsible for road building in their states, offered the possibility of an independent forum where the states and the federal government could discuss engineering issues in a non-political environment. In addition, AASHTO provided a vehicle for carrying the ideas of the highway engineering community to Congress.

That structure appealed to Page as a foundation for establishing a federal–state partnership to get the country moving toward good roads. But, Page died suddenly in 1918 at the age of 48, only two years after the landmark 1916 Federal-Aid Road Act was enacted. At the time of his death, he was attending a meeting of AASHTO's executive committee to discuss disappointing progress on highway construction. An AASHTO tribute upon his death said that Page "contributed much to smooth the ways of travel, to turn aside the stones over which we stumble, to widen the avenues along which we must work, and has made safer, brighter, and lighter the Nation's pathways for the feet of commerce, liberty, and happiness."[10]

Thomas H. MacDonald, who directed national highway policy from 1919–1953, was a staunch champion of the federal–state partnership in building roads.
Courtesy of FHWA

Page's successor, Thomas H. MacDonald, who had served as chief engineer for the Iowa Highway Commission, was recommended by AASHTO to become Bureau of Public Roads director. MacDonald shared Page's belief in the power of engineering expertise to build good roads and in the potential of a strong federal–state partnership. His goal for the nation's transportation was clear from the start of his long tenure as BPR chief—"My aim is this: we will be able to drive out of any county seat in the United States at thirty-five miles an hour and drive into any other county seat—and never crack a spring."[11] MacDonald led the Bureau of Public Roads for 35 years, working closely with AASHTO to strengthen the federal–state partnership.

The Hell Gate Bridge under construction in New York City circa 1915.

Transportation Turning Point
The Progressive Era Advances Good Government and Good Roads

AASHTO was born during the Progressive Era, a time of social and political reform based on the belief that fact- and data-based technicians could solve the country's problems. Progressives pushed for greater government involvement in public affairs to improve public services, build schools, construct roads, strengthen conservation and sanitation efforts, encourage transportation safety, and more.[12] The era spawned the good government movement and advanced the good roads movement by pressing for more science and less politics in meeting public needs. The Progressive Era also produced the City Managers' Association, now the International City/County Management Association (ICMA), also created in December 1914 with a goal of promoting scientific-based problem-solving, efficiency, and professional management in America's cities. The eight city managers who met in Springfield, Ohio, on December 2, 1914, to create their new organization, had something in common with the state highway officials who met 10 days later in Washington, D.C.—they were all engineers.

Building State Expertise

The idea of a strong federal–state partnership to build a transportation system depended on strong state highway and later transportation agencies with engineering expertise equal to or even deeper that federal capacity. That goal was a work in progress when the first federal-aid bill passed in 1916. The bill included a provision requiring the establishment of state highway departments headed by engineers in order to shift power and responsibility for highway construction to states and away from cities and counties. States had to have administrative highway departments that met federal criteria in order to qualify for federal funds.

In 1916, 11 of the then 48 states didn't have highway departments. By 1919 every state had formed a highway department that met the federal criteria.

Legislation That Helped Transform America

A 1976 Federal Highway Administration book celebrating the evolution of America's highways since the country's founding identified nearly 100 national laws which had had "a significant impact on the growth and development of the Federal-Aid Highway System." And, there have been more federal laws passed since 1976 which furthered development of America's highway and transportation system and refined the federal–state partnership.

However, over the past 100 years of transportation achievement, three federal laws stand out for their impact in shaping America's transportation system.

1. **Federal-Aid Road Act of 1916.** Although somewhat flawed as implementers would quickly learn, this law created a framework for a state-built and maintained national highway system, supported by federal aid. Page's sudden death, World War I, and renewed debate about whether to build a national system of state-owned and operated highways or a system of federally built and owned highways slowed progress on long-awaited road improvements. By war's end, more than 570 Federal-aid projects had been approved for construction, but only five were finished, netting 17.6 miles of road. The slow progress led to deep disappointment among good-road supporters and state highway officials who had hoped for rapid transformation.

2. **Federal-Aid Highway Act of 1956.** This measure, signed into law by President Eisenhower, led to construction of the Interstate system.
   - Title I authorized $25 billion as the federal share for the cost of building the national system of defense highways between 1957 and 1969, and
   - Title II (the Highway Revenue Act of 1956) established the Highway Trust Fund and required that the road construction program be operated on a pay-as-you-go basis.

The Federal-Aid Highway Act of 1956 also declared that completion of the system of Interstate highways was "essential to the national interest" and that a component of the national interest was "national defense." Connecting construction of the national highway system to national defense needs—particularly when that argument was made by a victorious World War II general during the early days of the Cold War—opened some previously closed minds.

Construction of the Interstate system with AASHTO playing a vital coordinating role among the state highway departments showed the federal–state partnership in action. It took more than 40 years to build the 46,931-mile Interstate system at a cost of nearly $129 billion.

Francis C. "Frank" Turner, the federal highway official who has been widely credited as the chief architect of the Interstate System.
Courtesy of FHWA

"The Interstate System will never be finished because America will never be finished."

~ Frank Turner, Federal Highway Administrator, 1969–1972

3. **Intermodal Surface Transportation Efficiency Act of 1991 (ISTEA).** Signed into law by President George H.W. Bush, ISTEA was the most sweeping restructuring of surface transportation programs since authorization of the Interstate system. ISTEA introduced the concept of integrated, multi-modal transportation and provided more flexibility to state and local government officials for developing the best mix of surface transportation projects to meet local, regional, and state needs.

President George H.W. Bush signs ISTEA into law. *Courtesy of FHWA*

Just as the 1916 federal-aid law paved the way for more than 50 years of road construction, ISTEA established the foundation for multi-modal transportation planning and action which is shaping the next century of transportation achievement.

Transportation Turning Point
The Highway Trust Fund

The Highway Trust Fund was created by the Highway Revenue Act of 1956 to support construction of the Interstate system. While it was originally set to expire in 1972, the trust fund has been extended many times since 1956—most recently in 2012 by the *Moving Ahead for Progress in the 21st Century Act (*MAP-21). It remains the primary source of funding for the federal government's surface transportation programs and for the federal–state partnership that was created with AASHTO's founding in 1914 and put into action with construction of the Interstate system.

Today, money collected mostly from excise taxes on gasoline and certain other motor fuels provide about 95 percent of all contributions to the Highway Trust Fund. Contributions are credited to two separate federal accounts—one for highways and one for mass transit. Other sources of revenue to the Highway Trust Fund include excise taxes on trucks and trailers, on truck tires, and on the use of certain kinds of vehicles. Money from the Highway Trust Fund is provided to the states on a reimbursable basis through six formula programs to support state infrastructure projects.

A lot has changed since 1956 which has created significant shortfalls in the Highway Trust Fund's ability to meet current and future transportation needs. Americans are driving less, vehicles are far more fuel efficient than they were in 1956, and there has been increasing resistance to gas tax increases.

A Balanced and Productive Partnership

AASHTO's role as a convener and facilitator of the 52 highway departments has been instrumental in establishing and sustaining a successful federal–state partnership over the past 100 years. "AASHTO is where we all come together to create and sustain a national transportation system that overlaps 50 states," said Malcolm Dougherty, Director of the California Department of Transportation. That was the idea in 1914 and remains true today. The Interstate system, the most significant outcome of the federal–state partnership in this century of transportation achievement, is noted for its design and construction consistency across the 50 states, its rational numbering system, its smooth state-to-state connections, and its safety features. That consistency emerged from AASHTO committee work on construction and materials standards and specifications.

Former New Mexico DOT Secretary and Missouri DOT Director Pete Rahn
Courtesy of HNTB

"The fact that AASHTO was there allowed the federal government to cooperate with the states around highway construction," said Pete Rahn, 2008 AASHTO President, and former secretary of both the New Mexico and Missouri Departments of Transportation. "The Interstate system wouldn't have been as successful without AASHTO playing that important role."

The federal–state partnership that evolved over 100 years was built on a series of federal laws that AASHTO and the states played a role in crafting, a framework for sustained collaboration among the 52 transportation departments under the AASHTO umbrella, and personal working relationships among people who recognized the vital role transportation plays in daily life, the economy, and the country's future.

"Friendly cooperation between the several States and the Federal Government has been one of the outstanding results of the work and purposes of this Association. But, perhaps the greatest accomplishment is that [AASHTO's] work and influence have brought about a large measure of right thinking on highway matters."

~ Warren W. Mack, President, AASHO, 1939, and Chief Engineer of Delaware

Former AASHTO President Warren W. Mack
Courtesy of Delaware Public Archives

Transportation Turning Point

Federal Legislation That Contributed to This Century of Transportation Achievement

1912 **Post Office Appropriation Bill of 1912** began the trend of federal aid for construction of highways and pulled the reluctant farmer into the good-roads campaign.

1916 **Federal-Aid Road Act of 1916** established the first federal-aid framework and the federal–state partnership for road building.

1921 **Federal-Aid Highway Act of 1921** solidified the federal–state partnership by allowing states to manage their own road building and allocated half of the federal transportation budget for roads that are interstate in nature.

The arrival of a shipment of U.S. air mail in Washington, D.C., in 1927.

Courtesy of Library of Congress; Photo by Harris & Ewing

An American Airlines Douglas DC-3 plane being filmed for a movie in 1943.

Courtesy of Library of Congress, Prints & Photographs Division, FSA/OWI Collection

1925 **Air Mail Act of 1925,** known as the Kelly Act, provided for the transportation of mail through contracts with the Post Office which contributed to support for better roads.

1926 **Air Commerce Act of 1926** established federal requirements for the oversight of air traffic, aircraft, navigational facilities, and safety measures.

1932 **The Revenue Act of 1932** established the first federal tax on gasoline. The tax, earmarked for deficit reduction, lasted only one year.

1944 **The Federal-Aid Highway Act of 1944** called for a national system of Interstate highways and directed the U.S. Public Roads Administration to establish construction and operational standards for that system.

1956 **Federal Aid Highway Act of 1956** established the highway trust fund and the framework for the Interstate system.

1961 **Housing and Urban Development Act of 1961** was not broad-based in scope but it did mark the first significant federal funding assistance for public transit by providing $50 million for loans and $25 million in grants for demonstration pilot projects in mass transportation.

1962 **Federal-Aid Highway Act of 1962** required the formation of metropolitan planning organizations (MPOs) in urban areas with populations greater than 50,000 to coordinate regional transportation planning and allocation of federal funds to meet regional needs.

1964 **The Urban Mass Transportation Act of 1964** provided federal funds for large-scale urban public or private rail projects in the form of matching grants to cities and states and created the Urban Mass Transportation Administration, now the Federal Transit Administration.

1964 **The Civil Rights Act of 1964** ended segregation in public places and gradually reduced ways in which transportation projects could infringe on the rights of the under-represented and under-served individuals and groups.

President Lyndon B. Johnson signing the Civil Rights Act of 1964.
Photo by Cecil Stoughton, White House Press Office

1966 **The Highway Safety Act** established the National Highway Safety Standards to reduce traffic accidents.

1969 **The National Environmental Policy Act (NEPA)** established the nation's first comprehensive environmental policy and goals and required transportation agencies to consider the impact of road projects on the environment.

1970 **The Clean Air Act of 1970** regulated air emissions from stationary and mobile sources. Combine with NEPA, these two federal laws established a connection between transportation and the environment.

1973 **The Federal-Aid Highway Act of 1973** provided funding for existing interstate and new urban and rural primary and secondary roads, funded a highway safety improvement program, permitted states to use the Highway Trust Fund money for mass transit, and prohibited the Federal Administration from approving highway projects in any state with a maximum speed limit of more than 55 miles per hour.

1983 **The Surface Transportation Assistance Act of 1982** established the Motor Carrier Safety Assistance Program and its companion **Highway Revenue Act of 1982** increased the gasoline and diesel tax by five cents per gallon to help reverse the trend of highways and bridges deteriorating faster than they could be repaired.

President Ronald Reagan signs into law the Surface Transportation Assistance Act of 1982 and the Highway Revenue Act of 1982.

1987 The Surface Transportation and Uniform Relocation Assistance Act of 1987 extended highway user fees another five years, funded the Strategic Highway Research Program and allowed states to raise the speed limit to 65 miles per hour on rural Interstate highways.

1991 The Intermodal Surface Transportation Efficiency Act of 1991 (ISTEA) introduced the concept of integrated, multi-modal transportation.

1995 President Bill Clinton signs into law the **1995 National Highway Designation Act**—a measure designating approximately 160,955 miles of roads—including the Dwight D. Eisenhower System of Interstate and Defense Highways and various other routes likewise important to the nation's economy, defense, and mobility—as a single network called the National Highway System (NHS).

1998 Transportation Equity Act for the 21st Century (TEA-21) was a six-year $216 billion surface transportation reauthorization which continued the framework established by ISTEA.

2005 Safe, Affordable, Flexible, Efficient, Transportation Equity Act: A Legacy for Users (SAFETEA-LU) extended programs established under ISTEA and TEA-21 and provided $286 billion in federal-aid funding.

2008 The Passenger Rail Investment an Improvement Act of 2008 focused on strengthening the United States passenger rail network through expansion of Amtrak, establishment of state-sponsored rail corridors, and development of high-speed rail corridors.

An Amtrak Acela Express train arriving at Union Station in Washington, D.C.

A sidewalk installation, resulting from the American Recovery and Reinvestment Act of 2009, along Rhode Island Route 114.
Reproduced by permission from Matt H. Wade. Matt Wade Photography; August 2009.

President Obama signing MAP-21 legislation into law.
Photo by Lawrence Jackson, White House Press Office

2009 American Recovery and Reinvestment Act of 2009 (ARRA) was a stimulus package of more than $787 billion, which included $48.1 billion for transportation infrastructure (including $27.5 billion for highway and bridge construction; $8 billion for intercity passenger rail; $1.3 billion for Amtrak; $6.9 billion for public transit; $1.1 billion for airport improvements).

The emblem for Recovery.gov, the official website of the American Recovery and Reinvestment Act of 2009.

2012 Moving Ahead for Progress in the 21st Century (MAP-21), the final surface transportation bill in this century of transportation achievement provided $105 billion in federal-aid funding, consolidated a number of federal transportation programs, and reformed the environmental review process.

"Birds have wings; they're free; they can fly where they want when they want. They have the kind of mobility that many people envy."

~ Roger Tory Peterson, American Naturalist, Ornithologist, Artist, and Educator

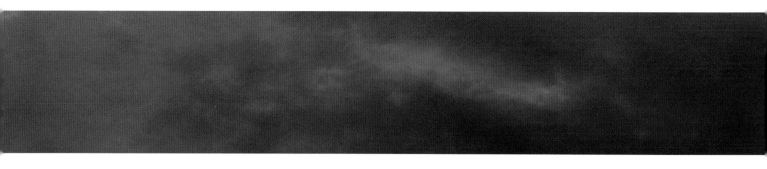

Chapter 4
A Nation on the Go

Everybody must get somewhere every day. Over the years, transportation needs have become more complex, and the system that meets those needs has continued to expand. The volume of coming and going is staggering:

- Residents and foreign visitors traveled about 4.6 trillion miles in the United States during 2010.
- A record 10.5 billion trips were taken on public transportation in 2012.
- An average of 85,000 passengers ride more than 300 Amtrak trains daily. In 2012, that added up to 31.5 million passengers.
- More than 25,000 domestic flights take off daily from airports in the U.S covering 640 billion passenger miles.
- Today, individuals in the United States travel an average of 13,000 miles per year, taking an average of four local trips that total 36 miles per day.
- More than 23 million children and teens ride 500,000 yellow buses to and from elementary and secondary schools across the country 180 days per year.[17]

The desire to get somewhere has been part of American life since the country's earliest days. In 1800 with a population of 5.3 million, long distance travel was difficult, time consuming, and unpredictable, mostly done on waterways or by horseback on limited and disconnected roads. Cities and towns grew up around waterways because of the possibility of travel and access to goods.

Tourists in
San Francisco.

The Amtrak "Coast
Starlight" train at
California's San Luis
Obispo rail station.

A student getting off
of a school bus.

By the early 1900s, population had grown to 76 million spread across the growing country with increasing options for getting around. Bicycles, horse-drawn carriages and wagons, boats for inland travel on expanded waterways, railroads, and electric trolley lines created new opportunities for mobility. Eventually the automobile changed everything about getting around.

The following sections provide a picture of the evolution of personal mobility over the past century.

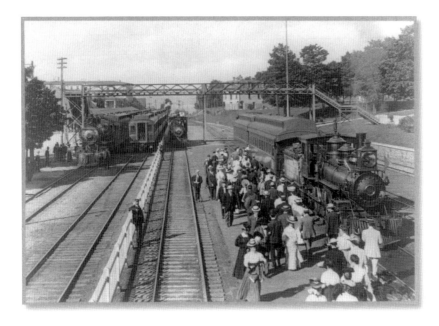

Railroads Rule the Day

In 1869, the last railroad tie was struck completing the Central Pacific and Union Pacific's transcontinental railroad. "The nation was expanding, the West was being opened, and the railroads ruled the day."[18] Between 1830 and 1890, active rail mileage in the United States grew from 40 miles in 1830 to nearly 164,000 in 1890 with the largest mileage concentrated in western states and regions from Texas to California. Improvements in technology including more powerful locomotives, steel passenger cars, and cleaner-burning coal made rail transportation even more attractive.

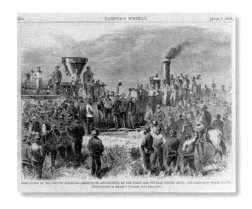

Railroads dominated long-distance travel in the early 1900s, carrying as many as 800 million passengers or 32 billion passenger miles annually and accounting for more than 70 percent of all intercity travel in the 1920s and early 1930s.[19] On any day in the 1920s, more than 20,000 passenger trains made journeys on 250,000 miles of track.[20] Gas and tire rationing during World War II led to record passenger rail travel—nearly 98 billion passenger miles in 1944 or about 90 percent of all wartime travel. After the war, personal automobiles, vastly expanded highways, and the rise of affordable air travel led to a steady decline in rail passenger travel in the 1950s and 1960s. By 2000, rail-passenger miles had plummeted to 15 billion despite significant population growth.[21]

Train Rides Inspire Songwriters

Stephen Goodman, a Chicago songwriter and folk singer, got the inspiration for *City of New Orleans*, while actually riding the Illinois Central train from Chicago in 1970 to visit his wife's grandmother. Goodman wrote about what he saw out of window and what he did on the train ride, including playing cards in the club car. When he learned that the train was scheduled to be decommissioned due to lack of passengers, he was encouraged to record the song to save the train. Goodman first recorded the song on his first album in 1971. It was later recorded by Arlo Guthrie in 1972 and Willie Nelson in 1984.

While it has gone through several changes in service and names over the years, Amtrak operates the 926-mile City of New Orleans daily connecting Chicago, Memphis, and New Orleans. Kankakee, which is mentioned in the song, is the second stop after the train leaves Chicago.

George Gershwin got the initial inspiration for *Rhapsody in Blue*, his first major classical work for piano and orchestra, while riding a train from New York to Boston in 1924. He described the train's inspiration this way: "It was on the train, with its steely rhythms, its rattle-ty bang, that is so often so stimulating to a composer—I frequently hear music in the very heart of noise. I hear it as a sort of music kaleidoscope of America, of our vast melting pot, of our unduplicated national pep, of our metropolitan madness."[22]

During their peak years, railroads were the go-to resource for long-distance travel and an important economic engine for the growing country, employing as many as two million people annually.

America's passenger rail system was operated by private, for-profit companies that were authorized by states and regulated by the federal government. In the late 1800s, the federal government operated a land-grant system giving millions of acres to new railroad companies in the wide open west that helped grow numerous rail lines in that part of the world. Even more important, growth of the railroads transformed American geography by providing large-scale movement beyond waterways. For example, the cities of Omaha, Tulsa, Wichita, and Denver grew rapidly around railroad depots when trains replaced canals, turnpikes, and steamboats as the preferred transportation mode.

New York Penn Station, circa 1020.
Courtesy of Library or Congress

In 1916, railroad track mileage peaked at 254,000.[23] It went downhill from there when Americans chose the automobile and the highway over the railroad. And, while the automobile industry was growing and the AASHTO-led federal–state highway partnership was taking shape, railroad owners and government had less than a warm relationship. "The railways considered cooperation with government beneath them, akin to socialism, and policy makers returned their contempt," wrote Stephen B. Goddard in his book, *Getting There*. "The motor industry and government, by contrast, reached out to each other eagerly and created an enduring symbiotic partnership."[24]

Steam Locomotives: Functional and Flashy

During the railroad heyday, steam engines were both functional and, in some cases, quite beautiful, such as the famous 20th Century Limited from New York to Chicago, the Hiawatha between Chicago and Minneapolis-St. Paul, and the Daylight between San Francisco and Los Angeles. Steam locomotive No. 1401 was a work horse for the Southern Railway operating out of Charlotte, North Carolina, from 1926-1952. It was part of the South Railway's Ps-4 type locomotives that could haul 12-15 passenger cars weighing about 700-1,000 tons at 80 miles per hour on level track. Carrying 14,000 gallons of water to generate the steam power, it could travel 150 miles between water stops. And the handsome Ps-4s were painted green and gold to set them apart from the traditional black American steam engine. Eight Ps-4 engines, including No. 1401, were used for President Franklin Roosevelt's funeral train from Warm Springs, Georgia, to Washington, D.C. in April 1945. Diesel locomotives which were cheaper to operate and maintain gradually took over in the 1950s, and all of the Southern Railways steam engines were retired by 1953.[25]

A Southern Railroad Crescent Limited locomotive in Alexandria, Virginia, circa 1926.

The Amtrak "Coast Starlight" passenger train heading north out of San Jose, California, in May 1971.
Reproduced by permission from Drew Jacksich

Amtrak Takes Over Passenger Rail

In 1969, three of the surviving railroads, the Pennsylvania Railroad, New York Central, and New York, New Haven, and Hartford Railroad merged to form the Penn Central—which declared bankruptcy a year later. Shortly after the bankruptcy filing, Congress created Amtrak, a government corporation to operate the Penn Central passenger lines and selected remaining inter-city service. Amtrak began operating passenger train service on May 1, 1971. Today, Amtrak operates a nationwide rail network serving more than 500 destinations in 46 states and the District of Columbia. It has more than 21,300 miles of routes and about 20,000 employees. In 2012, more than 31.2 million passengers road Amtrak trains including a record 11.4 million passengers on the busy northeast corridor between Washington, D.C. and Boston.

A station platform for Minnesota's Northstar Line rail service.
Courtesy of Minnesota DOT

States Ramp Up on Passenger Rail

In some parts of the country, passenger train service is regaining a hold on inter-city travel as an alternative to the automobile or higher-priced regional airlines. State transportation departments, working in partnership with Amtrak, have focused on developing rail plans, supporting expansion of passenger service, and upgrading rail infrastructure to improve service and ensure rail safety.

"Passenger rail was central to the development of this region and remains important today for long trips," said North Dakota Director of Transportation Grant Levi said. "We have a lot of people coming to the state to work in the energy industry, and they continue to rely on the railroad to get them here."

In recent years, more than 14 million passengers have traveled annually on state-supported rail lines outside the busy northeast corridor with the numbers rising. For example, train lines from Raleigh to Charlotte, North Carolina; Portland, Oregon to Seattle, Washington; and in upstate New York—all operated by their state transportation departments—have seen ridership increases from 13 to 150 percent in recent years. More than 5.2 million passengers are carried annually on California's state-owned rail lines.

States have also continued their AASHTO-developed collaborative efforts to support interstate/intercity rail travel. For example, the Vermont and Massachusetts transportation departments worked on two major projects to restore and expand the Vermonter service in northern New England.

An Amtrak Cascades passenger train traveling near Mount Rainier in Washington.
Courtesy of Washington State DOT

In North Carolina, the "City of Durham" commuter locomotive pulls into a train depot.
Courtesy of North Carolina DOT

Public Transit Meets Early Mobility Needs

From the country's earliest days, public transit met people's daily mobility needs. It was a relatively inexpensive and accessible way for people to get to work, school, worship, and recreation. While lacking the overall independence and flexibility later afforded by the automobile, public transit options were generally seen as improvements over trains which were loud, uncomfortable, and not ideal for urban settings.

The primary form of public transportation in the late 19th and early 20th centuries was electric streetcars operated by private companies under franchise agreements with the cities. Across the growing country, streetcars and later buses and subways provided day-to-day transportation options, peaking in 1946 when public transportation ridership reached 23.4 billion or 165 rides per capita. In the 1920s, despite the growing popularity of cars and gradual private disinvestment in streetcars, public transit still dominated downtown travel in big cities. For example, in 1924, 85 percent of downtown trips in New York City and 65 percent in Los Angeles were made by public transit. In 1928 and 1929, the percentage of downtown trips made using public transportation in Philadelphia and Chicago was 79 and 78 percent, respectively.[76]

Trolleys and people crossing New York City's Brooklyn Bridge during the early 20th century.

Streetcars at a terminal in Oklahoma City, Oklahoma, circa 1939.
Courtesy of Library of Congress, Prints & Photographs Division, FSA/OWI Collection

1940 Snapshot
By the Numbers

U.S. POPULATION **132,122,446**

FEDERAL SPENDING **$9.47 billion**

UNEMPLOYMENT RATE **14.6 percent**

AVERAGE ANNUAL INCOME **$1,392**

AVERAGE COST OF AN AUTOMOBILE **$800**

COST OF A GALLON OF MILK **$0.34**

MILES OF ROADS **3,287,000**

REGISTERED MOTOR VEHICLES **32.5 million**

1940 Snapshot
Events

- Germany invades Norway, Denmark, the Netherlands, Belgium, and Luxembourg.

- The Battle of France comes to an end with the signing of an armistice with Germany, and the Battle of Britain takes place.

- Winston Churchill becomes British prime minister.

- Franklin D. Roosevelt is elected to an unprecedented third term as President.

- Women's stockings made out of nylon are first sold across the United States.

- The first McDonald's, a Barb-B-Q restaurant featuring car-hop service, opens in San Bernardino, California.

- Walt Disney releases the full-length animated films *Pinocchio and Fantasia*.

- Cartoon characters making their screen debuts include Bugs Bunny, Elmer Fudd, and Tom & Jerry.

- The Cincinnati Reds defeat the Detroit Tigers in the World Series.

Number Sources:
U.S. Census Bureau—
Historical National
Population Estimates;
www.infoplease.com;
Historical Statistics of the
United States, 1789-1945;
web.bryant.edu; Federal
Highway Administration
Highway Statistics:
Summary to 1975;
TheCostofLiving.com

Event Sources:
Wikipedia;
TheCostofLiving.com;
www.historyorb.com

Streetcars stored in a maintenance yard in Minneapolis, Minnesota, circa 1939.

Courtesy of Library of Congress, Prints & Photographs Division, FSA/OWI Collection

But as private investment in streetcars deteriorated, the scope of service, particularly in smaller cities declined. Buses began to replace streetcars as the preferred option for public transit. Between 1926 and 1940, streetcar and rapid transit ridership decreased by 42 percent while bus ridership increased by 58 percent.

In the 1960s, big city mayors sought federal support to revitalize public transportation. Federal funding was authorized in 1961 and 1964 for loans and demonstration projects and capital grants. That funding helped modernize fleets and expand service, but ridership growth has been slow. In 1972, public transportation ridership hit its lowest point in the 20th century at 6.6 billion rides or 31 rides per capita.

Regional Transit District Serves Small Communities

The New Mexico Rio Metro Regional Transit District provides a variety of services between municipalities in Bernalillo, Sandoval, and Valencia counties to meet mobility needs in a rural section of the state. The District's mission is to manage a regional, integrated, multi-modal public transportation network that is fiscally responsible, innovative, and efficient. Rio Metro manages the New Mexico Rail Runner commuter rail and operates and/ or funds bus routes within the three-county area and to other transportation markets including Santa Fe, Taos, and Socorro. The Rail Runner is the state's first commuter rail system providing seven day a week service to 13 stations along a 96.5 mile corridor. If offers a variety of bus services

The New Mexico Rail Runner Express commuter train arriving at a station
Courtesy of MTAP Archives

including fixed route, demand response, and commuter buses to meet diverse transportation needs in the region. The transit district is funded by a $1/8$-cent gross receipts tax with half of the revenues dedicated to rail and half to the overall Rio Metro system and is governed by the Mid-Region Council of Governments in collaboration with the New Mexico Department of Transportation.

Emerging Public Transit Needs. "Public transit isn't an urban vs. rural issue," said Iowa Department of Transportation Director Paul Trombino. "It is a quality of life issue." The key challenge in meeting transit needs is understanding that one size doesn't fit all—certain tools will work in some areas, but not others. In rural areas where population is widely distributed over large areas, on-call service helps meet specific transportation needs, particu-

A rural highway in Vermont.
Courtesy of MTAP Archives

larly for older residents who either don't have cars or are no longer able to drive. "Access to some kind of public transportation is particularly important in a state like North Dakota, in part, because of limited and spread out medical services," said Grant Levi, Director of the North Dakota Department of Transportation. "So it is important to provide periodically scheduled bus service to give people rides to the city when they need them."

Transportation Fuels Civil Rights Activism

Because of the vital role transportation plays in daily lives, segregated buses were "lightning rods" for civil rights activists and "volatile arenas for race relations in the south."[27] In 1955, Rosa Parks refused to give her seat on a Montgomery, Alabama, city bus to a white man as required by a city ordinance. Her action led to a 381-day boycott of the city bus system by African Americans and civil rights activists which helped launch the national civil rights movement.

Interstate bus travel was also a centerpiece of the civil rights struggle. In 1944, Irene Morgan was arrested in Middlesex County, Virginia, for violating a state law on segregation when she refused to sit in the segregated section on a Greyhound bus traveling from Virginia to Maryland. Although interstate transportation was supposed to be desegregated, Virginia enforced segregated seating within its borders. Morgan appealed her conviction all the way to the U.S. Supreme Court. In a 1946 decision, the Court ruled that the

Several of the Freedom Riders conferring at the Greyhound Terminal in Birmingham, Alabama, in May 1961.
Reproduced by permission from the Birmingham News/*Landov.*

Virginia law was unconstitutional because the Commerce Clause protected Interstate travel. In 1960, the Supreme Court in Boynton v. Virginia ruled that segregation of interstate transportation facilities including bus terminals was also unconstitutional. Yet segregation of interstate buses and terminals continued.

In May 1961, an integrated group of 13 "freedom riders" left Washington, D.C., on Greyhound and Trailways buses headed for New Orleans to demand unrestricted access to buses and terminal restaurants and waiting rooms. The freedom riders encountered resistance, hatred, and violence along the way, and many were jailed. Additional freedom rides continued throughout the summer of 1961. On September 22, 1961, under pressure from the Kennedy administration to quell the violence, the Interstate Commerce Commission announced that, beginning on November 1, 1961, all interstate buses would be required to display a certificate that read: "Seating aboard this vehicle is without regard to race, color, creed, or national origin, by order of the Interstate Commerce Commission."[28]

Transportation networks also supported civil rights activists for other major events in the movement. For example, thousands who attended the 1963 March on Washington came to the city on buses and trains including 450 busloads of activists from Harlem and many more from cities across the country including Boston, Philadelphia, Milwaukee, Little Rock, and St. Louis. More than 1,500 buses came to Washington that day. Special trains began leaving New York City's Penn Station at 2:00 a.m.[29]

Bicycles Pave the Way to Personal Mobility

In the late 1800s, bicycles provided the first real opportunity for personal mobility. When the pneumatic-tired safety bicycle was introduced in the 1890s, usage grew rapidly. "The bicycle was what made the Gay Nineties gay," wrote one bicycle historian because it was a practical investment for commuting to work and family leisure. Improvements in bicycle technology and safety also opened this independent mode of transportation to women who opted for common-sense dressing (no bustles and corsets) for bike riding. In 1896, Susan B. Anthony said "the bicycle has done more for the emancipation of women than anything else in the world."[30]

The League of American Wheelmen, as bicyclists were known then, was founded in 1880 and headquartered in Boston, to defend the rights of cyclists and advocate for paved roads and improved riding conditions for the more than 100,000 cyclists throughout the country. Known today as the League of American Bicyclists, the organization is committed to creating a bike-friendly America for everyone.[31]

The enthusiasm for that mode of transportation in the U.S. can be traced to such events as the 1876 Centennial International Exposition, which was held in Philadelphia to commemorate the 100th anniversary of the signing of the Declaration of Independence in that city. One of the British buildings at that fair featured an exhibit of high-wheeled bicycles brought over from Europe. Those bicycles caught the attention of many Americans at the fair and helped popularize that means of mobility on this side of the Atlantic over the next several years. Bicycles gained an especially strong and fervent following in Northeastern and Midwestern cities. For those urban residents, bicycles were both a respite from the everyday drudgeries of city life and the opportunity to take leisurely trips through the countryside.

While bicycles remained popular throughout the 20th century, particularly for youngsters and pre-driving teens, they are enjoying a widespread renaissance today among adults who are attracted to their fuel savings, health benefits, vehicle emission reduction, congestion relief, and economic advantages. Bike sharing programs in cities across the country, expansion of bike lanes and trails, bike clubs, and increased interest in "active transportation" have made biking once again a desirable transportation option.

Organizational Turning Point
AASHTO Promotes
U.S. Bicycle Route System

The U.S. Bicycle Route System (USBRS) is a national network of officially numbered interstate bicycle routes that connect cities, suburbs, and rural areas. The USBRS was formally established by AASHTO in 1978. In 1982, the association established that system's first two routes: Bicycle Route 1 in Virginia and North Carolina; and U.S. Bicycle Route 76 in Virginia, Kentucky, and Illinois. Nearly 6,200 miles of U.S. Bike Routes have since been established in 12 states: Alaska, Kentucky, Illinois, Maine, Maryland, Michigan, Minnesota, Missouri, New Hampshire, North Carolina, Tennessee, and Virginia, and more than 40 states are working to create additional routes. An AASHTO task force has been working to strengthen the bike route system since 2003 including creating the National Corridor Plan which outlined numbered corridors for cross-country cycling routes. AASHTO catalogues and officially designates the routes based on applications from state departments of transportation working with local agencies, organizations, and volunteers to plan and choose routes. Through its continuing work, AASHTO is helping to build support among federal and state agencies for non-motorized transportation.[32]

Top Right: Corridor plan for the U.S. Bicycle Route System.

Center Right: The logo for the U.S. Bicycle Route System, a national network of bicycle routes.

Center Left: U.S. Bicycle Route 20 at a covered bridge in Frankenmuth, Michigan.

Bottom Left: A cyclist traveling along U.S. Bicycle Route 76, which was established in 1982.

Images courtesy of Adventure Cycling Association

The Rise of the Auto Culture

"If I had asked people what they wanted," Henry Ford once said, "they would have said faster horses." While automobile technology existed in the 19th century, Ford made cars accessible to the American public by using an assembly line for production and paying his workers $5 a day, compared with the usual $2 for most laborers. He hoped the higher wages would improve productivity and even encourage workers to buy cars. In 1914, the year AASHTO was established, the Model T sold for $490, about one-quarter what an automobile cost 10 years earlier.[33]

In 1938, the owner of a 1921 Model T drove that vehicle to the White House to show if off there.
Courtesy of Library of Congress

When given an option, Americans overwhelmingly chose the freedom of their own route, their own schedule, and their own automobile over fixed rail lines and schedules. "Before Henry Ford built the Model T, most people rarely went more than 25 miles from home and only did that occasionally," said Kirk Steudle, director of the Michigan Department of Transportation. "The arrival of the automobile gave people freedom of life."

"I saw in their eyes something I was to see over and over in every part of the nation—a burning desire to go, to move, to get under way, anyplace, away from any Here. They spoke quietly of how they wanted to go someday, to move about, free and unanchored, not toward something but away from something. I saw this look and heard this yearning everywhere in every state I visited. Nearly every American hungers to move."

~ *Travels with Charley*, John Steinbeck

Transportation Turning Point

Model T's: Any Color as Long as It's Black

In 1914, Henry Ford's high-speed assembly lines increased car-building productivity from 12.5 worker-hours to assemble an automobile to one hour and 33 minutes. In fact, assembly lines produced cars faster than paint could dry. Only Japan black paint dried fast enough to keep pace with the assembly line, leading to Ford's quip that his Model T's were available in "any color as long as it's black."[34]

Americans embraced that freedom with gusto, purchasing cars in record numbers while America's highway system slowly caught up with the desire to drive. In 1900, there were 8,000 cars registered in the United States. By 1914, the year AASHTO was created, there were more than 1.7 million cars, making the federal–state road building partnership that AASHTO's founders envisioned urgent.

Motorists waiting to travel on the Kansas Turnpike when it opened in October 1956.
Courtesy of Missouri DOT

"Never before in the history of industry had a product gone from its first appearance to complete societal dominance in so short a time," wrote Earl Swift in *The Big Roads*. "In thirty years, America had become a nation on rubber wheels."[35]

Today, America still ranks highest in the world in terms of per capita vehicle ownership at 828 motor vehicles per 1,000 people with Canada and Japan following at 676 and 657 motor vehicles per 1,000 people respectively.[36]

By The Numbers
A Century of Growing Motor Vehicles Registrations

1900	**8,000**
1914	**1,664,000**
1924	**15,436,100**
1934	**21,544,700**
1944	**25,566,000**
1956	**54,211,000**
1970	**89,244,000**
1985	**127,855,000**
1995	**128,387,000**
2010	**134,880,000**[37]

First project finished under the 1956 Federal Aid Highway Act on I-70.
Courtesy of Kansas DOT

The economic impact of the automobile industry was dramatic. It sped up the demand for better roads which created thousands and thousands of jobs, particularly once construction of the Interstate began in 1956. Road trips on rapidly improving highways contributed to the rise of motels, gas stations, and low-priced quick-service restaurants such as Howard Johnson's and Stuckey's along the way. It also produced a growing need for skilled mechanics to keep cars running and fix problems.

With the Ford Motor Company and other automobile pioneers such as the Dodge brothers, William C. Durant, the Packard Brothers, and Walter Chrysler all spearheading industry growth from Detroit, the city grew rapidly as the world automotive capital. Its population jumped from 465,000 in 1910 to 1.8 million in 1950 when nearly every major automobile factory was located there. Competition from international companies gradually changed the economic picture for the Detroit-based automobile industry, but not the American desire to own cars and drive on rapidly improving highways.

Norman Rockwell Celebrates Transportation

Illustrator Norman Rockwell chronicled turning points in American life in the 300 covers he created for the *Saturday Evening Post* between 1916 and 1963. Many of Rockwell's illustrations highlighted the changing transportation scene including *Excuse My Dust* (1920), *Speeding Along* (1924), and *Downhill Daring* (1926) which highlighted the rise of the automobile; *First Flight* in 1938 paying tribute to airplane travel; *Commuters Waiting at Crestwood Train Station* (1946) showing public transportation; and *Going and Coming* (1947) a two-part illustration showing a multi-generational family road trip at the start and end of the day.

Cars and Superhighways Define a Generation

America's Interstate system and the baby boomer generation grew up together. The massive construction period from 1956 to 1966 saw the birth of superhighways that made personal mobility efficient, comfortable, and highly desirable. Hitting the road was a hallmark of baby-boomer life, and the culture of the time reflected the focus on mobility. It was the beginning of "mass motorization" of America.[38]

In the early 1950s, singer Dinah Shore urged people to "see the USA in your Chevrolet." While the song was intended to be an automobile advertisement, running from 1952 to 1960, it became Shore's signature song which she used to open and close her Chevy-sponsored weekly variety show. Other singers celebrated cars—Wilson Pickett sang about Mustang Sally (1963), Ronny and the Daytonas about the GTO (1964), and the Beach Boys about Little Deuce Coupe (1963). *Highway Patrol* and *Route 66* were popular television shows in the late 1950s and early 1960s.

And the road trip was the vacation of choice for baby boomer families. "We all packed into the family car and hit the road," said former Missouri DOT Director Pete Rahn. "All eight of us had assigned seats and happily took long trips."

The Interstate Transforms America

Polar Street Bridge Construction, St. Louis, Missouri.
Courtesy of Missouri DOT

While the idea of good roads as an economic and safety engine was on the minds of American leaders from the country's earliest days—and a considerable amount of progress toward that goal was made throughout the 20th Century—construction of the Dwight D. Eisenhower National System of Interstate and Defense Highways became the most significant transportation achievement of the past 100 years.

The impact of the Interstate System—presently numbering 46,931 miles—is well documented in books, articles, exhibits, and more. It was cited as the 11th most significant engineering achievement of the 20th century by the National Academy of Engineers (NAE). In announcing the selections at an NAE National Press Club event in February 2000, astronaut Neil Armstrong said: "With 44,100 miles of limited-access, multiple-lane roads without a single stop sign or stop light, [the Interstate system] is a model of efficiency and an engineer's dream. While it clearly improves the lives of all who travel on it and are served by it, its rating suffers because it is not worldwide."

Today the Interstate system is taken for granted, particularly by large segments of the population who have never known life without connected, consistently constructed, safe, dependable superhighways. Its impact on American life during the past century has been impressive including:

- Revving the nation's economic engine by creating jobs and stimulating growth and development across the country;
- Standardizing and upgrading highways throughout the country;
- Saving lives, time, and money by providing straight, smooth, consistent highways with no surprises from state to state; and
- Connecting rural and urban America through a network of reliable roads.

Transportation Turning Point
Named Highways Foreshadow the Interstate Era

The National Road. Presidents George Washington and Thomas Jefferson believed a cross-county road was essential to unify the rapidly growing country. President Washington worried that the population moving west of the Allegheny Mountains would "drift into alien orbits and would in a few short years be as unconnected to us…as we are with South America."[39] The vision for a national road to connect the nation took shape under President Jefferson in 1806 when Congress authorized $30,000 to build a road connecting Cumberland, Maryland, to the Ohio River. It was the first important road built with federal funds. By 1818, the road was completed from Cumberland to Wheeling, in present-day West Virginia, and mail coaches began using it. As construction continued, towns and villages grew up along its route, just as suburbs would grow along Interstate routes in the 1950s, 60s, and 70s. The National Road carried passengers westward and produce from frontier farms eastward in the mid-1800s. In 1926, it became part of US 40 and has largely been replaced by Interstate 70.[40]

The Lincoln Highway. Conceived and promoted by Indiana entrepreneur Carl G. Fisher, the Lincoln Highway was the first coast-to-coast connected road for automobiles. Fisher envisioned a rock road built to a standard previously unseen in the United States—"dry, smooth, safe, not just passable but comfortable in the rainy seasons. A road built for the automobile. For the future"[41] Dedicated on October 31, 1913, it was named for President Lincoln because of the popularity of the Civil War President. Eventually, it ran from Times Square in New York City to Lincoln Park in San Francisco through 14 states, 128 counties, and more than 700 cities, towns, and villages. A convoy of 70 good-road supporters scouted the route in 1913 from Brazil, Indiana, reaching Los Angeles in 34 days. In 1928, most of the Lincoln Highway became U.S. Route 30, and today's Interstate 80 follows much of the highway's original route.

1956 Snapshot
By the Numbers

U.S. POPULATION **168,903,031**

FEDERAL SPENDING **$70.64 billion**

UNEMPLOYMENT RATE **4.4 percent**

AVERAGE ANNUAL INCOME **$4,445**

AVERAGE COST OF AN AUTOMOBILE **$2,100**

COST OF A GALLON OF MILK **$0.97**

MILES OF ROADS **3,479,801**

REGISTERED MOTOR VEHICLES **65.2 million**

Number Sources:
U.S. Census Bureau—
Historical National
Population Estimates;
web.bryant.edu;
www.infoplease.com;
Federal Highway
Administration Highway
Statistics: Summary to 1975;
TheCostofLiving.com

Event Sources:
Wikipedia;
TheCostofLiving.com;
www.historyorb.com

1956 Snapshot
Events

- The Hungarian Revolution, the first major threat to Soviet control of Eastern Europe, takes place.

- Dwight D. Eisenhower defeats Democratic challenger Adlai E. Stevenson to win a second term.

Dwight D. Eisenhower and Richard M. Nixon on the campaign trail.

Reproduced by permission from Associate Press.

- The Italian ocean liner *S.S. Andrea Doria* sinks after colliding with the Swedish ship *S.S. Stockholm* off the coast of Nantucket.

- The first snooze-alarm clock is introduced by General Electric.

- The hard disk drive is invented at IBM.

- The best-selling single is "Heartbreak Hotel," which also becomes Elvis Presley's first number-one pop record.

- TV shows that make their debut include such longstanding daytime favorites as the game show *The Price is Right* and soap operas *As the World Turns* and *The Edge of Night*.

- The Summer Olympics are held in Melbourne, Australia, although the equestrian events take place instead in Stockholm, Sweden.

- New York Yankees Don Larsen pitches the only perfect game in World Series history against the Brooklyn Dodgers.

AASHTO Ensures Interstate Consistency

As the association of state highways departments, AASHTO led the process of ensuring that Interstate highways would be consistent in design, quality, appearance, and identification. AASHTO's progressive-era scientific values and member expertise produced the standards that are reflected in every one of the 46,931 miles.

A cartoon about U.S. numbered highways in American Highways magazine in 1926.

Numbering. Long before GIS systems made map-free travel easy, the AASHTO-led Interstate numbering system dramatically improved highway travel. Before numbered highways became the standard, there was a random system of named highways marked by painted colored bands on telephone poles. AASHTO designed an Interstate highway numbering system that distinguished north-south from east-west routes which was a mirror image of the U.S. highway numbering system to avoid duplication.

Overall Design. To ensure cross-country consistency and maximize safety, all Interstate highways used the same overall design. In announcing the agreed-upon standards in 1956, then-Secretary of Commerce Sinclair Weeks said the Interstate network would use "all known features of safety and utility to provide for safe and relaxed driving, economy of vehicle operation, and pleasing appearance" including:

- Generally four lanes with broad strips of turf down the middle;

- At least 12-foot wide traffic lanes with side shoulders "strong enough to be used by trucks as well as cars;"

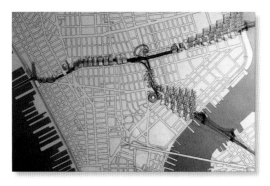

Lower Manhattan
Expressway Map,
January 1, 1967.

Courtesy of Library of Congress
Image by Paul Rudolph

Urban Highway Opposition

Despite fairly broad support, not every aspect of the Interstate system was welcomed with open arms. In particular, a plan to revitalize America's cities through construction of urban Interstates was blasted at a September 1957 symposium on highways in metropolitan regions. Journalist, sociologist, and historian Lewis Mumford was particularly harsh in saying the 1956 legislation was driven by America's love affair with the automobile rather than an understanding of how to restore cities. In his 1958 book, *The Highway and the City*, Mumford wrote: "A good transportation system minimizes unnecessary transportation; and, in any event, offers a change of speed and mode to fit a diversity of human purposes."

- Cloverleaf intersections, a minimum of side roads, and no railroad grade crossings;

- Controlled access with exits generally about three-miles apart except in densely populated areas; and

- Cross roads over or under main routes using bridges and underpasses.

Traffic flows smoothly along a freeway's interchange.

Pavement Materials. A seven-mile long test track in Ottawa, Illinois, proved to be a laboratory for testing the limits of design and materials for the new Interstate system. The process examined how traffic contributed to pavement deterioration on highways and bridges to help states use the best design, materials, and methods to ensure long-lasting, durable roads.

AASHO Road Test track near Ottawa, Illinois.

Consistent Signage. To ensure consistent signage, AASHTO asked state highway departments to submit designs for a new Interstate shield. In August 1958, full size versions of the selected shield finalists were set up along a route near the Ottawa, Illinois, highway test track. State officials then drove by the sample signs in various weather and lighting conditions to choose the most easily identified shield. The shield approved by AASHTO was from Texas, with elements of an entry from Missouri incorporated into the final version. Bertram D. Tallamy, the Federal Highway Administrator, officially adopted the new shield for nationwide usage along Interstate highways the following month. In cooperation with the U.S. Bureau of Public Roads, AASHTO then posted blue, green, and black signs with white lettering in an unopened stretch of the D.C. Beltway near Greenbelt, Maryland, for a two-week period. Hundreds of drivers drove by mock signs, and white lettering on a green background was selected. Nearly 58 years later, the blue Interstate shield and green directional signs are used on all of the 46,931 miles of Interstate highway throughout the United States.[42]

Community opposition to urban highways grew as people of all races joined together to preserve neighborhoods, save homes, and protect urban parks and historic places. Civil rights leaders took on the fight, calling the highway strategy an effort to build "white men's roads through black men's homes." The race riots of the 1960s have been blamed, in part, on urban Interstate construction which widened the gap between the suburban white middle class and the urban black working class who were losing their homes to road construction.

Urban highway wars continued for decades with the efforts to protect neighborhoods in many cities creating diverse coalitions and contributing to a renewed sense of community. In 1969, Massachusetts Governor Francis Sargent halted construction of I-95 through downtown Boston saying, "Never, never will this administration make decisions that place people below concrete."[43]

Aviation Shrinks the Country

In 1900, a cross-country train trip took about one week. Driving the same route took a month or more depending on the weather. Today, a non-stop, cross-country flight takes about five hours. Commercial flight as an accessible and generally affordable mode of personal transportation has brought people closer to the dream of unfettered bird-like mobility.

Passengers boarding a Fokker F.10 NC582K airliner, circa 1929–1935.

Reproduced by permission from Western Airlines Archives

Regional airlines began offering regularly scheduled passenger flights in the late 1920s. But it would take another 40 years for air travel to become popular, affordable, and widely used. The airline industry needed larger, faster, and safer planes in order to attract the traveling public on a regular basis. Highly publicized accidents, particularly the 1931 TWA crash that killed Notre Dame football coach Knute Rockne slowed the airline passenger industry significantly. That crash directly contributed to improvements in building safer airplanes because it was attributed, in part, to structural failure of the Fokker F-10A plane—specifically its all-wood cantilever wings. "The aviation industry, TWA, and Fokker could have no greater adverse publicity had the victim been the president of the United States himself," wrote airline historian R.E.G. Davies about the impact of the Rockne crash that occurred as the airline industry was shifting its focus from mail-only to a major push for increased passenger travel.[44]

Transportation Turning Point

Airline Travel Spawns a New Career Option for Women

An airline hostess arrives in Washington, D.C., in July 1941.

Courtesy of Library of Congress

In 1930, Boeing Air Transport introduced the first "stewardesses" after Ellen Church, a young nurse from Iowa, convinced the company to hire her and seven other nurses to attend to the comfort of passengers in flight including calming their nerves. Because early airplanes flew at lower altitudes, the stewardesses could point out landmarks while caring for passengers who got sick from frequent turbulence, using what were then called "burp cups." The addition of women to flight crews to serve the largely male traveling public quickly spread through the fledgling airline industry. In her book, *The Jet Sex: Airline Stewardesses and the Making of An American Icon*, historian and journalist Victoria Vantoch, wrote that stewardesses "paved the way for 1970s feminism, organized one of the most powerful female labor unions, fought discrimination in the workplace, and served as important ambassadors of America in the Cold War."[46]

More than 80 years later, male and female "flight attendants" (who are no longer nurses) carry out the same role on all commercial flights—attending to passenger comfort, supporting in-flight safety, and calming occasional white-knuckle fliers.[47]

Transportation Turning Point
Improved Mobility Transforms Baseball

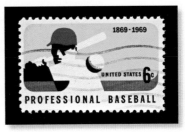

For nearly 80 years, major league baseball teams relied almost exclusively on trains to travel between parks. Teams were concentrated in the east and Midwest, all within a day's train ride from each other. A travel day was real time needed to get from one ballpark to the next rather than a day off to get settled, adjust to a different time zone, or take some extra batting practice. Before 1957, the average distance between ballparks was about 450 miles, and the maximum distance was 1,200 miles—a very long train ride but doable on the travel day between series. The growth of efficient, affordable, comfortable, and accessible airplane travel changed the geography of baseball. It made possible what has been called "one of the most heart wrenching moves in baseball history" when the Brooklyn Dodgers and New York Giants moved to California. Eventually, more western teams followed. Today, the average distance between parks is more than 1,100 miles with a maximum of 2,700 miles.[48]

Courtesy of Library of Congress

The debut of the DC-3 in 1936 began to turn the tide for passenger air travel. With a capacity of 21 passengers, all-aluminum-alloy construction, a hydraulic pump to raise and lower landing gear, noise-controlling plastic insulation, and more powerful engines, the DC-3 could fly from coast-to-coast in 16 hours which was a fast trip at the time. Other improvements that advanced the airline industry included radio communication, radar, and overall aircraft design including larger planes with more fuel efficient engines and pressurized cabins which made flight above 10,000 feet possible. Before that, passengers often became dizzy and even fainted because of diminished oxygen at higher altitudes. But the lower altitudes led to more weather-related air turbulence, which contributed to frequent motion sickness among passengers.

Equally important in the evolution of air travel was establishment in 1958 of the Federal Aviation Agency (later the Federal Aviation Administration) to oversee aviation safety including creating an air traffic control system to maintain safe separation of all commercial flights from take-off to landing. Air-traffic control became a high priority after a 1956 mid-air collision over the Grand Canyon killed 128 people and raised awareness of the nation's increasingly crowded skies.

Today, air travel is fast, safe, affordable, and immensely popular among the traveling public. Global positioning technology (GPS), sophisticated instrument landing systems, and weather management tools such as de-icing equipment and wind-shear warning devices have dramatically enhanced safety. According to the National Safety Council, airlines are consistently the safest mode of passenger travel based on deaths per 100 million passenger miles.[45]

Air Traffic Control
(87386298)

Photo by dbking–[1]. Licensed under Creative Commons Attribution 2.0 via Wikimedia Commons http://commons.wikimedia. org/wiki/File:Air _ Traffic _ Control _ (87386298). jpg#mediaviewer/ File:Air _ Traffic _ Control _ (87386298).jpg

Women Making Difference in Transportation History

From Harriett Tubman's role in leading more than 300 slaves to freedom along the Underground Railroad through Sally Ride's flight to space more than 100 years later, women have made their mark in transportation history. Here are a few examples:

1916 The Girl Scouts of America initiate an automobiling badge which requires girls to demonstrate their skills in driving, auto mechanics, and first-aid.

1920 Olive Dennis becomes the Baltimore & Ohio Railroad's engineer of service where she contributed to major improvements in rail cars including development of air-conditioned coaches, dimmers on overhead lights, and individual reclining seats.

1932 Amelia Earhart becomes the first woman to fly solo across the Atlantic.

1943 The Women Airforce Service Pilots (WASP) is created to fly military aircraft during World War II to free up male pilots for combat duty.

1952/1953 Ann Davison is the first woman to cross the Atlantic solo in a sailboat.

1955 Rosa Parks refuses to give up her seat on a city bus to make room for a white passenger, sparking a 381-day boycott of the city bus system.

1961 Jane Jacobs publishes *The Death and Life of Great American Cities,* a landmark book on city planning which still influences pedestrian and transit planning efforts today.

1962 Betty Crock is the first female highway engineer to join the Bureau of Public Roads.

1977 The Women's Transportation Seminar, later renamed Women in Transportation, is created to improve professional and personal advancement and develop industry and government recognition for women in transportation. It has more than 5,000 members in 2014.

1980 Lynn Rippelmeyer is the first woman to pilot a Boeing 747.

1983 Sally Ride becomes the first U.S. woman in space and, one year later, Kathryn Sullivan becomes the first woman to walk in space.

1997 Jane Garvey is the first woman to head the Federal Aviation Administration.

2001 Mary E. Peters is appointed as the first female Federal Highway Administrator, and in 2006 became the U.S. Transportation Secretary.

Aviation pioneer Amelia Earhart in 1928.

Jane Jacobs, the writer who fought against efforts to build a highway in her New York City neighborhood.
Courtesy of Library of Congress; photo by Phil Stanziola

The First Lady of Civil Rights Rosa Parks.
Reproduced by permission from Corbis © 1956.

Captain Lynn Rippelmeyer
Reproduced by permission from Seaboard Airlines.

Former U.S. Transportation Secretary Mary Peters
Courtesy of FHWA

"America will be defined as a nation by whether we can connect every citizen—rural or urban—to the 21st Century economy."

~ Anthony Foxx, Secretary, U.S. Department of Transportation
From his FAST LANE blog post of September 9, 2013.

Chapter 5
Moving Goods

Florida DOT Secretary
Ananth Prasad

Transportation is the backbone of the American economy. "We don't build roads and bridges because that's what we like to do," said Ananth Prasad, Secretary of the Florida Department of Transportation. "We do it to grow the economy." A strong, reliable, integrated transportation system means lower costs for freight shippers and receivers which mean goods can be produced and purchased less expensively which supports competition in the global marketplace.[49]

In the country's earliest days, the biggest challenges were delivering mail and getting crops from farms to markets. The scope of the freight system grew as rapidly as the country did. Waterways, rail-roads, and eventually highways and airplanes collectively created a network for moving goods that supported the young economy and remain essential in our own time. Even today, prompt delivery of mail and fresh crops remains important in every part of the country. "An efficient network of trucks, trains, barges, pipelines, canals, and airports gives businesses of every size the opportunity to thrive," said David Nichols, Director of the Missouri Department of Transportation. "Transportation brings mail to every household and strawberries to Kansas City in January."

The Golden Gate
Bridge in San
Francisco, California.

America's modern freight system is massive, complex, global, interconnected, and multi-modal. The system moves 48 million tons of goods worth $46 billion every day and serves 7.4 million business establishments, 117 million households, and more than 89,000 government units. Trucks carry the largest share of shipments traveling 500 miles or less over the country's 4.1 million miles of highways. In many cases, multiple modes are used to transport freight often based on the distance a shipment must travel.[50]

Freight's Early Days

The segment of the Erie Canal passing through Rochester, New York, in the early 20th century.
Courtesy of Library of Congress

Iron ore being unloaded from a vessel and onto railroad cars in Buffalo, New York, circa 1900.
Courtesy of Library of Congress

Development of the nation's freight infrastructure largely followed personal mobility patterns. Waterways were the first freight corridors. Coastal routes and inland rivers supplemented by connecting canals, locks, and channels provided the only economically feasible way of moving goods. Construction of the New York State canal system in the 1820s was instrumental in connecting Midwestern agricultural states to the cities and markets of the Northeast and expanding capacity for importing and exporting through the Great Lakes. The opening of the Panama Canal in 1914—just four months before AASHTO was created—allowed ships to pass between the Atlantic and Pacific Oceans, saving about 8,000 miles and further enhancing the country's maritime efficiency.

However, rivers, channels, and canals only go where the water flows. The rapid growth of railroads in the 19th century made waterways more productive by creating new connections that improved movement of agricultural and industrial goods, helped grow inland cities, and fueled the industrial revolution. Railroads were "steel tributaries" that broadened the reach of natural and constructed waterways.[51]

Despite the railroads' success as freight movers, the lack of reliable, connected, and consistently passable highways during the 19th and early 20th centuries left a huge gap in America's freight network, particularly for farmers who needed to get their crops to rail hubs. In 1893, General Roy Stone, the first head of the

Transportation Turning Point
A New England River City Prospers

In the country's early days, cities grew along waterways which provided both electric power and vital transportation connections. Norwich, Connecticut, is one example. The confluence of the Yantic, Quinebaug, and Shetucket Rivers in this small New England city, with a population of less than 20,000 in the late 1800s, opened a great waterway to Long Island Sound—the Thames River. Norwich became a cotton manufacturing powerhouse in the 1860s with construction of the Ponemah Mill complex, the largest cotton mill of the time. Norwich's vital transportation waterways were enhanced by chartering of the Norwich and Worcester Railroad in 1833. Good transportation contributed to the city's commercial growth as a firearms manufacturing giant which supplied weapons to the U.S. military and later as the home of the American Thermos Company which became a household brand throughout the world.[55]

The Modern Marine Transportation System

The success of today's marine transportation system (MTS) depends on efficient connections among all transportation modes. The system includes:

- 25,000 of navigable channels

- 239 locks at 193 locations

- The Great Lakes

- St. Lawrence Seaway

- 3,700 marine terminals

- 174,000 miles of rail connecting the lower 48 and Canada and Mexico

- 45,000 miles of interstate supplemented by 115,000 miles of other roadways

- 1,400 designated intermodal connections[52]

A loaded cargo ship sailing out of port.

Office of Road Inquiry in the U.S. Department of Agriculture (the predecessor to the Office of Public Roads and the U.S. Department of Transportation), described the deplorable condition of America's roads as a "crushing tax on the whole people" in squandered productivity, spoiled crops, and high food prices.[53] The fact that the federal government's first road agency was located in the Agriculture Department highlighted the vital connection between farmers and good roads.

AASHTO's role in creating the federal–state partnership that eventually built a national highway system helped expand the freight network that fueled the country's growing economy. Construction of a safe, reliable, and comprehensive system of roads was the remaining cog in the nation's early freight infrastructure.[54]

The Illinois Central Railroad's freight terminal at South Water Street in Chicago, circa 1943.
Courtesy of Library of Congress

Chicago: A Midwest Economic Powerhouse

Transportation improvements gave birth to inland cities. Chicago was one of the fastest growing cities at the start of the 20th century with more than 1.6 million residents and a booming economy. Connections to river, lake, and railroad transportation routes helped build the city's industrial, manufacturing, and commercial life. Mail order sales from two Chicago-based stores, Sears, Roebuck and Company and Montgomery Ward, further enhanced the city's economic power. "By 1900, the average American had come to depend on far-flung places for basic staples of life. Fruit from California, furniture from Chicago, and clothes from New York now crisscrossed the country with speed and ease unheard of a century before."[56]

Chicago's Galewood railroad yard during the 1940s.
Courtesy of Library of Congress

A U.S. Army recruitment poster during World War I.
Courtesy of Library of Congress

Railroads Dominate Freight Transportation

Between 1860 and 1950, railroads dominated freight transportation, carrying everything everywhere. They handled daily mail, express packages, raw materials, food, and manufactured products. Railroads were at the center of the American economy—employing people and affecting the jobs of millions more in agriculture, manufacturing, or distribution.[57] In 1860, railroads carried an estimated 3.2 billion ton-miles (one ton of freight carried one mile). By 1900, the freight load had jumped to 141 billion ton-miles.[58]

Business boomed for the railroads during World War I. In addition to carrying more than 90 percent of wartime passengers including taking almost all American soldiers to their departure ports for active duty, railroads moved nearly all military cargo from factories to east and west-coast ports, and 69 percent of all intercity freight miles reaching a then-record of 746 billion ton-miles in 1944.

But the railroads heyday as the center of freight movement began to fade after World War I as trucks and airlines seized more of the freight market. By 1950, railroads were in rapid decline.

Today there are six dominant North American freight rail carriers—CSX, BNSF, Norfolk Southern, Union Pacific, Canadian Pacific, and Canadian National—which together carry about 40 percent of the nation's goods based on distance and weight. Tom Zoellner, in his book *Train* describes the freight rail business in 2014 as "still reasonably healthy" albeit with a much lower profile. "A train is like a broom or a hammer: an

Freight Game Changer—Intermodal Containers

Malcom P. McLean, a truck driver who grew up on a small farm in Maxton, North Carolina, transformed the shipping industry in the 1950s when he redesigned truck trailers to include a portable, stackable container that could be moved easily into the hull of a cargo ship. His vision—which emerged from his years as a trucker waiting for hours while stevedores unloaded one crate at a time from truck to ship and vice versa—was not just one or two containers, but hundreds on one ship. McLean patented a steel-reinforced box with specially designed corners and "twistlocks," that made it easy for containers to be gripped for loading and stacking.

Malcom McLean, who revolutionized the use of shipping containers, at Port Newark in 1957.

While the idea of shipping freight in large boxes wasn't new, it had never been broadly implemented, in part, because of government regulations and union opposition.

McLean gave up ownership of his well-established trucking business to create a shipping company called SeaLand Industries to implement his intermodal container concept despite having no experience in the shipping industry. In 1956, the same year construction of the Interstate system began, SeaLand Industries launched the first containerized shipping trip from the port at Newark, New Jersey, to Houston with 58 boxes loaded onto a converted oil tanker. The containers arrived in Houston safe and secure where they were loaded onto trailer beds attached to trucking fleets that spread out over Interstate highways to deliver those goods.

Container cranes and container ships in full operation at Terminal 5, operated by Sea-Land in 1966.
Courtesy of Port of Seattle

The transition to containerized shipping reduced the cost of loading and unloading freight dramatically—from $5.86 per ton of loose and loaded cargo in 1956 to 16 cents per ton for containerized cargo.

1956 clearly was a pivotal year in America's transportation history. AASHTO and the state highway departments were moving quickly to build the long-imagined national highway system which was a catalyst for the birth of interstate trucking. Together, trucks, highways, and intermodal container shipping were transforming America's freight system.

Eventually, the productivity advantages and cost efficiencies of container shipping led to its broad use throughout the global marketplace. By the end of the 20th century, container shipping was transporting about 90 percent of the world's trade cargo.[62] However, without the simultaneous construction of the Interstate system to move intermodal containers to and from ships, the boxes that "made the world smaller and the world economy bigger" would have had limited impact.

Transportation Turning Point
A Midwest Perspective on
21ˢᵗ Century Freight Movement

A thriving business in Asia buys equipment to move heavy machinery that is manufactured in a small, rural town in southwest Minnesota. A small city at the northern edge of Minnesota is home to a window manufacturer that sells its products to customers in South America. A leader in electronic parts manufacturing based in northwest Minnesota depends on its regional airport to guarantee rapid-order fulfillment worldwide. All of the points in the transportation system that enable our products to get from A to B matter, from the trucks hauling oversized loads on county roads and bridges, across the Interstate, to a rail terminal, to a ship that leaves Los Angeles to sail across the Pacific. America's transportation system provides a constant, reciprocal, and growing connection to the world. Investment in transportation is an investment in our economic vitality.[63]

~ Minnesota Department of Transportation

Postmaster General James Farley with flight covers sent during the 1938 National Airmail Week.
Courtesy of Library of Congress

Workers handling mail bags at a Louisville & Nashville Railroad station in Florida in 1940.
Courtesy of Library of Congress

A worker removing mail bags from a railroad car in Montrose, Colorado, in 1940.
Courtesy of Library of Congress

Moving Mail Launches the Freight Industry

Delivering mail was at the heart of the evolution of America's transportation system, particularly growth of the country's freight network. The U.S. Post Office, which was established by the Continental Congress in 1775, often led the way in using new transportation systems before they were used more widely for passenger or freight travel. Mail delivery evolved from foot to horseback, stage coach, steamboat, railroad, bus, automobile, and airplane with interim experiments with balloons, helicopters, and pneumatic tubes.[64] Rail dominated mail delivery through much of the early 20ᵗʰ century, peaking in 1930 when more than 10,000 trains moved mail. By 1970, the railroads carried virtually no mail.

The first comprehensive approach for processing and delivering mail via trains was introduced in 1862 with an experimental route on the Hannibal and St. Joseph Railroad. That improved, higher-speed means of mail distribution subsequently expanded to other lines, and in 1869 the Railway Mail Service was created. Throughout the rest of the 19th century, the RMS continued to grow and thrive across the nation. That service became a major force in the U.S. mail delivery network. By the 1920s, however, the RMS (which would be re-designated the Postal Transportation Service in 1942) was suffering from the steep decline in passenger and business traffic on trains nationwide.

From 1941 through 1974, as the railroads continued to decline, buses were used for mail delivery. The Highway Post Office grew from three primary routes in 1941 using veteran railway postal clerks to more than 200 in the 1950s. Post office clerks processed and sorted mail on moving buses that were simultaneously delivering it from town to town. The Highway Post Office made its final run on the Cincinnati to Cleveland, Ohio, route, 33 years after the first experimental run. Incidentally, the last remaining Railway Post Office made its final run three years later between New York City and Washington, D.C.

A worker loading mail bags into rail cars at Chicago Union Station during World War II.
Courtesy of Library of Congress

The Post Office played a particularly important role in opening the airways for delivery of goods—and eventually for personal transportation. Airmail began in the early 1900s with 31 experimental flights in more than 16 states, followed by broad airmail service in 1918. By 1920, the Post Office was

Transportation Turning Point
Connecting California to the Country

California grew quickly when gold was discovered there in 1848, and pioneers flocked to the country's west coast. In less than two years, California grew from fewer than 7,000 residents to more than 60,000. In the state's earliest days, the Post Office contracted with the Pacific Mail Steamship Company to bring mail to California. It went by ship from New York to Panama, by rail across Panama, and then to San Francisco by ship, usually taking more than four weeks for a letter to reach its destination. An overland mail system using a stage line generally took months to arrive. The long delays in receiving mail and news from the other end of the country left Californians feeling isolated. For example, when California became a state in 1850, it took six weeks for the news to reach Los Angeles. The Pony Express, which was in service between April 1860 and October 1861, temporarily improved mail-delivery times for California from weeks or months to approximately just 10 days. It would take the establishment of transcontinental railroad lines in the decades after the Civil War, followed by the introduction of airmail service during the 20th century, to more consistently, closely, and comprehensively connect that rapidly growing state to the rest of the country.[65]

delivering mail from coast to coast with interim stops where mail was transported locally on trains. Mail was carried on trains at night and airplanes by day. Nevertheless, the combination air-rail mail service sped up cross-country delivery by 22 hours over rail only.

The scope of airmail service continued to expand from government-operated mail-only flights until commercial flights began in 1926. By September 1, 1927, all airmail was carried under contract to commercial flights.

The Post Office's early ventures into airmail laid the foundation for eventual growth of the world-wide air transport structure. Charles I. Stanton, an early airmail pilot, who later headed the Civil Aeronautics Administration, described the early evolution of airmail and air freight service this way:

Actress Marion Weldon participating in the celebration of National Airmail Week in May 1938.

Courtesy of Library of Congress

> *"We planted four seeds...They were airways, communications, navigation aids, and multi-engine aircraft. Not all of these came full blown into the transportation scene; in fact, the last one withered and died and had to be planted over again nearly a decade later. But they are the cornerstones on which our present world-wide transport structure is built, and they came, one by one, out of our experience in daily, uninterrupted flying of the mail."*[66]

Organizational Turning Point
AASHTO and the Panama Canal Share Anniversaries

"ANCON" in Gatun locks.
Courtesy of Library of Congress

AASHTO and the Panama Canal arrived on the transportation scene within four months of each other in 1914. Both had major impacts on the next 100 years of transportation progress. Their shared centennials are marked by continuing change and impact. A $5 billion expansion of the Panama Canal will widen and deepen the canal, double its capacity, create new container shipping efficiencies between Asia and the United States, and possibly alter shipping patterns to create new economic development opportunities for both port cities and inland regions. Recognizing that waterborne trade is a cornerstone of the 21st century economy, AASHTO is working with states and the federal government to strengthen the country's marine transportation system to ensure a strong and efficient freight system for the next 100 years.[67]

Post Office and Private Services Compete to Move Small Packages

The Post Office and private delivery services competed early in the 20th century to deliver small goods for the rapidly growing mail-order business. The Post Office launched parcel post services in 1913 with thousands of small packages mailed throughout the country in the first few days of operation. The availability of parcel post led to rapid expansion of the mail-order houses. Sears Roebuck & Company and Montgomery Ward, the two largest mail-order houses, saw their revenues triple after five years of parcel post delivery.

Private messenger and delivery services fought against parcel post, but rural residents, who loved the Post Office's rural free delivery and made up 54 percent of the country's population, strongly supported parcel post to handle their mail-order purchases. American Messenger Company, established in 1907, was the leading private parcel service. Using motorcycles and later Model T's, the company initially handled special delivery mail for the U.S. Post Office and then expanded to deliver packages for retail stores. American Messenger became Merchants Parcel Delivery in 1913, adopted the color brown as its identifying mark in 1916, and became the United Parcel Service in 1919, later known at UPS.

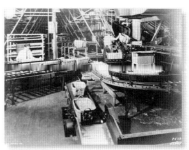

Interior views of Sears Roebuck & Company Mail Order Plant in the Merchandise Building, Chicago, Illinois, circa 1918.

Courtesy of Library of Congress

Post Office Department Parcel Post. Rural Free Delivery circa 1914.

Courtesy of Library of Congress; Photo by Harris & Ewing

"We all know that roads properly built to meet modern highway traffic conditions can help materially to reduce accidents. The saving of life and limb alone would justify the cost of modernizing our road system as quickly as possible."

~ President Harry S. Truman

In a 1955 letter he wrote as a former U.S. president to Senator Stuart Symington of Missouri.

In Washington, D.C., speed limits were lowered from 40 miles per hour to 35 within 24 hours after the Baruch Rubber Investigating Committee recommended the lower speed on a nationwide basis.

Courtesy of Library of Congress; photo by Albert Freeman, 1942

Chapter 6
Making America's Transportation System Safer

Investments in well-built roads, safer cars, and improved driver behavior have reduced highway accidents and saved lives during this century of transportation achievement. Over the past four decades, highway vehicle fatalities have declined by more than 35 percent despite a 130 per cent increase in vehicle miles traveled. But there is still a long way to go. Nearly 34,000 people died on America's highways in 2012 which translates to 93 auto fatalities per day. In addition, 236 million people were injured in traffic accidents in 2012.[68]

While the 2012 fatality total and a continuing decrease in 2013 to 1940s levels reflect a dramatic improvement in highway safety when viewed over time, most agree that zero fatalities is the right safety goal for the future.

The majority of transportation fatalities in the United States—94 percent in 2012—occur on the nation's highways. In comparison, other components of America's transportation system are relatively safe:

- In 2011 and 2012, there were *no* fatalities on commercial and commuter air carriers over 17.4 million flight hours and 9.4 million departures.
- Train fatalities have averaged about 600 annually during the past 10 years while transit deaths averaged less than 100 per year during the same period.
- The highest incidence of water-related fatalities occurs in recreational boating with more the 750 deaths in 2011.

"It is apparent that there is no single answer to the national traffic safety problem. Instead, increased safety and a resulting decrease in the death and injury toll will result from an intensified and coordinated traffic safety program...We cannot tolerate the human and economic waste which is occurring as a result of these traffic accidents."

~ President John F. Kennedy, April 1963
Responding to a report from the presidential committee on traffic safety.

Traffic accident at
14th and Q Streets, NW,
in Washington, D.C., circa
1920.
Courtesy of Library of Congress

Lethal Roads

Few could have envisioned the explosion of traffic fatalities as Americans took to the road when
Henry Ford made the Model-T accessible and affordable. But, the rapid growth of cars driven by
inexperienced and untrained drivers on poorly constructed roads proved to be a lethal combination.
There were 117 traffic fatalities in 1904, 10 years before Model T's became widely available. By 1920,
a new automobile rolled off the assembly line every six seconds and an auto fatality occurred every
16 seconds. In 1925 more than 930 people died in automobile accidents in New York City, more than
a third of them children. That same year, automobile accidents killed more people in Illinois than
diphtheria, measles, scarlet fever, typhoid, and whooping cough combined when those diseases were
fairly common and not yet controlled by vaccinations.[69]

An accident involving the
car circa 1920–1921 in
Washington, D.C.
Courtesy of Library of Congress

By the Numbers
Motor Vehicle Fatalities in the United States

	Total Fatalities	Population	Vehicle Miles Traveled
1904	172	82.2 million	N/A
1914	4,468	99.1 million	N/A
1924	18,400	114 million	105 million
1934	34,240	126.4 million	216 million
1944*	23,165	138.4 million	213 million
1954	33,890	163 million	562 million
1964	45,654	192 million	846 million
1972**	*54,589*	209.9 million	1.26 billion
1984	44,257	235.8 million	1.72 billion
1994	40,716	260 million	2.36 billion
2004	42,836	293.6 million	2.96 billion
2008	37,423	303.8 million	2.98 billion
2012	33,561	314.4 million	2.95 billion[71]

*Gas rationing and reduced driving during World War II led to a drop in fatalities from 1942–1945.
**Highest number of traffic fatalities on highways over the past century.

Organizational Turning Point
AASHTO Leads Safety Efforts

With consistency and interstate collaboration as its hallmarks, AASHTO played an important role from the beginning of the transportation safety movement both because of its engineering expertise and its capacity to bring state highway departments together to solve problems across state lines.

In 1922, before the first National Conference on Street and Highway Safety convened, AASHTO's Subcommittee on Traffic Control and Safety had begun working on naming and marking the nation's highways and standardizing traffic control devices to make America's roads safer. The committee's work led to publication of the first *Manual on Uniform Traffic Control Devices* in 1927 which has remained the bible on managing highway traffic for more than 85 years. Today AASHTO, the Federal Highway Administration, and 15 other organizations work together to review and constantly update the manual to ensure familiarity and consistency on tools for managing traffic on highways everywhere.

AASHTO has broadened and deepened its focus on safety through the work of its Standing Committee on Highway Traffic Safety which is charged with addressing specific safety issues, promoting constant awareness of the need to enhance highway safety, and ensuring that safety remains a top priority. Over the past century, AASHTO's safety work has evolved from the basics – standardizing road names and stop signs—to providing sophisticated tools for strategic safety planning and quantifying the safety-related effects of transportation decisions.[70]

The driving public was slow to react to the dangers of driving in America. Despite the growing fatality rate, people took to the roads in increasing numbers, driving faster whenever conditions permitted. Widespread traffic congestion in heavily populated areas was, in fact, a life saver because it forced slower, more cautious driving. National leaders began to take notice when the growing fatality rate was decried by many as a national scandal.

Tackling Transportation Safety

Secretary of Commerce Herbert Hoover convened the first National Conference on Street and Highway Safety on December 14, 1924—10 years after AASHTO was created. It was the first in a series of safety conferences over the next three decades to examine causes of traffic fatalities, identify strategies and solutions, and make highway safety a national priority.

Two couples sitting in a vintage 1910 Ford automobile at the Automotive Industry Golden Jubilee in Detroit in 1946.
Courtesy of Library of Congress

Participants in the 1924 national conference recognized the need for uniformity—in motor vehicle laws, signage, and road design—to improve highway safety. It was a theme that would dominate the continued evolution of the country's transportation system. And AASHTO was particularly well-positioned to be the arbiter of uniformity through its state highway department members.

The recommendations that emerged from the first national conference on safety dealt with car, driver, and road improvements including:

- Standardization of hand signals to communicate planned driver actions;
- Improved and more consistent highway design including standard widths to accommodate vehicles passing in opposite directions, fewer hills and curves, emergency off-road stopping areas every 300 feet on rural roads to avoid mid-road stops, and painted white centerlines on roads to indicate no passing sections;
- Use of standard, easily recognizable signs warning of upcoming hazards, particularly railroad crossings where 10 percent of all fatalities occurred;
- Better design of automobile headlights to brighten the road ahead without blinding oncoming drivers;
- Development of a "device" for cleaning rain and snow from automobile windshields while driving
- Clearer distinction between the accelerator and brake pedal on all automobiles and stronger brakes capable of stopping an automobile in 50 feet from a speed of 20 miles per hour; and
- Voluntary action by states to establish motor vehicles laws and policies including titling and registering all motor vehicles and licensing drivers.

A farmer changing automobile license plates in San Augustine, Texas, in 1939.

Courtesy of Library of Congress; photo by Russell Lee, 1903-1986

Conference participants concluded that it would be impossible to set one speed limit for broad use throughout the country, but that traveling at a speed of more than 35 miles an hour should be considered "unfeasible and reckless."[72]

Transportation Turning Point
Speed Limits Influence Highway Safety

In May 1901, Connecticut set the first state speed limits for motor vehicles— 12 miles per hour in cities and 15 miles per hour on country roads. The law also required drivers to slow down upon approaching or passing horse-drawn vehicles and coming to a complete stop to avoid scaring animals. Further adoption of speed limits was slow over the next three decades. As late as 1930, a dozen states had no speed limits. Although setting speed limits was considered a state responsibility, the federal government intervened in 1974 when President Richard Nixon signed a law setting a national speed limit of 55 miles per hour to deal with rising fuel prices and fuel shortages. In 1987, Congress allowed states to increase speed limits to 65 miles per hour on rural roads. The National Highway System Designation Act of 1995 repealed the national speed limit, giving full responsibility back to the states.[73]

While the 1924 National Safety Conference didn't produce measureable results—traffic fatalities increased by seven percent in 1925 crossing the 20,000 mark—it established highway safety as a national priority, reinforced the need for sustained attention to building better roads, and emphasized the importance of standardization in America's transportation system. Those themes would guide future action on highway safety and were central to AASHTO's work on the design and construction of highways, particularly the Interstate system.

Transportation Turning Point

Windshield Wipers Meet a Safety Need

The first manually operated windshield wipers were invented by Alabama-native Mary Anderson in 1904 well before the 1924 National Conference on Highway Safety highlighted the need. Anderson traveled to New York City from her Alabama home where she saw horseless carriages for the first time and noticed drivers constantly stopping to remove snow and ice from their windshields by hand. To solve the problem, she designed and won a patent for a spring-loaded rubber blade that was manually operated by a lever from inside the car. But the invention did not catch on because automobile use was still somewhat limited, the manual lever was difficult to operate without a passenger in the car, and automobile makers thought the moving blade would be more distracting than helpful. Her patent eventually expired. As use of cars expanded, however, the need for wipers became more obvious. In 1921, Fred and William Folberth invented automatic windshield wipers—initially called "Folberths"—that were powered by a tube connected to the car's motor. In 1967, Robert Kearns patented intermittent power wipers. Today water-sensing technology makes it possible for wipers to self-activate when rain hits the windshield and adjust automatically as it rains harder.[74]

As Commerce Secretary, Hoover convened another safety conference in 1926, followed by a 1930 conference when he was President. At the opening of that 1930 conference, Hoover described highway safety as a "humanitarian and economic problem which touches every man, woman, and child in the land." President Franklin Roosevelt hosted one safety conference during his first term.

President Harry Truman, a long-time advocate of good roads who had personally overseen construction of all-weather roads that brought all farms in Jackson County, Missouri, to within two miles of a concrete road when he was chief administrative judge there from 1927–1934, resumed the national focus on highway safety following World War II. He convened national safety conferences in 1946, 1947, 1949, and 1952. Truman personally led the conferences, demanding collective action to reduce what he called "the frightful slaughter on our streets and highways."[75] A seven-point action program emerged from the 1949 conference which called for:

1. Adoption of the Uniform Vehicle Code and the Model Traffic Ordinance;
2. More effective collection and analysis of traffic-accident reports to guide highway-safety activities;
3. Continuation of traffic-safety programs in American schools to provide guidance on preventing accidents prevention;
4. Operation of traffic-law-enforcement programs in cities and states to encourage voluntary observance of regulations and consequences for violations;
5. Use of engineering principles and techniques to eliminate or reduce physical hazards and promote safe control of traffic movements;
6. State adoption of policies and procedures for motor vehicle administration with special attention to driver licensing and vehicle inspection;
7. Continued public information outreach to spread the word about the importance of highway safety.[76]

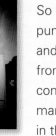

Transportation Turning Point
Electric Traffic Control Starts with a Birdhouse

A Salt Lake City policeman established the foundation for traffic signals to manage traffic and improve safety more than 100 years ago. Officer Lester F. Wire didn't feel safe when he was directing cars, trucks, buggies, and trolleys at a busy intersection in downtown Salt Lake City in 1912.

So he built a birdhouse made of plywood, painted it yellow, and punched six-inch holes on either side. He then dipped bulbs in red and green paint and used a manual switch to change the lights from red to green. By 1917, Salt Lake City had traffic signals at six connected intersections, all controlled simultaneously from one manual switch. It was the first interconnected traffic signal system in the United States.[77]

Licensing to Ensure Skilled and Knowledgeable Drivers

"You know the old story about when a fellow sticks a hand out in a car, he is going to stop, back up, turn right, or turn left," President Truman told the delegates to the 1946 Highway Safety Conference. "That is about as much as a lot of drivers know about the rules of the road."[78]

Truman was frustrated with the slow progress on driver-licensing systems to keep what he called "irresponsible, unfit, and chronic law violators" off the roads. It was a theme that he raised repeatedly at the four safety conferences he convened during his Presidency. As a U.S. Senator in the early 1940s, Truman had tried to pass legislation to establish uniform minimum standards for driver qualifications, but the bill failed in the House of Representatives when states' rights advocates successfully argued that the states, not the federal government, should regulate the operation of highways including establishing motor vehicle laws.[79]

Driver's licenses were initially little more than identification cards which could be acquired by mail for a small fee. Since testing or licensing hadn't been required to ride horses or drive carriages, few saw a need for new rules to govern driving horseless carriages. But the volume of cars driving at increasing speeds for longer distances and resulting accidents and deaths argued otherwise. In 1908, Rhode Island was the first state to test people on their driving ability before issuing licenses. New Jersey began requiring all drivers to pass both a driving skills and a written test in 1913. It took 51 years from Rhode Island's early adoption of driver testing for all states to require exams that assessed both the rules of the road and driving skills in order to get drivers' licenses.

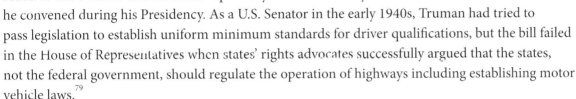

Transportation Turning Point
Evolution of New York Driver's License

New York State began issuing paper licenses to chauffeurs in 1910 including photos on the back. The first licenses for other drivers became available in 1918 and became required for all drivers in 1924. A year later, New York introduced a three-month learner's permit for 16- and 17-year-olds that allowed them to drive to school or work, but not in New York City. Beginning in 1925, the state added a reminder about the importance of reporting all accidents "under penalty of law" and a large "Safe Drivers Save Lives" message across the back of licenses. Because of the importance of drivers' licenses for official identification, the state began taking steps in the 1980s to combat false documentation by adding a color photo and a hologram. Today, New York drivers' licenses are laser-engraved and made of polycarbonate materials with two photos to minimize fraud.[80]

For a historic retrospective, visit *http://www.nytimes.com/interactive/2013/03/17/nyregion/17licenses-evolution.html.*

Safer Cars: Simple Strategies to Save Lives

Windshield wipers, non-blinding headlights, and more distinct accelerator and brake pedals were early improvements to make cars safer. Three major equipment improvements in the post-Interstate era had significant impacts on driver and passenger safety in cars.

Seat belts. In 1966, Congress passed the National Traffic and Motor Vehicle Act which required automakers to put front and back seat belts in all new cars. Unfortunately, the law did not require drivers and passengers to use the seat belts, and adoption was slow. Only about 25 percent buckled up on average for many years after seat belts became standard equipment. In 1984, New York became the first state to require drivers and front-seat passengers to wear seat belts all the time. Today, 49 states and the District of Columbia have mandatory seat belt laws at least for the driver and front-seat passengers with varying levels of enforcement. More than 86 percent of drivers and occupants now wear seat belts regularly with extremely positive safety results. Safety experts estimated that nearly 12,000 lives were saved in 2011 because accident victims were wearing seat belts.[81]

Child safety seats. A child crashing into or through a windshield after a sudden stop was a parent's nightmare in the 1960s. Even the arrival of seat belts did not improve riding safety for children because they were too small to be held in place safely. While some child seats were manufactured in the 1930s, they were intended to make it easier for a driving parent to see a child in the back seat rather than for the child's safety. The first child safety seats designed for crash protection were developed in the 1960s with significant pressure from advocacy groups such as Physicians for Automotive Safety and Action for Child Transportation Safety. State laws requiring use of child safety seats followed with Tennessee leading the way in 1978. Today, all 50 states and the District of Columbia have laws requiring safety seats and restraints for children based on their age and size.

Airbags. The technology for automobile "safety cushions" was developed in the 1950s, but they were not used widely by auto makers until the 1970s. Some safety experts believed airbags carried more risks than advantages, particularly for children and smaller people. With improved technology, data showed that the combination of airbags and seat belts reduced the risk of dying in a head-on collision by 30 percent. The Intermodal Surface Transportation Efficiency Act of 1991 (ISTEA) required that all cars and light trucks in the United States have airbags on both sides of the front seat by 1998. Since then, airbags have become standard equipment on all new cars and have had a significant impact on highway safety.

Highway Hypnosis

The very features that were intended to make superhighways safer than other roadways initially caused worries about risks of miles and miles of sameness. The drive for uniformity, some feared, could lull drivers into a state of near hypnosis, Frank Turner, deputy commissioner, chief engineer, and then director of public roads during the Interstate years, boasted about a system that was "so uniform you can't tell what state you are in except as you look at the sign." Safe roads, he argued, offered no surprises and required no sudden moves. However, the risk to drivers not accustomed to such uniformity was potentially falling asleep under the spell of passing miles. As the Interstate expanded, some safe driving campaigns provided advice on how to combat highway hypnosis or "turnpike trance" including listening to the radio, talking with passengers, watching the landscape, and stopping periodically on long trips. Over time, fast food restaurants and roadside stops grew up along the Interstate's exits providing options for travelers to break the monotony. And, in the long run, the uniformity of the Interstate system has proven to be one of its greatest safety assets.[82]

Safer Roads: Engineering Solutions to Reduce Fatalities

Good roads are safer roads. In the early days of this century, passable roads were the goal. AASHTO, with its deep engineering knowledge and access to state department expertise and experience, played a vital role in developing modern road-building approaches that, over the years, contributed to safer highways.

The Interstate system became a model for safe roads. Its uniformity—at least two travel lanes going in each direction separated by a median, standard lane widths and shoulders, gently banked curves to keep cars on the road, gradual hills, and limited access—has been its greatest safety feature. Traffic fatalities would be significantly higher without the Interstate system, which data shows is twice as safe as other roadways.[83]

Engineering strategies that state transportation departments have developed over the years to support safer roads include:

- Rumble strips to reduce run-off-the-road crashes by alerting drivers that they are drifting;
- Median barriers to minimize cross-over accidents;
- High-visibility lane markings; and
- Traffic calming designs such as roundabouts that manage traffic flow and reduce intersection collisions.

Centerline rumble strips have reduced traffic fatalities and injuries on Minnesota's rural two-lane roads by 12 percent since 2012.

Courtesy of Minnesota DOT

Transportation Turning Point
Mothers Against Drunk Driving

Candice Lightner created Mothers Against Drunk Driving (MADD) in 1980 shortly after her 13-year-old daughter, Cari, was killed by a drunk hit-and-run driver in Fair Oaks, California. MADD's mission is to stop drunk driving, support those affected by drunk driving, prevent underage drinking, and push for stricter alcohol policy. In 2006, MADD launched a campaign to eliminate drunk driving in the United States using a combination of current technology such as alcohol ignition interlock devices, law enforcement, and grassroots activism.

Safer Drivers: Licensed, Skilled, Focused, and Alert

President Truman believed knowledgeable and skilled drivers would make America's roads safer. He was right—driver testing and strict licensing requirements including special requirements for younger and older drivers have contributed to safer highways. But skill alone does not eliminate highway accidents. Impaired driving caused by alcohol, distractions, and fatigue remain major causes of traffic fatalities and injuries. Alcohol, in particular, is a factor in 40 percent of fatalities annually—down from 51 percent in 1990, but still a major safety problem. Despite the impact of zero tolerance enforcement, high arrest rates, educational campaigns, and the work of advocacy groups, drunk drivers caused more than 13,000 deaths in 2010.

Distracted driving, which is defined as any activity which causes drivers to take their eyes off the road, hands off the wheel, or mind off the primary task of driving safely even for a split second, is on the rise as a safety risk. Texting while driving is the most alarming distraction, and young people are particularly at risk. To combat distracted driving, states and the federal government have worked together to combine laws that ban texting and using hand-held cell phones while driving with effective enforcement and aggressive public education campaigns.

The federal–state partnership through AASHTO that guided development of the transportation system over the past 100 years carries over to highway safety through joint campaigns to raise awareness of the high risks of impaired or distracted driving.

21ˢᵗ Century Highway Safety

"We are on the cusp of significant improvement in highway safety," said AASHTO Executive Director Bud Wright. "We need to invest in strategies that will continue the trend." The incremental decrease in traffic fatalities over the past four decades from a high near 55,000 in 1972 to an average of 33,000 over the past four years is cause for optimism. Together, AASHTO, the Federal Highway Administration, and many state transportation departments are pushing toward a more aggressive outcome— zero fatalities.

How many fatalities on America's highways are acceptable? That's a question highway officials have grappled with since the early 1920s when everyone realized that 20,000 was way too many. As traffic fatalities increased over the next 50 years, slowing the growth became the annual goal.

Today, the "toward zero deaths" vision calls for a culture of safety in which any traffic fatalities are no longer acceptable. Four key strategies guide the zero fatalities movement:

- Considering motor vehicle crashes a public health crisis rather than just a transportation challenge;
- Bringing a wide range of stakeholders together to embrace the strategy;
- Using data to identify and monitor national priorities; and
- Encouraging dramatic steps to produce dramatic results.[84]

Transportation Turning Point
State Highway Fatalities Decline to 1940s Levels in Several States

The nationwide commitment to zero fatalities showed great promise as this century of transportation achievement came to a close. In 2013:

Iowa reported 317 fatalities, the lowest number of traffic deaths since 1944.

Ohio had 982 motorist and pedestrian deaths, the lowest total since the state began keeping records in 1936.

New Jersey state police reported an all-time low of 542 traffic deaths.

South Carolina saw a 17 percent decrease in traffic deaths compared with 2012.

Wyoming reported 85 people killed in traffic accidents, the lowest number since 1945.[85]

Transportation Turning Point
Bicycles and Automobiles Sharing Safe Roads

Bicyclists and automobile drivers have always had a lot in common. The rapid growth of cycling during the last half of the 19th century set the stage for the automobile. Early in the 20th century, bicyclists and drivers lobbied together for good roads to support safe and reliable mobility.

William Martin, champion six-day bicycle rider of the world.
Courtesy of W40476 U.S. Copyright Office; photo by Eisenmann, New York

Early bicycles with huge front wheels were both uncomfortable and risky as riders' heads were as much as eight feet above the road—a long fall on a rough road. When the "safety bicycle" with two equal-sized rubber tires made its debut in the 1870s, biking gradually became safer although still uncomfortable on bumpy, muddy roads and was more widely embraced.

Today bicyclists and drivers share modern roads, many with specifically defined bike paths to accommodate increased bike traffic and improve safe coexistence with cars. Bicycle fatalities account for two percent of all traffic deaths, but the number has been inching upward in recent years—a 9 percent increase from 2010–2011. To improve safety, about half of the states have passed laws that require drivers to stay at least three feet away when passing bicyclists. The distance law is particularly important on roads without bike paths or paved shoulder.

Like driving, bicycle experts say rider behavior including knowledge of good biking practices on busy roads will contribute to increased safety.

The Washington and Minnesota Departments of Transportation were among the first to embrace the zero-highway-death concept in 2000 and 2003. Minnesota DOT Director Charles Zelle said embracing the zero deaths vision was one of the department's most important milestones over the past 10 years, focusing particularly on collaboration as a strategy to reduce traffic fatalities. "MnDOT and our partner agencies work at the state and local levels to raise public awareness, implement safety-focused engineering solutions such as cable-media barriers, support enforcement efforts focused on peak crash times and behaviors, and facilitate emergency response to save lives," Zelle said.

In Minnesota, the zero deaths strategy has produced measureable results in the 10 years since it was adopted. In the last decade:

- The number of motor vehicle occupants killed who were not wearing seat belts decreased by 59 percent.
- The number of people killed in alcohol-related crashes decreased by 49 percent.
- The number of people killed in speed-related crashes decreased by 60 percent.
- The number of drivers under the age of 21 killed in speed-related crashes decreased by 61 percent.
- The number of drivers killed in distracted-driving-related crashes decreased by 55 percent.[86]

More states have adopted aggressive fatality reduction strategies with leadership from AASHTO and the Federal Highway Administration and partnerships within their states. Like much of AASHTO's collaborative work with states, the toward zero deaths strategy is built around a shared goal, state-specific actions to carry out the goal, and regular information sharing to learn from each other.

It's a model that has worked since 1914 in every facet of America's transportation system.

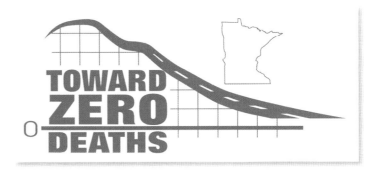

The logo for Minnesota's Toward Zero Deaths program, which focuses on reducing injuries and deaths on the state's roads.
Courtesy of Minnesota DOT

Cable median barriers installed along roads can reduce traffic fatalities by at least 90 percent.
Courtesy of Minnesota DOT

"If you can dream it, you can do it."

~ Walt Disney

Delaware's I-95 Newark Toll Plaza Highway Speed E-Z Pass Lanes.
Courtesy of Delaware DOT

Chapter 7
The Drive for Innovation

This century of transportation achievement is filled with dreams that became reality through persistence, collaboration, and research. The impressive scope of transportation innovations over the past century includes:

- More than four million miles of paved roads;
- Connected waterways including inland rivers, canals, and levees;
- 46,931 miles of coast-to-coast superhighways using consistent design, standard signage, and easily understood numbering;
- A nationwide rail system that supports freight movement and passenger travel;
- Public transit systems including subways and buses in most major cities that provide safe, efficient commuter travel;
- Affordable motor vehicles to improve personal mobility;
- Vastly improved pavement materials that provide a smooth ride and last longer;
- Now standard but once revolutionary advancements to make cars safer such as electric starters, windshield wipers, seat belts, airbags, and anti-lock brakes; and
- Air travel for rapid freight movement and personal travel.

And more…

This chapter highlights the vital role that collaborative research has played in creating America's transportation system during the past 100 years and the innovations that will shape transportation in the coming years.

AASHTO Promotes Innovation

From its earliest days, AASHTO viewed itself as an incubator—a laboratory with 52 experimental stations—for new ideas and best practices to improve the nation's transportation system. AASHTO's early leaders emphasized that transportation challenges could best be addressed through collaborative work among skilled engineers. "Finer roads will be built as they are needed," said AASHTO President Warren W. Mack, chief engineer of Delaware, during his time as AASHTO president in 1939. "Our engineering skill is fully the equal of any nation. Given sufficient funds, engineering skills can produce the desired result."[87]

AASHTO's 100-year commitment to collaboration helped shape the research infrastructure that has led to comprehensive and significant transportation advancements and provides a foundation for the next 100 years. "Research drives innovation, and innovation strengthens our transportation system," said Michigan Department of Transportation Director Kirk Steudle. "That's why sustained investment in research is vital to the future of our transportation system."

"Do you know what my favorite renewable fuel is? An ecosystem for innovation."
~ Thomas Friedman

Texas DOT traffic command center circa 1966, TRB logo, and HRB logo.
Courtesy of Transportation Research Board

Research Capacity Grows Over the Century

In 1920, AASHTO, the state highway departments, and the Bureau of Public Roads joined together to create the National Advisory Board on Highway Research of the National Research Council to exchange of information and research results about highway technology. With federal funding, the Advisory Board served as a forum for improving highway engineering. It was renamed the Highway Research Board in 1925 and became the Transportation Research Board (TRB) in 1974 to reflect the increasingly multi-modal focus of America's transportation system and its broadened research agenda. Today, TRB is one of six major divisions of the National Research Council and continues to maintain close ties with the state transportation departments.

Collaborative transportation research took a huge leap forward in 1962, when the state highway departments, the federal government, and AASHTO created the National Cooperative Highway Research Program (NCHRP) financed by pooled state and federal funds. Its mandate was to advance the state of highway technology for all states and provide technical guidance across the highway transportation sector.

During its first year of operation, NCHRP's launched 34 projects valued at $3.5 million. For more than 50 years, NCHRP has coordinated projects to help solve complex transportation problems, carry out research on emerging challenges, and develop standards for how highways are designed, built, operated, and maintained, often working through AASHTO's network of standard-setting committees. With an annual research budget of $35 million, NCHRP has carried out countless applied research projects that have contributed to safer, greener, smarter, and more cost-effective highway solutions.[88]

North Dakota DOT Director Grant Levi

Like the Interstate system, the partnership that led to and continues to support NCHRP is as significant as the transportation innovations its research has produced. By pooling funds to address shared challenges through NCHRP, state departments of transportation leverage their research investment to produce broader and deeper impacts. "For a small state like North Dakota, the collaborative research is vital," said Grant Levi, Director of the North Dakota Department of Transportation. "We're not big enough to have a large research department, and yet we benefit from and participate in the most advanced and innovative research."

Transportation Turning Point
NCHRP Works

Over 50 years, NCHRP cooperative research has helped state agencies meet the challenges of a changing transportation landscape. Highlights of its impacts include:

- Supporting a lasting commitment to safer transportation through 23 guidebooks that provide strategies to reduce highway injuries and fatalities

- Keeping bridges on the cutting edge through improved construction, management, and maintenance approaches based on applied research

- Developing strategies for assessing and addressing highway capacity issues to reduce congestion and improve the movement of people and goods

- Helping state transportation departments become greener through strategies that support environmental sensitivity without compromising the transportation system

- Developing principles and tools for smarter spending and system preservation through asset management

- Always seeking the next big concept in pavement design to ensure continued progress and improvements[89]

Road Tests Shape Early Highway Research

Beginning in 1909 and continuing through the early 1960s, road tests were the primary research method for assessing optimal materials and design to produce long-lasting roads. Most of the earliest road tests were carried out by local governments.

The first well-documented state-administered road test was the Bates Experimental Road in 1920 and 1921 in Illinois. With up to $100 million authorized to construct a statewide rural highway system, the Illinois Division of Highways built a 2.5-mile test segment on state property near Springfield, Illinois, to determine the best materials to use for rural roads carrying significant truck traffic. "To undertake a program of this size without definite scientific knowledge of the behavior of certain pavement under truck traffic and rural conditions—without knowing definitely how to design pavements to sustain truck traffic—was deemed unwise," wrote Illinois Chief Highway Engineer Clifford Older in a 1922 report summarizing the findings of the road test.[90]

The experimental road had 63 sections, each about 200-feet long built with paving materials that were currently in use or recommended. A 1921 New York Times article praised the road test approach for its scientific, non-political approach to highway research. "[The experimental road]

Highway officials inspecting experimental work done in Arlington, Virginia, by the U.S. Bureau of Public Roads

Multiple Programs Support Multi-Modal Transportation Research

As the transportation system has grown more complex and more multi-modal, the range of organizations carrying out and sharing information on vital research has also grown. These groups support and build on work by federal agencies, AASHTO, and the Transportation Research Board. In addition to the National Cooperative Highway Research Program, some important research resources in the transportation world include:

Airport Cooperative Research Program (ACRP)—Carries out applied research on problems that are shared by airport operating agencies.

Council of University Transportation Centers (CUTC)—Provides a forum for improving and enhancing research and education and for better integrating research with academic education, training, and technology transfer.

Long-Term Pavement Performance Program—Provides rigorous long-term field experiments on currently in-use pavements.

A surveyor at work at Alaska's Ted Stevens Anchorage International Airport, with a cargo jet taking to the skies above.

National Cooperative Freight Research Program—Carries out applied research on problems facing the freight industry.

National Transportation Product Evaluation Program—Provides quality and responsive engineering for the testing and evaluation of products, materials, and devices that are commonly used by state DOTS.

Research in Progress Online Database—Provides easy access to current or recently completed transportation research projects funded by the Federal government, state DOTS, and universities.

Surface Transportation Environment and Planning Cooperative Research Program—Improves understanding of the complex relationship between surface transportation, planning, and the environment.

Strategic Highway Research Program 1 and 2—Established by Congress to develop and evaluate techniques to combat deteriorating highways (SHRP 1) and to investigate the underlying causes of highway crashes and congestion (SHRP 2).

State Planning and Research Program—Encourages state DOTs to develop, establish, and implement research, development, and technology programs that anticipate and address transportation concerns before they become critical problems.

U.S. Secretary of Transportation Norman Y. Mineta attending a college graduation ceremony.

Transit Cooperative Research Program—Supports efforts by the transit industry to develop innovative, near-term solutions to meet challenges and demands.

Transportation Research Information Service—Maintained by TRB, serves as the largest and most comprehensive bibliographic resource on transportation information.

University Transportation Centers—Connects recognized centers of excellence and institutions of higher learning to provide a vital source of leaders who are prepared to meet the nation's need for safe, efficient, and environmentally sound movement of people and goods.

has already aroused widespread comment and no political agitation," the Times wrote. "Through a series of tests under the auspices of the State Highway Department it is believed that it will be possible to determine the actual wearing qualities of various paving types and from those tests to develop a permanent highway surface for future use."[91]

The Bates Road Test concluded that concrete was the best material for highway building and provided a precise design to maximize the life of concrete roads including use of a longitudinal center joint to eliminate center line cracking. The Bureau of Public Roads conducted loading tests on concrete pavement in the early 1930s, but additional tests were slowed down by World War II.

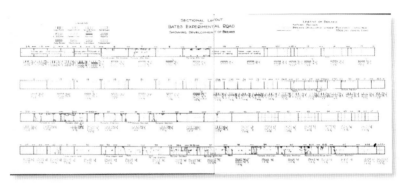

A diagram of the various sections of the Illinois-based Bates Experimental Road, where a pioneering study of highway pavement took place in 1922–1923.

Systematic efforts to gauge the service life of highway pavements and the impact of wheel loads gained new momentum after World War II with AASHTO's strong leadership and support. In 1948, AASHTO established procedures for launching and managing road tests. These research projects were generally financed jointly by two or more states to provide factual data for developing longer-lasting pavements to handle ever-increasing traffic. The first of those projects took place in Maryland in 1950 and 1951, known as Road Test One-MD. It was administered by the Highway Research Board and was financed by the District of Columbia and 11 states—Maryland, Connecticut, Delaware, Illinois, Kentucky, Michigan, New Jersey, Ohio, Pennsylvania, Virginia, and Wisconsin. The Maryland study used an existing road near LaPlata, Maryland, to test the impact of round-the-clock truck traffic on concrete pavements.

Following the Maryland Project, the Western Association of State Highway Officials (WASHO) sponsored a road test in 1953 and 1954 in Idaho at the suggestion of the AASHTO Highway Transport Committee to focus on the impact of heavy truck traffic on flexible (asphalt) pavements. The WASHO Road Test was also conducted by the Highway Research Board and financed by the Idaho, California, Colorado, Nevada, New Mexico, Oregon, Texas, Montana, Utah, Washington, and Wyoming highway departments,

A third road test sponsored by the Mississippi Valley Association of Highway Officials representing Midwestern states was abandoned in favor of a more comprehensive AASHTO-sponsored national research project.

The Road Test

The AASHTO (then known as AASHO) Road Test, the largest and most significant pavement research performed in the 20th century, was the primary source for information about design and construction of the Interstate system. Carried out from 1958 to 1960 at a cost of $27 million (in 1960 dollars) along a seven-mile loop of two-lane highway between Ottawa and LaSalle, Illinois, the road test focused on the impacts of moving truck loads on various asphalt and concrete pavement designs. Unlike the Maryland and WASHO efforts, the AASHTO Road Test covered both concrete and asphalt pavements.

Trucks driving along tangents of varied pavements as a key part of the AASHO Road Test.

An accelerometer that was used in the Bates Experimental Road Test in 1922–1923 to measure the acceleration of the wheels and axles of motor trucks.

There were 836 segments with six test loops of two double lane tangents and 16 bridges along the track, all built with different materials and engineering concepts. The Defense Department provided cars and heavy-duty trucks that drove over the road test loop relentlessly until November 1960 to see which pavement segments lasted the longest in the best shape.

Information on the best-performing segments was crucial in advancing knowledge about structural design, pavement performance, climate effects, and the impact of heavy loads. Findings from the test were used in 1960 and 1962 to develop the *AASHTO Interim Guide for the Design of Rigid and Flexible Pavement*.

Results from the road test still influence pavement design today and have resulted in other essential resource guides including the *AASHTO Guide for Design of Pavement Structures*. The road test also provided the foundation for more recent and similarly comprehensive technical studies including the Long-Term Pavement Performance program which began in1987 as part of the Strategic Highway Research Program (SHRP).

The AASHTO Road Test is generally considered a landmark in highway and bridge design that has never been equaled.

Research Focus Grows as Challenges Become More Complex

As the transportation system evolved in the second half of the century, the need for sustained research became even more important. The success of the AASHTO Road Test, in many ways, reinforced the need for and value of collaborative, applied research. Today, public, non-profit, and private organizations carry out research projects designed to promote transportation excellence. Many state departments of transportation have grown their research capacities to respond to state needs and challenges and which might provide useful information for other states.

AASHTO's Materials Reference Laboratory (AMRL) contributes to the overall success of construction research by:

- Assessing materials and testing laboratories throughout the United States and Canada for conformance with standards; and
- Accrediting laboratories to promote uniformity and quality laboratory testing.

Established in 1965, AMRL accreditation is the largest accreditation program of its kind and is highly valued and respected. The program currently serves more than 2,000 laboratories. AMRL's Laboratory Assessment and Proficiency Sample Programs were first introduced in 1966 covering soil, aggregate, and

bituminous materials. Over the years, AMRL's assessments have grown to include metals, plastic pipe, and spray-applied, fire-resistant material as well as proficiency samples for road-stripe paint. In 1988, the AASHTO Accreditation Program was established to provide formal recognition for construction materials testing laboratories that meet AASHTO-established standards.

A saw that is used as part of the concrete core testing process to assess the strength and durability of concrete materials for construction.

Transportation Turning Point
From Macadam to Superpave

Over this century of transportation achievement, more than four million miles of paved roads were built including the 46,931 Interstate system. That massive road construction effort demanded a similarly massive research effort into pavement materials to produce durable, long-lasting, and safe roads. Very early roads were built with tightly-packed and compacted stones called macadam, named after John McAdam who developed the construction method at the turn of the century. Macadam roads

Roadside construction work being done in the Dupont Circle area of Washington, D.C.

were later covered with tar (called tarmac) to bind the top layer of stones into a hard surface which lasted longer and reduced dust. Cement and asphalt eventually became the surfaces of choice for much of the Interstate system. Today, more than 95 percent of all paved roads in the country are asphalt. Ongoing public and industry research has produced major advancements in pavement technology focusing particularly on finding the best mix of materials to extend the life of roads. One research outcome that has significantly extended the life of asphalt roads is *Superpave*, a performance-based system that helps engineers mix asphalt pavements based on temperature, rainfall, and traffic volume. Other advancements in pavement technology have focused on reducing energy consumption through advancements such as warm-mix asphalt and recycling pavement materials and constantly monitoring pavement conditions using advanced tools such as profiling vans, ground-penetrating radar, and skid trucks to assess the impact of water on pavement, and weigh-in-motion scanners for truck traffic.[32]

Florida's Road Rangers Service Patrol responds to a variety of highway traffic incidents and helps keep vehicles moving along in the Sunshine State.
Courtesy of Florida DOT

In July 2013, AASHTO published a book of 109 high-value research projects carried out by 29 states, the District of Columbia, and the National Cooperative Highway Research Program—*Transportation Excellence through Research: Research Impacts.* The projects demonstrate the breadth of transportation research on topics including driver and pedestrian safety, impact of non-freeway rumble strips, use of streaming and digital media technologies, managing freight corridors, and eliminating weight restrictions on rail systems.[93]

Transportation Turning Point
The Google Automobile Offers a Driverless Prototype

Google Car.
Reproduced by permission from Steve Jurvetson.

The Google driverless automobile took its maiden public voyage in 2010 after logging more than 1,000 miles of entirely automated driving and 140,000 miles of driving with occasional human intervention. The automobile uses artificial intelligence software, a variety of sensors, a roof-mounted range finder, and a GPS navigation system to drive itself. A person sits behind the wheel during test runs to take control of the car, if needed, by hitting a red button, touching the brake, or turning the steering wheel. Since its 2010 unveiling, the Google automobile has been demonstrated and tested on public and private roads throughout the country to continue to refine its performance and to raise its profile. Several automobile manufacturers are participating in the Google research, and Volvo, Toyota, Ford, General Motors, Volkswagen, and Nissan are developing their own autonomous vehicles which are expected to go into production in less than 10 years.[94]

The technology that will make driverless cars commercially available within the next decade is already in use. The Tampa Bay International Airport, for example, was the first airport to use driverless people movers between remote gates and the main terminal, and ports in the Netherlands and Japan use some automated, driverless vehicles to move freight. Cruise control, which was first introduced as "auto-pilot" on the Chevrolet Impala in 1958, is now standard on most cars creating a partially driverless experience. Other pieces of the driverless technology puzzle already in use are adaptive cruise control which adjusts speed to keep pace with a lead car, self-parking, and automatic braking.

Refining the technology that will bring autonomous vehicles to the driving public may be the easy part. Driverless cars will require vast changes in the rules of the road including who (or what) is responsible for accidents—the automobile owner or the software manufacturer? For example, California's state vehicle code, like most states, has more than 40,000 provisions, all of which assume there is a driver in control of the vehicle at all times. To support advancement of the technology and begin to establish ground rules for self-driving cars, California, Florida, Nevada, and the District of Columbia were the first to pass legislation to allow automated vehicles to be tested on public roads.[95]

Smart Cars, Smart Roads, Smart Transportation

Research and advancements in intelligent transportation systems (ITS) have transformed America's transportation system-with exciting possibilities on the horizon. Examples of ITS systems already in use on America's highways include:

- Automatic high-occupancy-toll lane collection;
- Variable speed-limit signs which reduce the risk of rear-end collisions in areas where curves and tunnels reduce drives' sign distance;
- Advanced vehicle control and safety systems to prevent collisions;
- Dynamic messaging to alert drivers to accidents or upcoming traffic backups;
- Highway cameras to monitor traffic in real time;
- Sensors to collect real-time data on air and pavement conditions, precipitation, and other weather-related conditions such as de-icing chemicals on pavement;
- Public transportation information systems that provide real-time schedule information to plan personal trips;
- Electronic payment systems for toll collection, high-occupancy lane monitoring, and public transportation fares;
- Electronic customs clearance for commercial vehicles; and
- Emergency notification and warning systems in personal vehicles.

Gantries that have been built along North Carolina's Triangle Expressway to electronically charge tolls to customer accounts.
Courtesy of North Carolina DOT

Further advancements in intelligent highways and cars are just around the corner. Already cars are equipped with technology tools such as adaptive cruise control and sensors to detect lane changes, backup distances, and the distance between cars on the road. As Kenneth Woods predicted in 1957, highway and automobile engineers are talking to each other to explore vehicle-to-road communication and vehicle-to-vehicle communication. For example, a University of Michigan Transportation Research Institute project is testing vehicles that send signals to each other warning drivers of potential upcoming dangers such as traffic backups, cars stopped at signal lights, or even cars running through red lights.[96] The project is the basis for a national commitment to make vehicle-to-vehicle communication technologies standard equipment in the not-too-distant future.

John C. Allen displays a computation been used to help improve traffic planning.
Photo courtesy of New Jersey DOT

Connected and Driverless Vehicles

Connected vehicles represent a major shift in approaches to transportation safety and management. Several research projects are currently assessing the value of vehicle-to-vehicle and vehicle-to-road wireless communications to reduce accidents. A variety of wireless communications tools that allow vehicles to "talk" to each other can provide instant warnings—as many as 10 messages per seconds—to reduce crash risks from stalled traffic, lane change/blind sports, a predicted sudden stop, or intersection obstructions. Data that emerges from these studies will be used to estimate the long-term safety benefits of wireless communication tools.[97]

At the same time, research by automobile manufacturers and the National Highway Traffic Safety Administration is moving full speed ahead on driverless cars known as "autonomous vehicles." Just as the rapid growth of the Model T a century ago helped necessitate to advancements in road construction, technology advancements in today's vehicles will require deployment of new road technologies.

"The driverless car represents one of the most amazing breakthroughs in safety and quality of life in recent history," wrote Clifford Watson of the Brookings Institution. "Reaping the potential mobility benefits of automated vehicles will require reimagining the way we design and maintain highways."[98]

Transportation Turning Point
Connected Cars: There's an App for That

Technologists envision an entirely new driving experience ahead that goes beyond the safety benefits of car-to-car and car-to-highway connections. Among the possibilities are:

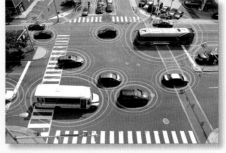

Image courtesy of U.S. DOT Research and Innovative Technology Administration

- Cars that self-diagnose mechanical problems, report on them, and find the nearest mechanic or auto parts store;

- Automatic navigation away from traffic bottlenecks and other delays before the driver gets to them;

- A parking location app that finds the most convenient location to a programmed destination taking into account how long the driver intends to stay; and

- Cars that can activate air conditioning at home before the driver arrives there.

A car, writes technologist James O'Brien, is no longer a mechanical device for travel alone. "More and more, consumers sit in a vehicle and expect a whole experience to surround them," according to O'Brien. "And like almost everything else in the 21st century, the experience is required to be interconnected."[99]

Transportation Turning Point
GPS Technology Leads the Way

In 1997, U.S. Secretary of Transportation Federico Pena said: "Most people don't know what GPS is today. Five years from now, Americans won't know how we lived without it."[100] While it took a little longer than five years, Pena was right. GPS replaced cumbersome, often out-of- date and hard-to-fold maps, making getting from point A to point B remarkably easy. It started with online resources such as MapQuest and Google Maps that plotted point-to-point routes that drivers could use as personal maps. Today, voice-enabled navigation systems are widely available in automobile dashboards and on smartphones. The worldwide GPS system was developed by the U.S. Department of Defense in the 1970s so that military units would always know their exact locations and that of supporting units. The system proved valuable during the 1991 Persian Gulf War, particularly to guide military vehicles across the wide-open, unmarked desert at night. The Defense Department GPS system, with 31 satellites located 12,500 miles above the earth, became open to the public worldwide in 2000.

"Twenty-five years from now, piloting one's own vehicles will seem weirdly anachronistic and unnecessary, like riding a mule to the mall. Just say the address, say "go," sit back and get on with your hologram."

~ Dan Neil; Auto Columnist

From "Who's Behind the Wheel? Nobody," The Wall Street Journal, *September 24, 2012.*

AASHTO Committees and Technical Services Advance Research Efforts

Experts from the 52 member transportation departments participate actively in national transportation research efforts through AASHTO's Standing Committee on Research (SCOR) and the Research Advisory Committee (RAC). The 16-member standing committee evaluates all transportation research programs in the United States and solicits research problems and challenges from all departments and committees. All 52 departments have seats on the advisory committee to ensure broad involvement in identifying research needs, review research in progress, and implement research results. The AASHTO research infrastructure plays a vital coordinating role among the state transportation departments and the many organizations involved in transportation research.

AMRL and AASHTOWare, the association's cooperative transportation software program, further help strengthen the country's transportation system by providing key technical resources and services that would otherwise be tough to obtain or unavailable altogether for state departments of transportation.

"It's time for [the nation's] interconnected system of roads and bridges and rails and runways and waterways to make the journey from a system that works for today's population to one that works for tomorrow."

~ "A to B" Video; Minnesota Department of Transportation

Chapter 8
The Ride Ahead

It's 2014. America's transportation system has come a long way in the past 100 years. The urgent need for good roads and the vision of an interconnected system of superhighways which drove AASHTO's creation and dominated its work for more than half of the century have both been achieved.

At the 2013 Washington Briefing, NHTSA Administrator David Strickland and FMCSA Administrator Anne Ferro participate in a panel discussion moderated by AASHTO President Michael Lewis.

The lasting legacy of this century of achievement is a transportation system that works. It moves people and freight using multiple modes, supports economic growth and community vitality, and offers great promise for the future through ongoing research and innovation. These transportation achievements and the role AASHTO played in building the federal–state partnership that made many of those achievements possible are worth celebrating.

But, the ride ahead is far from smooth.

Traffic along San Francisco's Golden Gate Bridge.

Today, America's transportation system is entering a new century of change, challenge, and opportunity. The challenges are many—a population that is both graying and growing, aging infrastructure, a complex and highly competitive global economy, and limited funds to meet enormous needs.

The following sections highlight challenges that are important to America's transportation future. These issues, which emerged from interviews with and input from leaders of state departments of transportation, are not intended to predict the future or cover all the challenges America's transportation system may face in the years ahead. Instead, they provide a snapshot of the issues that may influence the next century of transportation achievement.

By The Numbers

An Aging Transportation System

Roads

- Nearly 32 percent of major U.S. roads are in poor or mediocre condition.

- Vehicle miles traveled increased by 39 percent between 1990 and 2009, but newly constructed road mileage increased by only 4 percent during the same period.

Bridges

- Nearly 25 percent of the nation's bridges are classified as functionally obsolete or structurally deficient.

- 30 percent have exceeded their 50-year design life.

- The average age of the nation's 607,380 bridges is 42 years.

- More than two billion trips are taken daily across deficient bridges in metropolitan areas.

Public Transit

- In 2010, there were more than 430 interruptions per revenue mile in passenger bus service and 57 interruptions per revenue mile on light rail.

Ports

- Inadequate connections from port terminals to surrounding roads and rail lines cause significant delays when moving goods from ports to market.

Inland Waterways and Rivers

- Much of the water transportation infrastructure has not been upgraded since the 1950s.

- More than half of the locks along inland waterways are at least 50 years old.

- There is an average of 52 services interruptions per day on the water transportation system due to aging infrastructure.

Source:
The American Society of Civil Engineers 2013 Report Card for America's Infrastructure
www.infrastructurereportcard.org

Transportation Challenges for the Future

1. Creating new models for 21st century collaboration.

The state leaders who created AASHTO in 1914 to tackle the nation's transportation challenges believed collaboration among states and between the states and the federal government was the key to progress. They were right. While collaboration remains vital to transportation interconnectedness, the structure and approach may be different in the years ahead. "Whether public–private partnerships, multi-agency collaboration, or an expansion of existing stakeholder and public interaction in transportation planning and programs, daily transportation success requires connections between those shaping it and those interacting with it," said Rudy Malfabon, Director of the Nevada Department of Transportation.

Future collaboration to achieve transportation success will require (1) preserving and strengthening the partnership among state departments of transportation to recognize and respect diverse needs without losing national focus; (2) rethinking and redefining the federal–state partnership to operate in a changed transportation environment; (3) strengthening metropolitan planning and engagement of local officials in regional planning decisions; and (4) building stronger partnerships with customers and consumers to increase understanding of and appreciation for the vital role of transportation in quality of life.

2. Improving the transportation system to meet emerging mobility needs and to strengthen the economy.

A strong transportation system attracts businesses, creates jobs, and supports efficient movement of goods—in addition to meeting a wide range of mobility needs. State departments of transportation are playing more explicit roles in economic development by focusing on freight, trade, and movement of goods using diverse and interconnected modes. "As transportation professionals, we need to continue to make the point that investment in our nation's transportation infrastructure is essential to the economy," said Ananth Prasad, Secretary of the Florida Department of Transportation.

While much of the past century focused on building a new system to serve a country steadily growing in population and power, maintaining and maximizing the efficiency of that system will be an important challenge in the years ahead. Achieving that goal will require investing in preserving and modernizing older infrastructure to extend its life and meet new mobility needs. However, as the country grows and changes, preserving a transportation system that was built to meet 20th century needs will not be sufficient for the 21st century. "We can't settle for maintaining today's system," said former Virginia Secretary of Transportation Sean Connaughton. "We need to get Americans to understand the importance of making our transportation system better than it is today through strategic investments."

By the Numbers
What Lies Ahead

- By 2040, the U.S. population will reach 406 million with 11 percent of Americans age 75 and older requiring greater investments in public transit options.

- An annual capital investment of $101 billion is needed to maintain the nation's roads in their current condition and $170 billion annually to improve the nation's roads compared with the current $91 billion annual capital investment in roads.

- The U.S. air system's already crowded skies will carry more than one billion passengers annually, and air freight tonnage will grow by 200 percent.

- Total U.S. freight shipments will grow from 17.6 billion tons in 2011 to 28.5 billion tons in 2040—a 60 percent increase.

- Trade volume through ocean ports will double between now and 2021 and double again by 2030.

Source:
The American Society of Civil Engineers 2013 Report Card for America's Infrastructure
www.infrastructurereportcard.org

In Indiana, passengers board a bus along Route 2 of the transit service run by the Fort Wayne Public Transportation Corporation (Citilink).
Courtesy of MTAP

South Carolina's cable-stayed Arthur J. Ravenel Jr. Bridge (Cooper River Bridge) under construction.

U.S. Senator Barbara Boxer (D-CA) speaking about transportation priorities at the annual AASHTO Washington Briefing on Capitol Hill in February 2013.

3. Funding the nation's transportation system for the long run.
As predicted by AASHTO's founders in 1914, skilled engineers and sophisticated research have advanced the science of transportation over the century leading to a solid, albeit now-aging, transportation system. The future of America's transportation system will depend on identifying equitable, sustainable, and adequate revenue sources to replace a funding model that was created in 1956, based on fossil fuel taxes. "We are spiraling toward a place where we cannot adequately preserve the transportation system let alone meet new needs for our growing population without new funding models," said Mike Hancock, Secretary of the Kentucky Transportation Cabinet. The structure, sources, and amount of money available to build, operate, and maintain a great transportation system have always been on the front burner at the local, state, and federal levels.

Solving the challenge of long-term transportation finance remains the big issue for the future. Strategies for tackling this issue include new public funding models that rely on income sources other than gas taxes including public–private partnerships, infrastructure banks, subsidized bonding programs, and utility-based financing. States are leading the way in exploring new revenue models. For example, the state of Virginia created a new transportation funding plan that eliminates a gasoline tax in favor of a mix of sales taxes and user fees. The Indiana Department of Transportation is using a public-private partnership which involves leasing the Indiana Toll Road as the cornerstone of funding future state road and bridge projects. The Maryland Department of Transportation is exploring a public-private partnership to design, build, operate, and help pay for a 16-mile transit extension.

Transportation Turning Point
Metropolitan Planning Organizations

The Federal-Aid Highway Act of 1962 required the formation of metropolitan planning organizations in urban areas with populations greater than 50,000 to ensure that use of federal funds in the region is based on a continuing, cooperative, and comprehensive planning process which includes public participation. As of 2013, there were more than 340 MPOs in the country. The Intermodal Surface Transportation Efficiency Act of 1991 (ISTEA) revitalized and expanded the role of MPOs including requiring state transportation officials to connect with MPOs on to encourage collaboration on difficult transportation issues such as traffic congestion in metropolitan regions. In the years ahead, as population grows in urban centers and transportation needs change, the MPOs will become even more important to shaping transportation choices to meet diverse needs.

4. Leveraging technology in transportation system design, operation, management, and communication.

In 1962, a short-lived prime-time television animated series, *The Jetsons*, introduced a technology-driven life-style for a family living in 2062. While the cartoon was very "space age," many of the technologies that shaped the Jetsons' daily lives are here today nearly 50 years earlier than predicted in that television show. Those technologies include moving sidewalks, video phones, flat screen televisions, and voice-activated household tools.

Edwin Melendez, a regional transportation management center operator for the Florida DOT, monitors traffic incidents on the mini video wall at a work station.
Courtesy of Florida DOT

Technology has already transformed many aspects of the transportation system with incredible promise to enhance safety, reduce congestion, lower construction and operating costs, and help reduce carbon emissions. Tools already in use include smart cars, smart highways, wireless communication, voice-enabled navigation, automated traffic and work-zone management, and real-time transit scheduling.

Sam Sakran, a maintenance contractor for the Florida Department of Transportation, gathers the ends of fiber optic to be spliced together.

Physical Security Information Management (PMIS) systems have helped agencies such as the Massachusetts Transportation Bay Authority to better utilize and monitor video cameras, video control devices, and various other sensors.

Software that provides real-time data is also vital to the efficient, cost-effective management of state transportation systems. "Information about the transportation system is as important as the infrastructure we build," said Paul Trombino, Director of the Iowa Department of Transportation. "The emerging transportation era is about information, logistics, and constant real-time customer communication."

Iowa DOT Director
Paul Trombino III, P.E.

With endless potential, the challenge for transportation leaders and the research community is to develop and deploy technology tools which will have the greatest impact on achieving transportation goals. "All of these future technologies offer promise of paradigm-shifting improvements in our transportation systems, but making the leap from systems and investments that we have today to what we could have in the future has sometimes proved challenging in the U.S.," said Richard Davey, Massachusetts Secretary of Transportation and Chief Executive Officer. "Choices we make over the next century will determine whether we are courageous and inventive enough to adopt fundamentally new transportation technologies."

Massachusetts DOT
Secretary and CEO
Richard A. Davey

1973 Snapshot
By the Numbers

U.S. POPULATION **211,908,788**

FEDERAL SPENDING **$245.71 billion**

UNEMPLOYMENT RATE **4.9 percent**

AVERAGE ANNUAL INCOME **$9,154**

AVERAGE COST OF A CAR **$3,650**

COST OF A GALLON OF MILK **$1.31**

MILES OF ROADS **3,806,883**

REGISTERED MOTOR VEHICLES **125.7 million**

1973 Snapshot
Events

- Richard Nixon is inaugurated for a second term as U.S. President.

- U.S. military involvement in Vietnam ends.

- Egypt and Syria attack Israel on Yom Kippur to launch the fourth Israeli–Arab conflict.

- Spiro Agnew becomes the second U.S. vice president to resign from office.

- The U.S. Senate begins nationally televised hearings to investigate the Watergate break in.

- Billie Jean King beats Bobby Riggs in the "battle of the sexes" tennis match.

- Skylab, the first U.S. space station, is launched.

- The first handheld mobile telephone call is made by Martin Cooper in New York City.

- The Miami Dolphins beat the Washington Redskins in the Super Bowl VII to complete the National Football League's first-ever perfect season.

- Secretariat becomes the first horse racing Triple Crown winner in 25 years.

Number Sources:
U.S. Census Bureau—
2012 Statistical Abstract;
www.infoplease.com;
web.bryant.edu;
Federal Highway
Administration Highway
Statistics: Summary to 1975;
TheCostofLiving.com;
www.boomeret.com

Event Sources:
Wikipedia;
TheCostofLiving.com;
www.historyorb.com;
www.boomeret.com

5. Making zero deaths a reality.
"When it comes to transportation safety, you need to have a goal against which to measure progress," said 2011–2012 AASHTO President Susan Martinovich, former Director of the Nevada Department of Transportation. "But how can that goal be anything more than zero because everyone matters?" Safer cars, safer highways, improved driver behavior, campaigns to raise awareness, and technology improvements make zero fatalities a legitimate goal for the next century of transportation achievement. While driver behavior remains the bottom line in ensuring highway safety, the interaction of smart cars and smart highways is one of the most promising advancements for dramatically improving transportation safety.

6. Creating a more interconnected, multi-modal transportation system to move people and goods.
State departments of transportation have grown into their post-Interstate roles by managing, coordinating, and connecting diverse transportation modes that all developed separately. "We are becoming mobility managers to make connections that meet diverse transportation needs," said Iowa DOT

Director Paul Trombino. Developing strategies for moving people and freight on a more interconnected, multi-modal transportation system is a key challenge for the ride ahead.

Congestion on America's highways, an aging population that will require different types of transportation to meet the needs of those individuals, growing interest in car-free urban living, public support for transit funding initiatives, concerns about carbon emissions, and new transportation options such as bike and automobile sharing all contribute to a balanced multi-modal transportation system in the next century. "Coming back to a multitude of transportation options is about optimizing choices as a system rather than as alternatives to cars," said Michael Melaniphy, President and Chief Executive Officer of the American Public Transportation Association (APTA).

President and Chief Executive Officer of the American Public Transportation Association Michael Melaniphy

1993 Snapshot

By the Numbers

U.S. POPULATION **257,746,103**

FEDERAL SPENDING **$1409.39 billion**

UNEMPLOYMENT RATE **7.3 percent**

AVERAGE ANNUAL INCOME **$23,133**

COST OF A CAR **$12,750**

COST OF A GALLON OF MILK **$2.86**

MILES OF ROADS **3,905,211**

REGISTERED MOTOR VEHICLES **194.1 million**

NAFTA Initialing Ceremony.
Photo reproduced by permission from Wikimedia Commons.

Number Sources:
U.S. Census Bureau—
2012 Statistical Abstract;
www.infoplease.com;
Federal Highway
Administration 2012
Highway Statistics;
TheCostofLiving.com;

Event Sources:
Wikipedia;
TheCostofLiving.com;
www.historyorb.com;
www.boomeret.com

1993 Snapshot

Events

- Bill Clinton succeeds George H.W. Bush as the 42nd U.S. president.

- A bomb parked below the North Tower of the World Trade Center in New York City explodes, killing six and injuring more than 1,000.

- The North American Free Trade Agreement (NAFTA), creating a trilateral trade bloc for the U.S., Canada, and Mexico, is ratified by each of those nations.

- The dissolution of Czechoslovakia takes place, with the Czech Republic and Slovakia peacefully separating into two sovereign states.

- Adobe Systems introduces the first PDF file format.

- The National Center for Supercomputing Applications (NCSA) introduces version 1.0 of the Mosaic web browser, which helps further popularize the World Wide Web.

- The Food Network makes its debut.

- The Dallas Cowboys win their fourth Super Bowl.

- The Toronto Blue Jays win their second World Series in a row by beating the Philadelphia Phillies four games to two.

Multi-modal transportation also includes bicycles and pedestrians and the paths, bikeways, sidewalks, and pedestrian enhancements to ensure safer shared use of all transportation choices. According to the Rails-to-Trails Conservancy, small investments in active transportation options for everyday travel can improve mobility, reduce carbon emissions, enhance energy security, and improve public health.[101]

Efficient movement of freight will become even more essential to sustained economic competitiveness. Projected population growth to 406 million by 2040 will put more demands on an aging and stretched-to-capacity national freight system. Freight movement is expected to grow from nearly 18 billion tons annually in 2011 to nearly billion annual tons by 2040—a 60 percent increase. In addition to that projected growth, the transition from just-in-time delivery to real-time, on-demand delivery will put new pressures on freight networks.[102]

In New York City, canoeists compete in a race down the Bronx River.
Courtesy of New York State DOT

Cyclists traveling along the William C. O'Neill Bike Path in South Kingstown, Rhode Island
Courtesy of Rhode Island DOT

Stop along northeastern New Jersey's Hudson–Bergen Light Rail system.
Courtesy of MTAP

2013 Snapshot
By the Numbers

Number Sources:
U.S. Census Bureau,
www.census.gov;
www.infoplease.com;
Updates to the Federal
Highway Administration
Highway Statistics

Event Sources:
Wikipedia;
www.historyorb.com

U.S. POPULATION **317,012,926**

FEDERAL SPENDING **$3790 billion**

UNEMPLOYMENT RATE **7.2 percent**

AVERAGE ANNUAL INCOME **$44,322**

AVERAGE COST OF A CAR **$28,150**

COST OF A GALLON OF MILK **$3.50**

MILES OF ROADS **4,077,756**

REGISTERED MOTOR VEHICLES **253.2 million**

2013 Snapshot
Events

- Barack Obama is inaugurated for a second term as U.S. president.

- Pope Benedict XVI becomes the first pope in nearly 600 years to resign, and is succeeded by Pope Francis, the first Jesuit to lead the Catholic Church.

- Two bombs detonated at the Boston Marathon finish line kill three and injure 264.

- The U. S. federal government shuts down for 16 days until an interim appropriations bill is signed into law.

- The most powerful meteor to strike Earth's atmosphere in more than a century explodes over the Russian city of Chelyabinsk.

- The first new Mickey Mouse cartoon short in 60 years is released by the Walt Disney Company.

- The Boston Red Sox win their eighth World Series title and clinching that championship at Fenway Park for the first time since 1918.

- The Baltimore Ravens win their second Super Bowl in the team's 17-year history.

For the ride ahead, America needs a robust, multi-modal, and well-connected (both physically and digitally) freight system. The nation's marine transportation system with facilities on three coasts, the Great Lakes, and the inland waterways needs particular attention. With a wider and deeper Panama Canal, attention to improving United States ports and ensuring reliable connections to highways and railroads will be even more important.

7. Raising public awareness of the vital role transportation plays in daily life. Transportation is at the center of everyday life. Yet the public seems to take the transportation system for granted or even discount its importance until something happens—like an extreme weather event that shuts down vital systems. As the transportation system continues to evolve in the 21st century, engaging the public in ways that create a collective awareness of the vital role transportation plays in daily quality of life and the need for sustained investment will become even more important. Know-before-you-go, transparency, and real-time information are all hallmarks of the new transportation outreach.

South Dakota DOT Secretary Darin Bergquist

"Effectively marketing the enormous economic and quality-of-life benefits of a well-maintained, national, multi-modal freight and passenger system is critical," said Darin Bergquist, South Dakota Secretary of Transportation. "We must provide simple answers to

Transportation Turning Point
A Connected Inland Port Facilitates Freight Movement

The new Southwest Regional Intermodal Freight Transportation Hub at America's Central Port in Granite City, Illinois, connects six rail lines and four Interstate highways to two marine highways to move cargo from north central United States to the Gulf of Mexico and other international markets. "…[T]he hub will reduce shippers' costs, promote economic growth, and provide agricultural producers and manufacturers in America's heartland better access to global markets," wrote Acting Maritime Administrator Paul Jaenichen in the U.S. Department of Transportation's Fast Lane blog.[103]

two questions: (1) if [the transportation system] ceases to function as it does, what happens, and (2) how do we keep it functioning as it does today."

Social media is already a valuable tool for sharing information, improving the transportation experience, and raising awareness of transportation's impact and value. YouTube, Twitter, Facebook, and other social-media tools either under development or yet to emerge will continue to support powerful connections between transportation providers and users.

Indiana DOT
Commissioner
Karl Browning

"Americans have always been willing to pay for what is important to them," said Karl Browning, Commissioner, Indiana Department of Transportation. "So we need to be smart, creative, and forceful to establish a platform for future success."

Transportation Turning Point
Maglev and Hyperloop: Next Generation Trains

By 2050 or sooner, extreme-high-speed trains using still-under-development technology could be a reality. Magnetic levitation (maglev) trains are already in use in Shanghai from downtown to the airport and under development in Japan. The wheel-less trains are propelled by shifts in horizontal magnetic fields and can travel at speeds up to 310 miles per hour. The ride is smooth, quiet, and less polluting.

Meanwhile, Elon Musk, chief executive of Tesla Motors which builds electric cars and trains, has developed a concept for a solar-powered, city-to-city elevated transit system that could take passengers and cars from Los Angeles to San Francisco in 30 minutes at a speed of 800 miles per hour. Known as Hyperloop, the trains would transport people along aluminum pods enclosed in steel tubes.

While Maglev technology already exists for high-speed inter-city transportation, Hyperloop is an idea. At this stage, the cost of building either concept in the United States is prohibitive.

Organizational Turning Point
The New Language of Mobility

Making the case for transportation investment depends on increasing awareness of the benefits of that investment by using language that resonates with the public. A 2011 AASHTO research project concluded that people are willing to pay for transportation investments if they understand the value of a smarter, more efficient transportation system and are convinced that investments will be sustainable, locally driven, and used only for transportation. The project identified five keys to gaining public support for transportation investments:

1. Assurance that investments will create a future of sustainable mobility based on thoughtful planning.

2. Emphasis on technology and modernization to create the 21st century transportation system.

3. Attention to long-term planning that anticipates the future or is at least flexible enough to accommodate upcoming changes.

4. A commitment to accountable and transparent spending that is dedicated to meeting long-term transportation needs.

5. Establishment of a clear connection between transportation investment and jobs and economic development.[104]

8. Continuing to support and expand the commitment to environmental sustainability. In 2014, the transportation mission goes far beyond ensuring mobility. It supports the larger worldwide goal of economic, social, and environmental sustainability. Since passage of the Clean Air Act of 1970, transportation leaders have moved from compliance with environmental regulations to taking proactive steps to ensure that transportation projects fit into and enhance their communities and the environment. In 2001, AASHTO created the Center for Environmental Excellence to help transportation agencies incorporate environmental compliance, sustainability, and stewardship into transportation planning, project development, construction maintenance, and operations.

The importance of environment sustainability and the impact of climate change will continue to influence the direction of transportation planning and action in the years ahead. The scope of transportation environmental action is already broad, including but not limited to:
- Supporting and promoting mobility alternatives to reduce carbon emissions from fuel-burning vehicles;
- Connecting land use and transportation planning;
- Improving erosion control;
- Reducing water and salt pollution;

- Strengthening wildlife and forest conservation;
- Enhancing roadside cultural and aesthetic;
- Incorporating recycled and reused pavement materials;
- Advancing historic preservation, and
- Reducing noise pollution.[105]

Noisewall from the Shiloh Road Improvement Project which was an America's Transportation Award entry in 2011.
Courtesy of Montana DOT

"The role that the transportation sector plays in our changing climate will force all of us to rethink our transportation system, our use of vehicles powered by carbon-based fuels, and our employment, residential, and travel patterns," said Richard Davey, Massachusetts Secretary of Transportation. "This is an enormous challenge for the states…but it is also a huge opportunity to reconsider our behaviors and embrace new technologies and new ways of living that will not only preserve our future environment but also repair some of the damage done…by a transportation culture focused too exclusively on the private automobile."

Transportation Turning Point
States Support Zero-Emission Vehicles

States are working to reduce pollution caused by driving. Their strategies to accomplish this goal include encouraging and supporting use of electric cars and other zero-emission vehicles. For example, governors of eight states representing 23 percent of the United States auto market joined together in October 2013 to implement specific steps to overcome consumer resistance to electric cars. Plans include modifying building codes to make it easier to construct charging stations, using more zero-emission vehicles in public fleets, lowering electricity rates for home-charging stations, installing more electric charging stations along highways, and introducing or continuing tax breaks for electric vehicles users. The states in this partnership are California, Connecticut, Maryland, Massachusetts, New York, Oregon, Rhode Island, and Vermont.

Electric vehicle owner Druce Oberg at a charging station in Skyomish, Washington.
Courtesy of Washington State DOT

The Washington and Oregon Departments of Transportations joined together to create the "West Coast Electric Highway," a network of electric vehicle rapid-charging stations located every 25 to 50 miles along Interstate 5 and other major roadways in the Pacific Northwest. The highway is designed to give electric vehicle drivers "range confidence" which may support increased market demand for zero-emission vehicles.

By 2015, more than 200,000 zero-emission vehicles are projected to be on U.S. roads.[106]

AASHTO Programs Support Workforce Development

AASHTO's National Transportation Leadership Institute and TRAC & RIDES programs provide a foundation for continuing to shape, strengthen, and sustain the future trans-

portation workforce. Established in 1967, the National Transportation Leadership Institute addresses the management training and development needs state departments of transportation. TRAC & RIDES are designed to introduce students in grades K–12 to the work world of transportation and civil engineering. TRAC (Transportation and Civil Engineering) is a hands-on, educational outreach program that state departments of transportation offer free of charge to middle and high school students in their state. RIDES (Roadways into Developing Elementary Students) is designed to interest K–8 students in transportation careers while improving their math and science skills.

Students from Tupelo High School in Mississippi participating in the TRAC 2013 National Bridge Challenge competition in Providence, Rhode Island.

9. Shaping, strengthening, and sustaining the future transportation workforce.

The expertise of state transportation leaders and employees helped build the modern transportation system. Maximizing technical expertise and objective scientific knowledge and minimizing political influence was a guiding principle for the AASHTO founders and a sustained practice during this century of progress. When Virginia Highway Commissioner Henry G. Shirley, AASHTO's first president, died in 1941, he was praised for his technical expertise and his ability to function successfully in a political environment. "He consistently refused to mix politics with highway engineering" and kept "the largest single operation of the state on so business-like a basis that, although a political appointee, nobody thought of him as a politician," the Norfolk Virginian-pilot wrote.[107]

With one in every six workers in the United States labor force now 55 years of age or older and that ratio expected to be one in every five within a decade, dramatic personnel changes are inevitable

Cooperation and community involvement near Elkton, Oregon.
Photo courtesy of Oregon DOT

in transportation agencies. Building the future public-sector transportation workforce will also face the twin challenges of recruiting people to launch a career in transportation and motivating talented employees to stay on board.

In an increasingly fragmented and heated public policy environment, many of today's transportation leaders worry about growing the transportation brain trust for the future when engineering know-how must be combined with political and technology savvy in order to succeed. In particular, some of today's leaders fear that the best and the brightest future engineers will be drawn to the private sector more than to public service. "It is increasingly difficult to recruit engineers into state highway agencies because of the glamor of working in big corporations," said 1999–2000 AASHTO President Dan Flowers, former Director of the Arkansas State Highway and Transportation Department. "The future of our transportation system depends on exposing young people in school systems to the opportunities and challenges of public service in transportation as a career choice."

Arkansas SHTD Director Dan Flowers

The high-tech evolution of America's transportation system demands new skills to meet new challenges. "During AASHTO's earliest days, we had a lot of crew cut guys who dealt largely with concrete and steel," said Michael P. Lewis, Director of the Rhode Island Department of Transportation. "Today, we are more dependent on people who know technology and can integrate changing technologies into transportation systems. We need to bring that expertise to public service."

Many of today's transportation leaders say they considered public service a noble calling—an opportunity to make a difference in people's lives—something worth doing. "The public will not be well served in the future if transportation agencies cannot get the best people for this important job," said Kentucky's Mike Hancock.

Organizational Turning Point
AASHTO Focuses on Resilient Transportation Systems

In recent years, extreme weather has disrupted transportation systems throughout the country. Blizzards, hurricanes, tornadoes, derechos, dust storms, and massive and prolonged flooding have shutdown roads, transit systems, and rail service for extended time periods and severely damaged transportation infrastructure. In addition to costs of system repairs, transportation system shutdowns have dramatic economic impacts that extend beyond the immediately affected areas. In order to learn from and deal with future extreme weather events, AASHTO created a program to provide timely information, tools, and technical assistance to support state DOTs in maintaining resilient transportation systems. The primary goal is to ensure that transportation agencies are prepared for the worst and able to recover as quickly as possible, drawing on the experiences of and lessons learned from states that have faced severe weather events. In addition, through AASHTO's collaborative network, transportation leaders are able to incorporate new practices in operations and maintenance strategies, flexible design approaches, and emergency response plans to build more resilient systems.[100]

In the Boston area during 2011, Massachusetts DOT construction personnel help coordinate the lowering of prefabricated bridge units into place.
Courtesy of MassDOT

An engineer inspecting work on the San Francisco–Oakland Bay Bridge.
Courtesy of Caltrans

AASHTO Looks Ahead with Confidence

The federal–state partnership that developed from AASHTO's creation in 1914 helped build the transportation system that exists today. That partnership remains vital to tackling the challenges facing America's transportation system in the years ahead. "Through AASHTO, we focus on making transportation better in the United States as opposed to just in our states," said 2008–2009 AASHTO President and former Pennsylvania DOT Secretary Allen D. Biehler. "We really think about the whole transportation system, and that's essential to its future." As the issues facing state transportation systems become more complex and vary more widely from state to state, working together on shared priorities becomes more challenging. "Revenue pressures are causing states to look at ways of achieving transportation outcomes differently," said 2013–2014 AASHTO President Mike Hancock, Secretary, Kentucky Transportation Cabinet. "AASHTO's biggest challenge in the years ahead is keeping everyone together while they are working separately on their own challenges."

Pennsylvania DOT
Secretary Allen D. Biehler

Future collaboration among the states through AASHTO may require more attention to regional differences without losing a holistic focus on the national transportation system. "If we position ourselves to protect our turf, no one wins," said Utah Transportation Executive Director Carlos Braceras. "We need to constantly look for the combined transportation vision that reflects what we want for our states and for the country as a whole."

Utah DOT Director
Carlos Braceras, P.E.

In 1989, AASHTO marked its 75th anniversary by asking high school juniors and seniors from throughout the country to submit essays describing the important role transportation plays in everyday life. One of the winners, Maureen Reed of West Bloomfield, Michigan, summarized her view of transportation this way: "From coast to coast, for each and every transported good, transportation has changed and improved Americans' lives. Transportation united America and gives it the power to keep going."

Building on 100 years of transportation achievement, $7 trillion in transportation assets, and a commitment to collaboration and innovation, America has the power to keep going into the next century of transportation achievement.

Traffic along I-80.
Courtesy of Wyoming DOT

AASHTO's Centennial Shadowbox with 141 unique elements that tell the history of AASHTO.

©2014 One Of A Kind, Inc. Art Studio. Created by Lawrence M. Romorini.

"For nearly 100 years, AASHTO has been a meeting place for transportation officials working toward a safer, more efficient, and resilient national transportation system....AASHTO's story really is about more than cars, trains, trucks, and airplanes. It is a story of America and the link between mobility, economic vitality, and quality of life."

~ Michael P. Lewis, Director, Rhode Island Department of Transportation; 2012–2013 AASHTO President

"Saying transportation and America go together is like saying the brain and heart go together. How can one function without the other? What good is on without the other?"

~ Mary Carol Jones, Kemmerer, Wyoming

Grand Prize Winner of AASHTO-sponsored essay competition titled "Transportation and America—They Go Together" in 1989

Appendix A
AASHTO Executive Directors

Prior to 1920, there were no provisions in the AASHTO financing structure to pay a full-time secretary and various highway officials served the association in that capacity for the additional work, without compensation.

The first secretary of the association was Dr. Joseph Hyde Pratt, State Geologist and Engineer of North Carolina. He served until December 1921, when he was succeeded by John H. Mullen, Minnesota. Charles M. Upham, North Carolina, succeeded Mullen in 1922 and served until William Colfax Markham, Kansas, was named Executive Secretary effective January 1, 1923, and a permanent association office was established in Washington, D.C. to coordinate the growing transportation organization.

A brief biographical sketch of the former Executive Directors of the Association follows:

William Colfax Markham (1868-1961)

William Colfax Markham, editor and publisher, poet and playwright, was born in Bolivar, Ohio. He at tended the Academy of the Baldwin-Wallace College in Beria, Ohio, for three years. In 1886, he entered Baker University, Baldwin, Kansas, from which he graduated in 1891. He became the editor and publisher of the Baldwin (Kansas) Ledger.

Markham retained the ownership of the Ledger for 36 years and during those years he found time to engage in many public activities. He was postmaster of Baldwin for 13 years, and served as Secretary of the Kansas Postmasters Association, as well as Secretary of the National Association of Postmasters. He was also President of the Kansas State Editorial Association in 1917.

Markham served as the Legislative Representative for AASHTO from October 1921 to January 1923, at which time he became Executive Secretary. *American Highways* was first published in August 1922 and Markham had a great deal to do with the establishment and publication of this magazine during his tenure of office.

Markham held his position until 1942, when he voluntarily resigned, having served 22 years. He was given the honorary title of Executive Secretary, Emeritus.

Hal Henderson Hale (1902–1979)

Hal Henderson Hale was born in Morristown, Tennessee. He graduated from the University of Tennessee, with a B.S. degree in Civil Engineering in 1924, and started working for the City of Knoxville in the Department of Public Service. During 1925, he was a surveyor, U.S. Engineers Department, on TVA Surveys at Chattanooga, Tennessee.

From July 1926 to August 1933, he served the Knoxville City Engineering Department as draftsman, designer and office engineer; from August 1933 until March 1938, he was the City Engineer for Knoxville. For a short while in 1938, he served as an Associate Civil Engineer, Projects Planning Division, TVA, in Knoxville. In August 1938, he became Office Engineer, Atlanta District, Portland Cement Association, Atlanta, Georgia, in which position he served until late in 1941 when he moved to Washington, D.C., to become the Washington representative of the American Society of Civil Engineers.

On January 1, 1944 he became AASHTO's second Executive Director. He served until his resignation in December 1954 to take the post of Assistant to the Vice President of the Association of American Railroads in Washington, D.C.

Alfred Eugene Johnson (1907–1992)

Alfred "Alf" Eugene Johnson, the third Executive Director, was born in Harrison, Arkansas. Johnson attended the University of Arkansas, from which he received his B.S. degree in Civil Engineering. He decided on a highway career when he was a young schoolboy and the national highway cry was "Get Out of the Mud." Johnson was with the Arkansas State Highway Department in the field and the headquarter offices from 1929 until December 1954. Working up through the ranks as rodman, instrument man, resident engineer, designer, research engineer, and office engineer, he was named Assistant Chief Engineer in 1942, and was appointed Chief Engineer in 1947. He also served three special interim terms as Director of Highways of the Arkansas Highway Department while in the Chief Engineer's Office.

On January, 1955, Johnson became the third Executive Director of the Association. One of the highlights of Johnson's career included serving as Advisor to the Clay Committee in 1954, which formulated President Dwight D. Eisenhower's Highway Program (the Interstate System of National and Defense Highways).

Johnson, who was referred to as "The Coach" by the Chief Administrative Officers of the Member Departments, served as the Association's Executive Director until his retirement in 1972.

Henrik E. Stafseth (1919–2011)

On November 1, 1972, Henrik E. Stafseth, formerly Highway Director for the Michigan Department of State Highways, became the fourth Executive Director of the Association. Born in Lansing, Michigan, Stafseth attended Michigan State University earning a Bachelor of Science Degree in Civil Engineering in 1942. In 1946, Stafseth joined the Michigan Department of State Highways as Bridge Project Engineer.

He continued with the Michigan State Highways Department until 1950, when he left to become City Engineer for the City of St. Joseph, Michigan. In 1952, he resigned from the City Engineer's post and became Engineering Manager of the Lenawee County Road Commission in Michigan. July 1955 saw Stafseth accept a similar position, Engineer Manager, for the Ottawa County Road Commission in Michigan, a position he held until 1965. He was elected as a Delegate to the Michigan Constitutional Convention from October 1961 to May 1962, serving on the Finance and Taxation and Public Information Committees. Stafseth returned to the Michigan Department of Highways in 1965 to accept the position of Deputy Director for Planning and Governmental Liaison. In 1967, he was appointed Acting State Highway Engineer, and later in January 1968, was elevated to the post of State Highway Director. Stafseth resigned as the Association's Executive Director in 1979.

Francis B. Francois (1934–)

Francis B. "Frank" Francois took over the reins as Executive Director of the Association in 1980.

Born in Iowa and reared on a family farm, Francois earned his engineering degree at Iowa State University and his law degree at George Washington University. He has been active in the development and implementation of public policy for nearly three decades.

Before resigning his office to join the Association, Francois was a member of the County Council of Prince George's County, Maryland, an elected position in which he worked closely with transportation, public works, environmental and community development issues.

During his 18 years as a county official, Francois was President of the National Association of Counties in 1979–80 and President of the National Association of Regional Councils in 1972 and 1973, and served on many regional, state, and national committees concerned with federal, state, and local governmental issues.

A registered patent attorney, Francois engaged actively in a patent and trademark law practice before coming to AASHTO. He now resides in Chicago.

John Horsley (1942–)

John Horsley became Executive Director of the American Association of State Highway and Transportation Officials in 1999.

Previously, Horsley was nominated by the President and confirmed by the Senate as Associate Deputy Secretary of Transportation where he served from 1993 to 1999 as the Department's advocate for intermodal policies, quality-of-life initiatives and as liaison to state and local governments, U.S. Congress, and transportation constituencies.

A native of Washington State, Horsley was elected to five terms as County Commissioner in Kitsap County, a community west of Seattle. He was a graduate of Harvard, an Army veteran, a former Peace Corps volunteer and Congressional aide, and he completed some graduate studies at Georgetown. He is past president of the National Association of Counties, and was founding Chairman of the Rebuild America Coalition.

Bud Wright (1951–)

Bud Wright became the executive director of the American Association of State Highway and Transportation Officials in 2012. Wright upon joining AASHTO had nearly four decades of experience in both the private sector and as a top executive at the Federal Highway Administration.

Wright, who was a transportation consultant based in Alexandria, Virginia, prior to his appointment as AASHTO Executive Director, served as Executive Director of the Federal Highway Administration from 2001 to 2008, assisting the Administrator in establishing policies, programs, and priorities for the $40 billion annual Federal-aid highway program. As FHWA's chief operating officer, he was also responsible for a workforce of more than 2,500 transportation professionals and an annual operating budget of $400 million.

From 2001 to 2002, Wright was the FHWA program manager for safety. Before that, he was director of the Office of Budget and Finance, where he worked extensively on the Transportation Equity Act for the 21st Century (TEA-21). In 1992, he became the first non-engineer to serve as an FHWA state-level Division Administrator.

Wright began his career in 1975 as an economist in the FHWA Office of Planning. In 1986, he was selected for a congressional fellowship, serving with the Senate Appropriations Committee staff. In 1989–1990, he was a member of the National Transportation Policy Team, which developed former Transportation Secretary Samuel Skinner's National Transportation Policy.

He holds a B.A. in Economics from Virginia Polytechnic Institute and State University, Blacksburg, Virginia.

AASHTO Presidents

1914–1915, 1915–1916
Henry G. Shirley, *Maryland*

1916–1917
George P. Coleman, *Virginia*

1917–1918
William D. Uhler, *Pennsylvania*

1918–1919
Arthur R. Hist, *Wisconsin*

1919–1920
Paul D. Sargent, *Maine*

1920–1921
William S. Keller, *Alabama*

1921–1922
Charles M. Babcock, *Minnesota*

1922–1923
Charles J. Bennett, *Connecticut*

1923–1924
Fred R. White, *Iowa*

1924–1925
Frank F. Rogers, *Michigan*

1925–1926
Frank Page, *North Carolina*

1926–1927
Louis D. Blauvelt, *Colorado*

1927–1928
Frank T. Sheets, *Illinois*

1928
John N. Mackall, *Maryland*

1928–1929
Camden P. Fortney, *West Virginia*

1929–1930
Samuel Eckels, *Pennsylvania*

1930–1931
Henry H. Blood, *Utah*

1931–1932
Frederic E. Everett, *New Hampshire*

1932–1933
Charles H. Moorefield, *South Carolina*

1933–1934
Oliver S. Warden, *Montana*

1934–1935
Arthur W. Brandt, *New York*

1935–1936
Gibb Gilcrhist, *Texas*

1936–1937
Thomas H. Cutler, *Kentucky*

1937–1938
Charles H. Purcell, *California*

1938–1939
Warren W. Mack, *Delaware*

1939–1940
Henry F. Cabell, *Oregon*

1940–1941
J. Stanley Williamson, *South Carolina*

1941–1942
G. Donald Kennedy, *Michigan*

1942–1943
Brady Gentry, *Texas*

1943–1944
Samuel C. Hadden, *Indiana*

1944–1945
Herman A. McDonald, *Massachusetts*

1945–1946
M.J. Hoffman, *Minnesota*

1946–1947
C.W. Phillips, *Tennessee*

1947–1948
R.H. Baldock, *Oregon*

1948
W.W. Polk, *Illinois*

1949
C.W. Brown, *Missouri*

1950
D.C. Greer, *Texas*

1951
J.A. Anderson, *Virginia*

1952
B.D. Bellamy, *New York*

1953
C.M. Ziegler, *Michigan*

1954
A.E. Johnson, *Arkansas*

1955
George T. McCoy, *California*

1956
F.D. Merrill, *New Hampshire*

1956
Rex M. Whitton, *Missouri*

1957
W.A. Bugge, *Washington*

1958
C.R. McMillan, *South Carolina*

1959
R.R. Bartlesmeyer, *Illinois*

1960
David H. Stevens, *Maine*

1961
D.H. Bray, *Kentucky*

1962
J.C. Womack, *California*

1963
John C. Mackie, *Michigan*

1964
J. Burch McMorran, *New York*

1965
M.L. Shadburn, *Georgia*

1966
C.E. Shumate, *Colorado*

1967
E.M. Johnson, *Mississippi*

1968
J.O. Morton, *New Hampshire*

1969
Ross G. Stapp, *Wyoming*

1970
Douglas B. Fugate, *Virginia*

1971
W.J. Burmeister, *Wisconsin*

1972
J.C. Dingwall, *Texas*

1973
T.F. Airis, *District of Columbia*

1974
George H. Andrews, *Washington*

1975
J. Phillip Richley, *Ohio*

1976
Langhorne M. Bond, *Illinois*

1977
Robert N. Hunter, *Missouri*

1978
Darrell V. Manning, *Idaho*

1979
Thomas D. Moreland, *Georgia*

1980
Roger Mallar, *Maine*

1980
William A. Bulley, *Washington*

1981
Richard A. Ward, *Oklahoma*

1982
John A. Clements, *New Hampshire*

1983
Henry C. Gray, *Arkansas*

1984
William A. Ordway, *Arizona*

1985
Richard P. Braun, *Minnesota*

1986
Thomas D. Larson, *Pennsylvania*

1987
John R. Tabb, *Mississippi*

1988
Leno Menghini, *Wyoming*

1989
James P. Pitz, *Michigan*

1990
Kermit Justice, *Delaware*

1991
Hal Rives, *Georgia*

1992
A. Ray Chamberlain, *Colorado*

1993
Wayne Muri, *Missouri*

1994
Howard Yerusalim, *Pennsylvania*

1995
Wayne Shackleford, *Georgia*

1996
Wm. G. Burnett, *Texas*

1996–1997
Darrel Rensink, *Iowa*

1997–1998
David Winstead, *Maryland*

1998–1999
Dan Flowers, *Arkansas*

1999–2000
Thomas R. Warne, *Utah*

2000–2001
E. Dean Carlson, *Kansas*

2001–2002
Bradley L. Mallory, *Pennsylvania*

2002–2003
James C. Codell, III, *Kentucky*

2003–2004
John R. Njord, P.E., *Utah*

2004–2005
Bryan Nicol, *Indiana*

2004–2005
Jack Lettiere, Jr., *New Jersey*

2005–2006
Harold E. Linnenkohl, *Georgia*

2006–2007
Victor Mendez, *Arizona*

2007–2008
Pete Rahn, *Missouri*

2008–2009
Allen Biehler, *Pennsylvania*

2009–2010
Larry L. "Butch" Brown, Sr., *Mississippi*

2010–2011
Susan Martinovich, *Nevada*

2011–2012
Kirk Steudle, *Michigan*

2012–2013
Michael P. Lewis, *Rhode Island*

2013–2014
Michael Hancock, *Kentucky*

"After 100 years, I think it can be said about AASHTO that the model worked and continues to serve an important purpose. Every state is a member of AASHTO because leaders see value in its purpose and because collaboration, communication, and joint advocacy contribute to a stronger transportation system."

~ Bud Wright, AASHTO Executive Director

Appendix C
Resources

Books About Transportation

Blue, Elly. *Bikenomics: How Bicycling Can Save the Economy.* Independent Publishers Group (Chicago: 2013).

Counihan, Harold J. *Moving Maryland Forward.* Maryland Department of Transportation (Baltimore: 2008).

Jones, David W. *Mass Motorization + Mass Transit.* Indiana University Press (Bloomington, 2008).

Kasinsky, William. *The American Highway.* McFarland & Company, Inc., Publishers (Jefferson, North Carolina: 2000).

Kotkin, Joel. *The Next Hundred Million: America in 2050.* Penquin Books (New York, 2010).

Levinson, Marc. *The Box: How the Shipping Container Made the World Smaller and the World Economy Bigger.* Princeton University Press (Princeton, New Jersey: 2006).

McNichol, Dan. *The Roads that Built America.* Sterling Publishing Company (New York, 2006).

Steinbeck, John. *Travels with Charley: In Search of America.* The Curtis Publishing Company (New York: 1962).

Swift, Earl. *The Big Roads.* Houghton Mifflin Harcourt (New York: 2011).

Vanderbilt, Tom. *Traffic: Why We Drive the Way We Do.* Vintage Books (New York: 2008).

Zoellner, Tom. *Train.* Penguin Group (New York: 2014).

AASHTO Publications

AASHTO: Convention and Twenty-Fifth Anniversary. American Association of State Highway and Transportation Officials (Washington, D.C.: 1939).

AASHTO: The First Fifty Years, 1914–1964. American Association of State Highway and Transportation Officials (Washington, D.C.: 1965).

AASHTO 1911–1999, Moving America into the Future. American Association of State Highway and Transportation Officials (Washington, D.C.: 1999).

Above and Beyond: The Environmental and Social Contributions of America's Highway Programs. American Association of State Highway and Transportation Officials (Washington, D.C.: January 2008).

American Highways. Volume XLIII, Number 1. American Association of State Highway and Transportation Officials (Washington, D.C.: January 1965).

The States and the Interstates. American Association of State Highway and Transportation Officials (Washington, D.C.: 1991).

Waterborne Freight Transportation: Bottom Line Report. American Association of State Highway and Transportation Officials (Washington, D.C.: June 2013).

Federal Resources

America's Highways 1776–1976: A History of the Federal-Aid Program. U.S. Department of Transportation, Federal Highway Administration (Washington, D.C.: 1976).

Public Roads. Special Edition 1996. U.S. Department of Transportation, Federal Highway Administration (Washington, D.C.: June 1996).

Highway History. U.S. Department of Transportation, Federal Highway Administration, *https://www.fhwa.dot. gov/infrastructure/history.cfm*

Endnotes

[1] The mileage in each direction over which vehicles travel while in service for passenger use.

[2] U.S. Department of Transportation. *Transportation Statistics Annual Report 2012.* Research and Innovative Technology Administration, Bureau of Transportation Statistics (Washington, D.C.: 2013), pp. 1–3.

[3] Compiled from interviews with state directors of transportation and surveys submitted by state departments of transportation about AASHTO's centennial celebration.

[4] Mack, W.W. *A Quarter Century of Road Building.* Convention and Twenty-Fifth Anniversary, American Association of State Highway Officials (Washington, D.C.: 1939), p. 10.

[5] McNichol, Dan. *The Roads that Built America.* Sterling Publishing Co., Inc. (New York: 2006), p. 36.

[6] *Ibid.*, p. 114.

[7] Kaszynski, William. *The American Highway.* MacFarland & Company, Inc. (Jefferson, North Carolina: 2000), p. 210.

[8] Drawn from Richard Weingroff. "Building the Foundation: The Federal Aid Road Act of 1916." *Public Roads Special Edition*, Federal Highway Administration. (Washington, D.C.: 1996), pp. 1–3.

[9] *Ibid.*, p. 2.

[10] *Ibid.*, p. 3.

[11] McNichol, *op. cit.*, p. 63.

[12] Sage, Henry J. *The Progressive Era: The Great Age of Reform. http://sageamericanhistory.net/progressive/topics/progressive. html* (2012).

[13] McNichol, *op. cit.*, p. 59, and presentations by John Horsley, former AASHTO Executive Director, and Bruce Seely, Michigan Technological Institute, AASHTO Centennial Presentations. (Washington, D.C.: January 13, 2014).

[14] Swift, *op. cit.*, pp. 49–51.

[15] Weingroff, Richard F. "The Year of the Interstate." *Public Roads*, Jan/Feb 2006, Vol. 69, No. 4.

[16] Federal Highway Administration. Eisenhower Interstate Highway System Website, Frequently Asked Questions, *http://www.fhwa.dot.gov/interstate/faq.htm#question6*

[17] Data compiled primarily from *Transportation Statistics Annual Report, op. cit.*, pp. 19–24.

[18] McNichol, *op. cit.*, p. 35.

[19] National Museum of American History. *American on the Move Exhibition: Passenger Trains. http://amhistory.si.edu/ onthemove/themes/stories_42_7.html.*

[20] Zoellner, Tom. *Train.* Viking (New York: 2014), p. 97.

[21] National Museum of American History. *American on the Move Exhibition: Passenger Trains. http://amhistory.si.edu/onthemove/themes/stories_42_7.html.*

[22] *Songfacts. http://www.songfacts.com/detail.php?id=2878,* Amtrak City of New Orleans Route Guide, and Zoellner, p. 98.

[23] *Ibid.,* p. 64.

[24] *Ibid.,* p. 5.

[25] National Museum of American History. *America on the Move Exhibition: Steam Locomotive. http://amhistory.si.edu/onthemove/exhibition/.*

[26] Jones, David W. *Mass Motorization + Mass Transit.* Indiana University Press (Bloomington: 2008), pp. 54–56, 139.

[27] *The Story Behind the Bus.* The Henry Ford Online Collection, (2010), *www.thehenryford.org/exhibit/rosaparks/story.asp.*

[28] Compiled from Arsenault, Raymond. *Freedom Riders: 1961 and the Struggle for Racial Justice.* Oxford University Press, Inc. (New York, 2005); *Freedom Rides.* History.com Articles, *www.history.com/topics/freedom-rides; The Road to Civil Rights: The ICC Ruling.* Federal Highway Administration History, U.S. Department of Transportation, October 17, 2013.

[29] *The Road to Civil Rights: Getting to the March on Washington.* Federal Highway Administration, *op. cit.*

[30] This section is adapted from *A Quick History of Bicycles.* Bicycle Pedaling History Museum, Orchard Park, New York, *http://pedalinghistory.com/PHhistory.html.*

[31] The League of American Bicyclists website, *www.bikeleague.org.*

[32] American Association of State Highway and Transportation Officials. *A Century of Achievement for a Better Tomorrow Newsletter,* January 29, 2014; and Adventure Cycling Association. *10 Fast Facts: United States Bicycle Route System. http://www.adventurecycling.org/routes-and-maps/us-bicycle-route-system/10-fast-facts/.*

[33] *The Age of the Automobile.* U.S. History Online Textbook, 2013, *http://www.ushistory.org/us/46.asp.*

[34] Wikipedia. *Automobile. http://en.wikipedia.org/wiki/Automobile.*

[35] Swift, *op. cit.,* p. 88.

[36] *Transportation Statistics Annual Report 2012, op. cit.,* p. 19; and Wikipedia. *Motor Vehicle Ownership Trends. http://en.wikipedia.org/wiki/Motor_Vehicle.*

[37] Compiled from *The Age of the Automobile.* U.S. History Online Textbook, 2013, *http://www.ushistory.org/us/46.asp; Transportation Statistics Annual Report 2012, op. cit.,* p. 19; and U.S. Census Bureau. *The 2012 Statistical Abstract. http://www.census.gov/compendia/statab/cats/transportation/motor_vehicle_registrations_alternative_fueled_vehicles.html.*

[38] Jones, David W. *Mass Motorization + Mass Transit.* Indiana University Press (Bloomington: 2008), p. 111.

[39] Stevens, Larry. "The National Road: Infrastructure in its Infancy." *Right of Way,* July/August 2012, pp. 19–20.

[40] Longfellow, Rickie. *Back in Time: The National Road.* Federal Highway Administration, *www.fhwa.dot.gov/infrastructure/back0103.cfm.*

[41] Swift, *op. cit.,* p. 31.

[42] *The Roads that Built America, op. cit.,* pp. 114–123; and "U.S. Sets Standards for New Highways." *The New York Times,* July 22, 1956.

[43] Compiled from *The Roads that Built America, op. cit.,* pp. 139–161, and Weingroff, Richard F. "The Genie in the Bottle: The Interstate System an Urban Problems, 1939–1957." *Public Roads,* Sept/Oct 2000.

[44] Friedman, Herbert M. and Ada Kera Friedman. *The Legacy of the Rockne Crash,* May 2001; and Brondfield, Jerry. *Rockne: The Man, The Myth, The Legend.* Random House (New York: 1976).

[45] Compiled from *The Airline Handbook.* Airlines for America. Formerly the Air Transport Association (Washington, D.C.: 1995),

[46] *The Rise of the Airline Stewardess.* Slate Book Review of Victoria Vantoch. *The Jet Sex: Airline Stewardesses and the Making of an American Icon.* April 5, 2013.

[47] Watkins, James A. "A History of Commercial Airlines." Technology Blog, March 2011.

[48] Reisner, Alex. "Baseball Geography and Transportation." Published in *The Baseball Research Journal #35* (Cleveland: 2007), pp. 46–47.

[49] American Association of State Highway and Transportation Officials. *Waterborne Freight Transportation: Bottom Line Report.* (Washington, D.C.: June 2013), p. xi.

[50] *Transportation Statistics Annual Report 2012, op. cit.*, pp. 35–37.

[51] *Waterborne Freight Transportation, op. cit.*, pp. 1-1–1-3.

[52] "Norwich Memories: A Pictorial History of Norwich from the 1800s through the 1960s." *The Bulletin* (Norwich: 2013), p. 31.

[53] *Waterborne Freight Transportation, op. cit.*, p. 2-1.

[54] Swift, *op. cit.*, p. 15.

[55] Swift, *op. cit.*, p. 15.

[56] National Museum of American History. *America on the Move Exhibition: Transportation History 1800–1900. http://amhistory.si.educ/onthemove/themes/story_48_1.html.*

[57] "American Railroad Expansion (1870–1950)." *History Wired: A Few of Our Favorite Things,* Smithsonian Institution, accessed at *www.historywired.si.edu/detail.cfm?ID-225.*

[58] *America on the Move Exhibition: A Railroad for Santa Cruz, op. cit.*

[59] Zoellner, *op. cit.*, p. 97.

[60] Compiled from *The Roads that Built America* (McNichol) and *The Big Roads* (Swift).

[61] Compiled from *The Roads that Built America, op. cit.*, pp. 51–53 and *The Big Roads, op. cit.*, pp. 48–49.

[62] Compiled from *The Truck Driver Who Reinvented Shipping* (Anthony J. Mayo and Nitin Nohria, October 2005); *The Box: How the Shipping Container Made the World Smaller and the World Economy Bigger* (Marc Levinson, Princeton University Press, 2006); and *Waterborne Freight Transportation: Bottom Line Report* (American Association of State Highway and Transportation Officials, June 2013).

[63] Perspective provided by the Minnesota Department of Transportation in response to an AASHTO Centennial Project survey, August 2013.

[64] About.com. Inventors. *The Post Office Role in the United States Development.* Accessed at *www.inventors.about.com/library/inventors/blmilus2.htm.*

[65] About.com Inventors. *U.S. Postal System: 1775–1993.* Accessed at *www.inventors.about.com/library/inventors/blmailus3.htm.*

[66] Compiled from *United States Postal Service, About, Airmail.* Accessed at *www.about.usps.com/publications/pub100_/.*

[67] *Waterborne Freight Transportation: Bottom Line Report, op. cit.*; and National Association of Development Organizations Research Foundation. *Freight Transportation and Economic Development: Planning for the Panama Canal Expansion.* (Washington, D.C.: 2012), pp. 1–4.

[68] U.S. Department of Transportation. "2012 Motor Vehicle Crashes: Overview." *Traffic Safety Facts,* National Highway Traffic Safety Administration. (Washington, D.C.: November 2013).

[69] Swift, *op. cit.*, pp. 88–89.

[70] Wikipedia. *List of motor vehicle deaths in U.S. by year.* Accessed at e*n.wikipedi.org/wiki/List_of_motor_vehicle_deaths_in U.S.-by year*; and *Traffic Safety Facts.* National Highway Traffic Safety Administration (Washington, D.C.: May 2013).

[71] American Association of State Highway and Transportation Officials. *AASHTO Strategic Highway Safety Plan: A Comprehensive Highway Safety Plan.* (Washington, D.C.: 2005); and *Highway Safety Manual,* 1st Edition, Volume 1, American Association of State Highway and Transportation Officials (Washington, D.C.: 2010).

[72] U.S. Department of Transportation. *America's Highways 1776–1976: A History of the Federal Aid Program.* Federal Highway Administration (Washington, D.C.: 1976), pp. 127–132; and report of the National Conference on Street and Highway Safety (Washington, D.C.: 1930).

73 History.com. "Connecticut enacts first speed limit law." *This Day in History*, www.history.com/this-day-in-history/connecticut-enacts-first-speed-limit-law.

74 Compiled from *Inventor of the Week*, Lemelson-MIT at web-mit/invent/iow/Anderson.html, Mary Anderson, inventor in AmazingWomenInHistory.com at *www.amazingwomeninhistory.com/mary-anderson-inventor/*, and Rain-Sensing Wipers, J.D.Power.com at *autos.jdpower.com/content/consumer-interest/pUEL2vg/rain-sensing-wipers.htm*, February 24, 2012.

75 "President Harry S. Truman's Highway Safety Conferences." *Highway History*, Federal Highway Administration, *www.fhwa.dot.gov/infrastructure/safety01.cfm*.

76 Daily Kos. *How regulation came to be: The Truman Highway Safety Conferences.* Accessed at *www.dailykos.com/story/2013/02/17/1187836/-How-regulation-came-to-be-The-Truman-Highway-Safety-Conferences.*

77 KSL.com. *UDOT celebrates 100 years of the Utah-born traffic light* www.ksl.com/index.php?sid=22426453&nid=481, October 4, 2013.

78 "Address before the President's Highway Conference—May 8, 1946." *Public Papers of Harry S. Truman, 1945–1953*, Harry S. Truman Library & Museum, *www.trumanlibrary.org/publicpapers/index.php?pid=1548*.

79 Steffen, D. *How Regulation Came to Be: The Truman Safety Conferences.* February 17, 2013. Posted at *http://www.dailykos.com/story/2013/02/17/1187836/-How-regulation-came-to-be-The-Truman-Highway-Safety-Conferences*

80 "Evolution of the New York Drivers' License." *The New York Times.* Accessed at *http://www.nytimes.com/interactive/2013/03/17/nyregion/17licenses-evolution.html?_r=0.*

81 *Transportation Statistics Annual Report 2012, op. cit.*, pp. 72 and 74.

82 Swift, *op. cit.*, pp. 255–258.

83 American Association of State Highway and Transportation Officials and TRIP. *Rough Roads Ahead.* p. 18; and *The Roads that Built America, op. cit.*, pp. 10–11.

84 *Toward Zero Deaths: The National Strategy on Highway Safety.* AASHTO Presentation, March 2012; and *Toward Zero Deaths: National Strategy on Highway Safety.* FHWA Brochure, U.S. Department of Transportation, Washington, D.C.

85 Wilson, Reid. "Traffic Deaths Decline to 40s Levels in Several States." *The Washington Post*, January 3, 2014.

86 Minnesota Department of Transportation. *Minnesota TZD: 10 Years of Progress.* Minnesota Department of Health, Minnesota Department of Public Safety, March 2013, p. 4.

87 Mack, *op. cit.*, p. 10.

88 *NCHRP at 50 Years.* Published by the Federal Highway Administration, American Association of State Highway and Transportation Officials, and the Transportation Research Board, 2012

89 Compiled from *NCHRP at 50 Years, op. cit.*

90 *Bates Experimental Road Test.* State of Illinois, Department of Public Works and Buildings, Division of Highways, Bulletin 19, January 1922.

91 "Road Tests for Motoring." *The New York Times*, December 18, 1821.

92 Adapted from McNichol. *The Roads that Built America, op. cit.*, pp. 25–26 and 235–237; and Counihan, Harold J. *Moving Maryland Forward.* pp. 6–7 and 182–183.

93 American Association of State Highway and Transportation Officials. *Transportation Excellence through Research: Research Impacts.* July 2013.

94 Halsey, Ashley, III. "Let the Car Do the Driving." *The Washington Post*, November 3, 2013.

95 Compiled from Thurston, Susan. "Florida transportation leaders say automated cars not too far off." *Tampa Bay Times*, November 14, 2013; Seal, Dean. "Driverless car hits Smart Road." *Collegiate Times*, September 13, 2013; Clark, Maggie "States Take the Wheel on Driverless Cars." *The Pew Charitable Trusts Stateline Consumer Infarction*, July 29, 2013, and Markoff, John. "Google Cars Drive Themselves, in Traffic." *The New York Times*, October 9, 2010.

96 Privacy and Security Blog. *Toyota testing smart cars that talk to each other and the road.* November 2013. www.networkworld.com/community/blog/toyota-testing-smart-cars-talk-each-other-and-road.

[97] *Questions & Answers About DOT's Safety Pilot Model Deployment.* Safety Pilot Connected Vehicle Technology, U.S. Department of Transportation, National Highway Traffic Safety Administration (Washington, D.C.: 2012).

[98] Winston, Clifford. "Paving the Way for Driverless Cars." *The Wall Street Journal* (New York: July 17, 2012).

[99] O'Brien, James. *Connected Cars: How Long Must We Wait?* October 9, 2013, Published online at *www.mashable. com/2013/10/09/connected -car-platforms*.

[100] Rosenberg, Matt. "Global Positioning System: Eight Things You Need to Know about GPS." *About.com: Geography*, *www.geography.about.com/od/geographictechnology/a/gps.htm*.

[101] Rail-to-Trails Conservancy. *Active Transportation for America: The Case for Increased Federal Investment in Bicycling and Walking.* (Washington, D.C.: 2008), p. 7.

[102] U.S. Department of Transportation, Research and Innovative Technology Administration Bureau of Transportation Statistics. *Transportation Statistics Annual Report 2012.* (Washington, D.C.: 2013), p. 34.

[103] Jaenichen, Paul "Chip". "Linking Rivers, Rails and Roads at America's Central Port." *Fast Lane: The Official Blog of the U.S. Department of Transportation*, August 19, 2103.

[104] American Association of State Highway and Transportation Officials. *The New Language of Mobility: Talking Transportation in a Post-Recession World.* (Washington, D.C.: March 2011).

[105] American Association of State Highway and Transportation Officials. *Above and Beyond: The Environmental and Social Contributions of America's Highway Programs.* (Washington, D.C.: January 2008).

[106] Bernstein, Lenny. "A plug for zero-emission vehicles." *The Washington Post*, October 5, 2013; and West Coast Electric Highway, *www.westcoastgreenhighways.com*.

[107] "State Officials Pay Tribute to Highway Head at Funeral." *Associated Press*, July 17, 1941.

[108] American Association of State Transportation and Highway Officials. *Impacts of Extreme Weather on Transportation: National Symposium Summary.* (Washington, D.C.: 2013).

AASHTO Extends Our Thanks to All of Our Centennial Sponsors:

Visionary Sponsors

Milestone Sponsor

HDR

Pioneer Sponsors

Leadership Sponsors

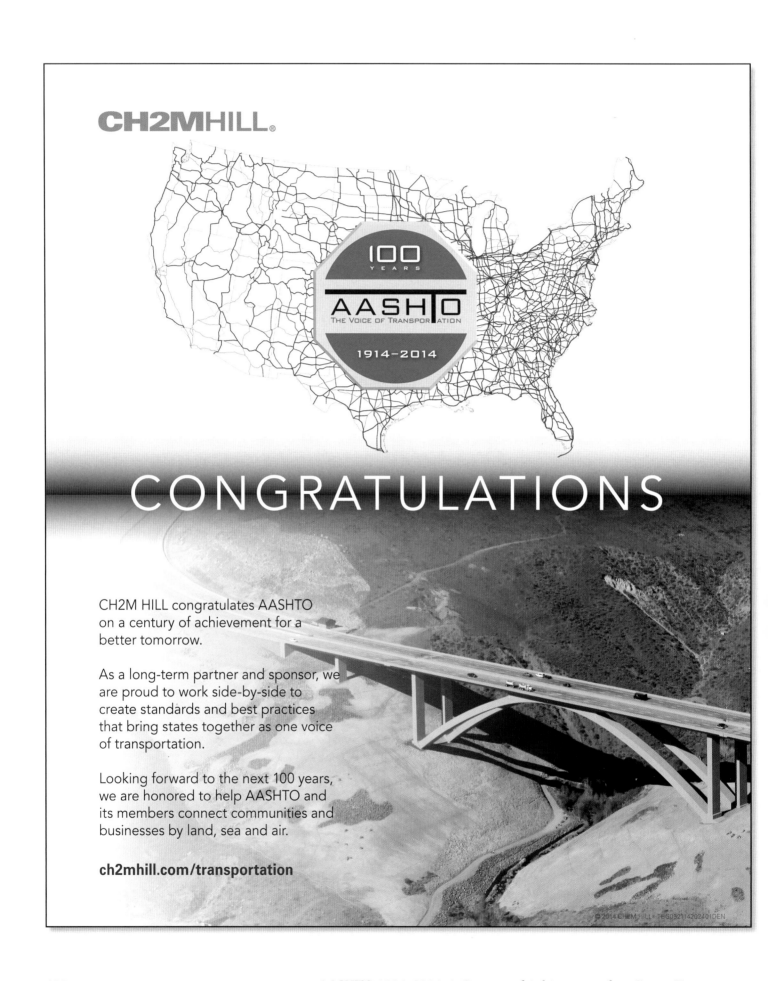

CH2MHILL

CONGRATULATIONS

CH2M HILL congratulates AASHTO on a century of achievement for a better tomorrow.

As a long-term partner and sponsor, we are proud to work side-by-side to create standards and best practices that bring states together as one voice of transportation.

Looking forward to the next 100 years, we are honored to help AASHTO and its members connect communities and businesses by land, sea and air.

ch2mhill.com/transportation

Welcome to the Centennial Club!

100 YEARS

AASHTO
THE VOICE OF TRANSPORTATION

1914–2014

From your partners at the
American Road & Transportation
Builders Association

Together, our members build a better America!

Transportation Makes America Work

Transportation Investment Advocacy Center.

www.artba.org

www.tmaw.org

www.transportationinvestment.org

A *Century* of Shared Progress!

Congratulations on

100 years.

AECOM congratulates our partner, the American Association of State Highway and Transportation Officials, on a century of achievement. We wish the organization a happy anniversary as they enter another century for a better tomorrow.

Have you experienced Autodesk lately?

Which proposal will differentiate you from the competition?

How would you prefer to gather feedback on design alternatives?

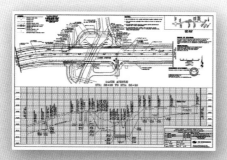

Which will help stakeholders understand how a proposed project will look from their backyard?

Discover the benefits of BIM for Infrastructure with the Autodesk® Infrastructure Design Suite, featuring Autodesk® AutoCAD® Civil 3D®. Add the groundbreaking technology in Autodesk® InfraWorks 360™ software and go beyond model creation, sketching, and visualization with capabilities to author, engineer and evaluate design alternatives in context.

- Better understand and communicate project risk, intent, and options before a project is built
- Maintain more consistent data, context, and processes across the project lifecycle
- Respond more quickly to change with processes that are smarter, faster and mobile

Discover for yourself what's really possible in civil design: autodesk.com/bim-for-infrastructure

AUTODESK.

Bridging
the gap
between idea
+ achievement

This is where great begins.

Congratulations AASHTO on 100 years of excellence

Info Tech, Inc. is proud to be celebrating
30 years as an AASHTOWare® contractor

www.infotechfl.com

Congratulations, AASHTO!
Thank you for keeping America moving for 100 years.

CAMBRIDGE
SYSTEMATICS
www.camsys.com

From your friends at Cambridge Systematics.

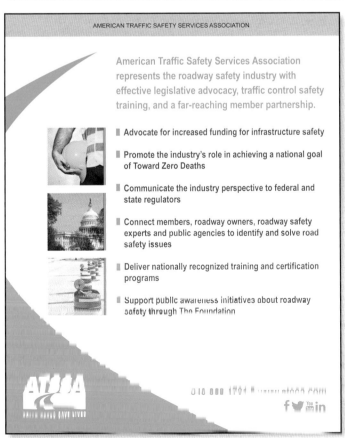

AMERICAN TRAFFIC SAFETY SERVICES ASSOCIATION

American Traffic Safety Services Association
represents the roadway safety industry with
effective legislative advocacy, traffic control safety
training, and a far-reaching member partnership.

▌ Advocate for increased funding for infrastructure safety

▌ Promote the industry's role in achieving a national goal
of Toward Zero Deaths

▌ Communicate the industry perspective to federal and
state regulators

▌ Connect members, roadway owners, roadway safety
experts and public agencies to identify and solve road
safety issues

▌ Deliver nationally recognized training and certification
programs

▌ Support public awareness initiatives about roadway
safety through The Foundation

ird
INTERNATIONAL ROAD DYNAMICS INC.

Congratulations to AASHTO on a Century of Achievements!

We make highways talk

www.irdinc.com

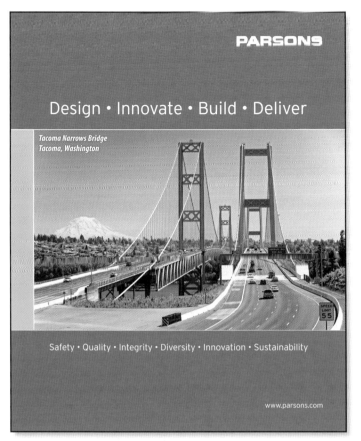
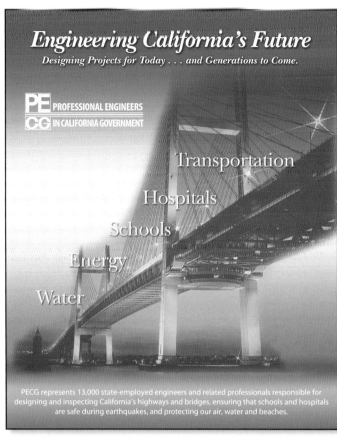
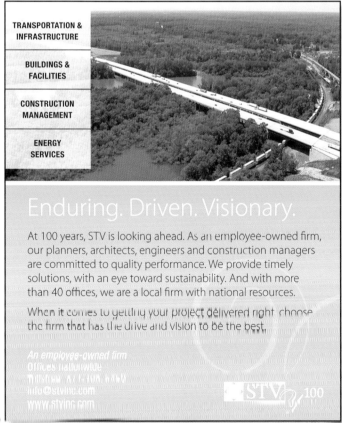
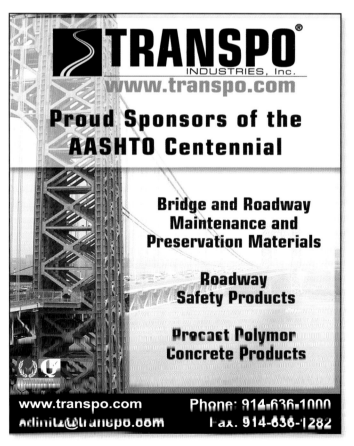

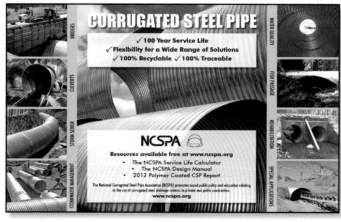

Highlights & History
AASHTO Member States

ALABAMA

Alabama Department of Transportation

John Cooper
Director

YEAR FORMED **1911**

FTE **4,252**

KEY FACTS
TOTAL STATE ROAD MILES
(OWNED BY STATE HIGHWAY
AGENCY) **10,911**

STATE-OWNED BRIDGES **5,738**

TRANSIT TRIPS PER YEAR
6.57 million

After 103 Years, ALDOT Is Just Getting Started

The Alabama Department of Transportation (ALDOT) was celebrating its third birthday 100 years ago, with three full-time employees managing less than 4,000 miles of improved roads. By contrast, today ALDOT has 4,400 employees and supervises 11,000 miles of highway transporting 104 million miles of travel daily. And, its responsibilities have been diversified to include 5,745 bridges, two below-water traffic tunnels, a 1,000-mile interstate system, and two ferry boats.

And, with the massive 52-mile Birmingham Northern Beltline just beginning construction, as well as a new Mobile Bay Bridge on the horizon, ALDOT is continuing to meet the public's appetite for better, more efficient transportation options.

As with the past 100 years, Alabama will face severe challenges in the future. Weather is one challenge with Alabama's northern counties subject to occasional ice and snow storms, a Gulf Coast battered by periodic hurricanes, and the entire state subject to menacing tornadoes. Other long-time antagonists will remain present, as well. Securing available funding will continue to be a concern, as will maintaining a skilled work force and dealing with environmental requirements.

But if you believe those tasks are daunting, take yourself back a century to a time when automobiles were having a tough go of it on Alabama's roads. At that time, all road construction was by counties, financed with bonds or county warrants. The main role of what was then known as the State Highway Commission was to educate those counties on the need for constructing roads along economical and engineering lines, as well as use of the best local construction materials.

Whether the road work was done under contract by the county, or through the use of county inmate labor, the construction methods were primitive by today's standards. The only power machinery for road construction was gas or steam rollers and rock crushers. All work was performed by teams of horses or mules. Grading was done with wheeled scrapers, slip scrapers, and fresno scrapers. Material was hauled in slat bottom wagons that held from one to two cubic yards.

When the first federal aid became available in 1917, Alabama found that there were no state matching funds available.

As a remedy, voters ratified a state bond issue of $25 million in 1921 to be used for the construction and maintenance of roads with the understanding that it would be used in conjunction with federal appropriations. A year later, 58 projects comprising 361 miles of road in 32 counties were completed and another 47 projects in 36 counties saw 476 miles under construction. Another $25 million bond issue followed a few years later, also to match federal funds.

Alabama also received a boost from the federal government through its distribution to the states of military surplus from World War I. Automobiles, trucks, tractors, and road machinery were obtained at nominal cost to the state.

The 1920s and 1930s in Alabama saw inadequate highway financing, increased road use and an unsympathetic public who, perhaps unjustly, dubbed the period "The Patch Road Era." But in reality, Alabama's views reflected the nation's ills, particularly the "do nothing" governments that characterized the Roaring 20s and The Great Depression of the 30s. And, some note that state highway personnel made the most of a bad situation and, in spite of their disadvantages, made some sound improvements in the road system during those eras.

One of the primary problems they faced, and still face today, is Alabama's topography which does not enhance inexpensive road construction. The extensive waterways of the state, which have been so often heralded, were a major obstacle to road builders. The Tennessee, Alabama, Tombigbee, and Chattahoochee rivers and their tributaries necessitated costly bridges. The mountains in northern Alabama are beautiful to tourists but troublesome for engineers.

The $25 million bond issues of the 1920's were helpful, but did not provide sufficient funds to cope with the increased automobile traffic or provide necessary maintenance. The number of motor vehicles in Alabama had increased from 9,000 in 1914 to over 312,000 in 1939 while the total miles of road only grew from 50,000 to 65,000. Of the money available, little was provided for keeping roads passable.

In addition, primitive equipment continued to plague road building. Most of the construction accomplished during this period was by animal power or human labor. There were a few steam-powered drag-lines, shovels, rollers, Holt or Best crawler tractors, concrete mixers, rock crushers, and bituminous plants in use. Maintenance equipment was either

horse or truck powered. Even Mother Nature was unfavorable to Alabama engineers, particularly in 1928–1929. During that period, unprecedented rain wrought extensive flood damage throughout the state and caused an estimated $10 million in highway damage.

In 1939, construction of a $4 million, 3,389-foot tunnel across the Mobile River began. Consisting of seven sections, from 255 feet to 298 feet in length, each segment was floated down the river and lowered into a huge trench 47 feet below the surface. Alabama's first underwater tunnel was completed in 1941. It was originally estimated that 1,250 cars would use the tunnel each day. By the early 1970s, over 25,000 were passing through daily.

Pre-World War II innovations in Alabama's road system were better road design, more road maintenance, the opening of new river bridges, the formation of a group dedicated to check final quantities before payment on contracts, progress in highway marking, as well as a winter training school.

However, the war had a severe impact on ALDOT. Over 600 employees left for the armed services. Regular federal aid was suspended. All department work was correlated with the war effort. Access roads to military installations became the principle construction objective. No construction could be initiated without special government permit.

At the war's end, gasoline rationing was terminated and the standard of living rapidly rose which led to an increase in car and truck ownership. And that meant an increasing demand for more and better roadways. In addition, the 1949 legislature enacted a statute requiring the department to assume maintenance of the streets through municipalities which were traversed by state highway routes. This added 164 miles to ALDOT's maintenance system.

The first interstate highway to be opened to traffic in Alabama was a 28-mile section of I-65 in 1959. Nine years later more than 50 percent was completed with only 27 percent remaining to be placed under contract.

The most dramatic development in the Alabama interstate system, however, was begun in 1969 with the contract letting of the Mobile Tunnel as part of Interstate 10. This twin tube project was by far the largest undertaking of any project in the history of the state's system with the largest single contract ever let in Alabama's interstate program ($47.5 million). The 3,000-foot-long structure took nearly three and a half years to build. It was opened to traffic in early 1973.

The five existing mainline interstates (I-10, I-20, I-59, I-65, and I-85) within Alabama were completed by the mid-1980s.

In 1979, ALDOT began construction of a new controlled access highway under the Appalachian Development Highway Program that would connect Memphis and Birmingham. This route was added to the interstate system by Congress

and designated as I-22. Approximately 96 miles of I-22, from the Mississippi line to Jasper, Alabama, was completed in 2005, with another 25-mile segment added by 2007. The last section that will connect I-22 with I-65 and U.S. Highway 31 is currently under construction. It is interesting to note that from the 1950s to the 1990s, Alabama spent $1.5 billion to build its interstate system. That is the same cost that has been needed to construct this lone 96-mile highway.

In February 2014, ALDOT began construction on the Birmingham Northern Beltline project, a 52-mile, multi-lane interstate connector that will essentially complete an outer loop around Alabama's largest city. The total project is expected to take more than 25 years to build.

ALASKA

Alaska Department of Transportation and Public Facilities

Patrick J. Kemp, P.E.
Commissioner

YEAR FORMED **1911**

FTE **3,500**

KEY FACTS
TOTAL STATE ROAD MILES (OWNED BY STATE HIGHWAY AGENCY) **5,606**

STATE-OWNED BRIDGES **807**

TRANSIT TRIPS PER YEAR
5.13 million

FREIGHT RAIL ROUTE MILES **506**

Since statehood in 1959, the Alaska Department of Transportation and Public Facilities, originally known as the Alaska Department of Highways, has grown to include 254 airports, 11 ferries serving 35 communities, 5,619 miles of highway, and 720 public facilities throughout the state of Alaska. As the largest state in the union and two-and-a-half times the size of Texas, with more coastline than all of the other states combined, transportation across Alaska is as versatile as the scenery, wildlife, and people who call The Last Frontier home. From the urban center of Anchorage to the rural villages in coastal and Arctic regions of the state, the Alaska Department of Transportation and Public Facilities keeps Alaska moving.

The old joke that Alaska is just outside Anchorage is both true and false. Anchorage was established in 1914 as a railroad construction port for the Alaska Railroad, which was built between 1915 and 1923. Anchorage has since grown into Alaska's largest city and is the hub of the state.

Getting to Anchorage is easy any time of year, whether traveling by air, land, or sea. Two scenic highways connect Anchorage to the rest of the major roads in the state; the Glenn Highway

heads north to Denali National Park via the Parks Highway and east to the Wrangell–St. Elias National Park and Preserve; and the Seward Highway leads south to the Kenai Peninsula and west toward Cook Inlet. The Alaska Railroad connects Anchorage with Denali, Fairbanks, Girdwood, the Mat-Su Valley, Seward, Talkeetna, and Whittier. The Alaska Marine Highway ferries dock at several ports such as Whittier, Homer and Valdez, which are all connected to Anchorage by road or rail. Anchorage is also home to Ted Stevens Anchorage International Airport, the state's largest international airport and the nation's second largest cargo airport.

Alaska's economy boomed in 1967 with the discovery of Prudhoe Bay, the largest oil field in North America. By 1975, the Dalton Highway was complete, providing the only over-land connection from the Prudhoe Bay oil fields to the rest of the world. Often referred to as "Alaska's Road to the Bank," the 415-mile highway begins at mile 73 of the Elliott Highway, near Livengood, and ends near the Alaska Department of Transportation & Public Facilities owned Deadhorse Airport at Prudhoe Bay.

Built to secondary road standards, the Dalton Highway was originally

constructed by the Alyeska Pipeline Service Company to support construction and maintenance of the oil pipeline. The Alaska Department of Transportation & Public Facilities took over the road in 1978. The entire highway, up to Prudhoe Bay, opened to the public in 1994. More than 70 percent of the traffic on the Dalton Highway is comprised of heavy trucks. Since the road opened to the public, recreational travel has increased 300 percent with an average of 190 vehicles per day.

No matter where the road goes in Alaska, the journey and view is sure to be remarkable. Of the 15 scenic byways recognized by the state of Alaska, five are nationally recognized. The George Parks Highway, Glenn Highway, and Haines Highway–Valley of the Eagles are National Scenic Byways, and both the Seward Highway and Alaska Marine Highway are All-American Roads.

Connecting Alaska's two largest cities—Anchorage and Fairbanks—the George Parks Highway travels through spectacular wilderness into the heart of Alaska. Named after territorial Governor George A. Parks, the highway was completed in 1971. The highway provides access to Denali National Park and Preserve and offers a number of

opportunities to see North America's tallest peak, Mount McKinley—known by Alaskans as Denali, which means "the great one."

The Glenn Highway National Scenic Byway travels a path carved by ancient glaciers. Following the braided Matanuska River for over half its length this byway winds through 135 miles of the most impressive terrain on earth. Winters present a splendid sky show when the northern lights dance among the snow-capped mountains, while summers bring endless days to roam in fields of wildflowers and ancient forests.

The Haines Highway–Valley of the Eagles connects the Southeast Alaska community of Haines with Haines Junction in the Yukon Territory. First used by the Chilkat Indians, the highway became a packhorse trail to the Klondike goldfields in the late 1880s. In 1943, the U.S. Army used the highway as a military access road during World War II. This byway is encompassed by lush coastal rain forest as it makes its way up the St. Elias Mountains, and into Canada where the forest gives way to alpine tundra and connects with the Alaska Highway in Canada.

Recognized for its scenic, natural, historical, and recreational values, the

127-mile Seward Highway holds triple designation: USDA Forest Service Scenic Byway, Alaska Scenic Byway and All-American Road. Departing Anchorage, the first 50 miles of the Seward Highway skirts the base of the Chugach Mountains and the shore of Turnagain Arm, where it is common to see beluga whales, Dall sheep, waterfalls, and eagles. The remainder of the drive courses through the Kenai Mountains, offering dramatic views of wild Alaska.

The Alaska Marine Highway System, the only marine route recognized as an All-American Road, celebrated its Golden Anniversary in 2013 by embarking on a year-long celebration highlighting the storied history of the system's vessels and communities. Since its start 50 years ago, the Alaska Marine Highway System has grown to connect an area covering 3,500 miles and 35 port communities, from Alaska to Canada to Washington. In its 50th year, the fleet of 11 vessels carried 330,000 passengers and 110,000 vehicles.

When considering Alaska's enormous size, it comes as no surprise that the Alaska aviation system is the largest in North America. Nearly 82 percent of Alaska communities are not accessible by road, making aviation more than a convenience or a luxury—aviation is essential in the Alaskan way of life. Alaska has 405 public use land-based airports, 54 heliports, and approximately 855 recorded landing areas, not including the thousands of lakes and gravel bars across the state of which the Alaska Department of Transportation & Public Facilities owns and oversees operations of 254.

Whether in Anchorage or the smallest community at the tip of the Aleutian Chain, air service is the lifeline that connects all Alaskans to other communities in the state, to the Lower 48, and to the world. Alaska's airports serve the transportation needs of the state's residents, support the movement of materials and goods, contribute substantially to the economy, and enable delivery of critical medical services.

The Alaska International Airport System, comprised of Ted Stevens Anchorage International Airport and Fairbanks International Airport, is also owned and operated by the Alaska Department of Transportation & Public Facilities.

Fairbanks International Airport (FAI), located in the heart of interior Alaska, serves 1 million passengers annually, and is the second largest airport in the state. In addition to being an economic engine for the Fairbanks community, FAI is the aviation hub for interior Alaska and is the diversionary airport for international freighters flying to the Anchorage International Airport.

Ted Stevens Anchorage International Airport (ANC) is the major air gateway to the state of Alaska for both passengers (over 5 million passengers per year) and cargo (over 2 million tons of cargo per year). Its strategic location makes it an important technical stop and trans-load hub for air cargo freighters flying between Asia and North America. It is also home to Lake Hood Seaplane Base, which is recognized as the largest and busiest seaplane base in the world.

ANC consistently ranks within the top six of the world's busiest air cargo airports; as well as the number two cargo airport in the United States. It was recently named the number one air cargo airport in North American by Air Cargo World Magazine, winning this prestigious award for the third consecutive year in a row.

Alaska's transportation system is a multi-billion dollar endeavor that provides for the safe and efficient movement of goods and people to, from, and within the state. Numerous challenges, some common across the nation and some unique to Alaska, affect the state's ability to deliver transportation facilities and services, and the public's ability to fully use and enjoy them. Expanding transportation routes and facilities is essential to ensuring continued job creation and economic vitality.

ARIZONA

Arizona Department of Transportation

John S. Halikowski
Director

YEAR FORMED **1974**

FTE **4,248**

KEY FACTS
TOTAL STATE ROAD MILES
(OWNED BY STATE HIGHWAY
AGENCY) **6,750**

STATE-OWNED BRIDGES **4,700**

TRANSIT TRIPS PER YEAR
90.31 million

FREIGHT RAIL ROUTE
MILES: **1,679**

In the past quarter century, Arizona has experienced tremendous growth, its population almost doubling. Three hundred days of sunshine annually, a diverse landscape and wide-open real estate opportunities have long made Arizona a beacon of inspiration for individuals looking to make a life for themselves. Rapid growth, however, presented a number of challenges to the state's transportation system.

Since the 1950s, highway safety and capacity, and the economic connection between metropolitan Phoenix and rural towns have been major concerns. By the 1990s, population growth had created a pressing demand for new, expanded, more efficient transportation connectivity in metropolitan Phoenix. As the Arizona Department of Transportation (ADOT) worked to meet that demand, however, connectivity with rural areas also became an increasingly important issue that came with its own set of challenges, including mitigating impacts to communities, wildlife, and the natural beauty of the Sonoran Desert and mountains in Arizona. With strong leadership from agency directors who later advanced to high-level federal positions—Director Mary Peters became the U.S. secretary of transportation and Director Victor Mendez led the

Federal Highway Administration—and a recognized history of innovation, the Arizona Department of Transportation was well-positioned to meet those challenges.

Meeting Metropolitan Demands: The Regional Freeway System
As the 1980s came to a close, ADOT neared completion of its most expensive highway-construction project to date and faced an enormous challenge in metropolitan Phoenix. In 1990, the final segment of Interstate 10 was completed, finishing the 2,460-mile-long highway that runs from California to Florida. Because the path of the freeway ran through historic Phoenix neighborhoods, designers devised an innovative plan that set the 10-lane freeway below street level for six blocks. Above the freeway, construction crews lined up 19 bridges side by side, creating a tunnel effect for motorists, and built a 30-acre public park atop the bridge decks. Locals call this stretch of I-10 the "Deck Park Tunnel," even though it does not meet the formal definition of a tunnel. More than 260,000 vehicles pass through the "tunnel" each day.

With I-10 and I-17 finished, ADOT turned its attention to meeting the needs of rapid population growth in

the sprawling metropolitan area, which covers much of Maricopa County and part of northwest Pinal County. In 1970, Phoenix ranked 20th in the nation for city population, according to U.S. Census Bureau data. By 1990, it was the ninth largest and growing quickly. From 1990 to 2010, Arizona's population increased 74 percent to 6,392,017 people, with most of the growth occurring in Maricopa County. In 2010, the population of Maricopa County (3,817,117) exceeded the entire state of Arizona's 1990 population (3,665,228), and Phoenix had become the nation's sixth-largest city.

With population booming, voters approved a half-cent sales tax devoted almost exclusively to funding construction of a new Regional Freeway System in metropolitan Phoenix. This victory was significant for transportation as voters had voted down similar initiatives in the past. Proposition 300 secured funding for the first phase of a freeway-expansion program that included five new highways, totaling 169 miles, constructed by 2011 in metropolitan Phoenix. The first two that broke ground were State Route 51 and the Agua Fria and Pima freeways, which form two of the three sections of Loop 101, which serves the western, northern and eastern

portions of the metropolitan area. By 1990, the first segment of SR 51 opened. Around the same time, construction crews completed the Superstition Freeway in Phoenix's East Valley, finishing a two-decade-long project. By 2001, Loop 101, a 60-mile highway consisting of three freeway segments (Agua Fria, Pima, and Price) was completed. The 15-mile-long SR 51 was finished two years later; its northern segment intersecting Loop 101 in northern Phoenix. In 2008, Governor Janet Napolitano renamed SR 51 the Piestewa Freeway in honor of Lori Piestewa, an Arizonan who was the first Native American woman killed in combat while serving in the U.S. military during Operation Iraqi Freedom.

Throughout the construction of the Regional Freeway System, ADOT used rubberized asphalt—an Arizona-pioneered mixture of regular asphalt and rock and "crumb rubber" made from shredded, used vehicle tires—as a pavement preservation strategy. Rubberized asphalt provides motorists a smoother ride and reduces traffic noise by an average of four decibels. Furthermore, by recycling 1,500 tires for every lane of every mile of rubberized asphalt, ADOT keeps millions of tires out of landfills. One 10-mile, six-lane stretch of highway

alone repurposes 90,000 old tires. In 2003, ADOT's Quiet Pavement Program spent $34 million resurfacing 115 miles of Phoenix-area freeways. Now, most freeways in metropolitan Phoenix are paved with a top layer of rubberized asphalt. The practice has become increasingly common on rural highways, too.

By the time Proposition 300 expired in 2006, it had generated $5.7 billion for constructing new Phoenix-area freeways. The Regional Freeway System was not complete, however, and in 2004, voters approved Proposition 400, extending the half-cent sales tax for an additional two decades and assuming a broader scope. The tax continued to support the Regional Freeway System, but it also provided for improvements to local streets, expanded bus service and construction of 58 miles of light-rail transit, representing a major shift toward multi-modal transportation in Phoenix.

With the continued support of Proposition 400, the construction of Loop 202, the 51-mile long two-freeway system (Red Mountain and Santan) that circumnavigates southeastern suburbs of Tempe, Mesa, Chandler and Gilbert, finished in 2008. Meanwhile, in northwestern metropolitan Phoenix, construction on Loop 303 began. Crews had completed 39 miles of the highway by 2014. Most recently, construction began on SR 24 in 2012 to increase access to far-southeastern suburbs.

If estimations prove correct, Proposition 400 will bring in $14.3 billion by 2025.

Connecting to Rural Arizona

In 2010, about 64 percent of Arizona's population lived in the Phoenix metropolitan area, and another nine percent were distributed between Tucson and Flagstaff, the two other largest population hubs in Arizona. The remaining 25 percent lived in a small or rural town, totaling 1.8 million people spread across the sixth-largest state, by area, in the United States. Though diverse, this population supports a significant portion of the state's economy and presents a particular challenge for simultaneously strengthening economic connectivity with other states and countries and preserving it within the state. Modernizing and operating the rural highway system to accommodate tourism traffic has offered a distinct set of challenges requiring ingenuity and innovation.

Since Congress designated the CANA-MEX Corridor in the Intermodal Surface Transportation Efficiency Act of 1991, the idea of a commerce corridor linking Mexico with Arizona's economic centers and Nevada has been discussed. ADOT has shown its commitment to facilitating commercial transportation and trade with Mexico by working with the federal government to improve access to ports of entry along the international border in Nogales and the Yuma area. ADOT built SR 195, which connects San Luis Port to I-8, and at the Mariposa Port in Nogales, it realigned and

widened SR 189, allowing easier and faster access to I-19. I-11, currently still in the planning stage, could enhance connections from Mexico to Phoenix and Las Vegas—two of the largest cities in the country not connected by an interstate. I-11 and the Intermountain West Corridor Study have no funding for construction, but Congress designated the Phoenix-to-Las Vegas segment as part of the Moving Ahead for Progress in the 21st Century legislation.

In addition to increasing national and international connectivity, ADOT has supported the many smaller economies that depend on the State Highway System. The Beeline Highway, the local name for SR 87 and the first major rural highway to undergo modernization in recent times, opened to traffic in 1958 and gave Phoenix residents a direct 70-mile escape to the cool climes of Payson, northern Arizona and the Mogollon Rim—home to the world's largest stand of ponderosa pine trees. As the area grew in popularity, the two-lane highway became prone to congestion and eventually exceeded the national average for traffic crashes on similar highways. To maintain the tourism vital to the survival of northern towns along the Mogollon Rim, ADOT began reconstructing SR 87 in 1989. The project finished in 2001 and resulted in a four-lane, divided highway that was more efficient and safer for motorists. FHWA awarded ADOT a merit award for environmentally sensitive measures taken to preserve archaeological sites and the surrounding landscape and its inhabitants.

A similar stretch of highway on US 60—necessary for tourism and no longer capable of safely carrying high-volume traffic—required modernization in

the 2000s. In 2008, construction crews widened the 10-mile stretch of highway through Gonzales Pass in Tonto National Forest to four lanes, replacing a narrow two-lane road. Not only did the new roadway reduce head-on collisions, but it also finished eight months early and $2.5 million under budget. Upon the project's completion, the Arizona-based Valley Forward organization awarded it the prestigious President's Award for Environmental Excellence for its efforts to maintain the natural environment surrounding the roadway, which included salvaging and replanting 18,000 cacti and native Sonoran Desert plants, implementing wildlife crossings to divert animal traffic away from the roadway and installing innovative parallel roadway ditches and sediment-settling basins to prevent stormwater pollution.

ADOT also has dedicated nearly half a billion dollars to widening and improving US 93, which is the main highway for motorists traveling between Phoenix and Las Vegas. In 2010, Arizona and Nevada worked together to accelerate construction of the Mike O'Callaghan-Pat Tillman Memorial Bridge at Hoover Dam. The structure is currently the world's highest concrete arch bridge. Previously, traffic crossed the Colorado River by driving over the dam's narrow roadway, resulting in heavy traffic and bottlenecks on US 93, a key route for interstate transit, especially after security increased following 9/11. The new bridge allows motorists to bypass the dam. In 2012, the American Society of Civil Engineers awarded the bridge an Outstanding Civil Engineering Achievement Award. The project also received recognition for implementing first-of-its-kind wildlife overpasses. Because the highway cut through bighorn sheep habitat, it isolated the animals from the region's only significant water source at the Colorado River, making it difficult for the animals to maintain genetic diversity and recover from disease. In response, ADOT partnered with the Arizona Game and Fish Department to find a solution. The two agencies tracked a portion of the sheep population, and based on the data collected, ADOT built three wildlife bridges within 15 miles of the Hoover Dam bridge.

In 2013, two projects—one unplanned and another planned—began work in Northern Arizona. After a landslide destroyed a portion of US 89 near Page, Arizona, the roadway was impassable, forcing a 23-mile closure that required a 115-mile detour. While geotechnical analysts worked to devise a long-term solution for rebuilding that section of the highway, ADOT acted quickly to find a reasonable short-term fix. In only three months, ADOT worked with the Navajo Nation to agree to pave Navajo Route 20, turning the previously dirt 44-mile roadway into Temporary US 89 and vastly shortening the detour route. Around that time, ADOT also received a $21.6 million federal grant to make improvements to a bridge on the I-15 Virgin River Gorge corridor in the northwestern corner of Arizona. This sum was the largest awarded in 2013 by the Transportation Investment Generating Economic Recovery program.

Work to widen SR 260 along the Mogollon Rim began in 2000 and is a long-term, ongoing project. Construction should take two decades because of difficulties due to working through mountainous terrain. Like Gonzales Pass, SR 260 will use wildlife crossings to reduce collisions between motorists and animals, and will continue preserving and conserving water on construction sites and finished roadways.

Because tourism is the economic lifeblood of many small Arizona towns, ADOT has also undertaken improving economic connectivity throughout the state in a number of ways not related to constructing highways. ADOT's award-winning print publication, Arizona Highways magazine, both showcases the majestic beauty of Arizona's natural landscapes and directs tourists toward destinations and activities for all interests, from wine-tasting tours to fishing hotspots. ADOT also owns and operates Grand Canyon National Park Airport, which serves 300,000 passengers annually, and will continue to improve the airport's facilities to ensure the safety and comfort of travelers who take in America's second-most visited national park. In addition to modernizing Arizona's rural highways, these ventures are ways that ADOT supports rural economies and transportation within the state.

Looking Forward

If population projections and trends continue, ADOT will have ample opportunity to make use of rubberized asphalt, environmentally sensitive highway designs and partnerships to connect economic centers. Some metro and rural projects might even soon blend together. Population models forecast that the combined populations of Maricopa, Pinal, Pima, Yavapai and Santa Cruz counties could double by 2050, growing to more than 10 million people. These counties comprise the "Sun Corridor Megapolitan," which links the Phoenix and Tucson metropolitan areas and extends to the United States–Mexico border. Existing and planned roadways would not be enough to handle such an influx of residents. New transportation development in the megapolitan might take on a form other than new highways. In 2011, ADOT began to study the feasibility of a passenger rail between Phoenix and Tucson. Though the project has no construction schedule or funding, ADOT has advanced the possibility of multi-modal transportation options to Arizona. Just as it confronted massive population growth at the end of the 20th century, Arizona will meet new, possibly-still-unknown challenges in the 21st century.

For more transportation history in Arizona, visit *azdot.gov/HistoryReport*.

By Dani Weber and Doug Pacey

ARKANSAS

Arkansas State Highway and Transportation Department

Scott Bennett, P.E.
Director

YEAR FORMED **1913**

FTE **3,542**

KEY FACTS

TOTAL STATE ROAD MILES (OWNED BY STATE HIGHWAY AGENCY) **16,414**

TOTAL PUBLIC BRIDGES **12,645**

STATE-OWNED BRIDGES **7,236**

TRANSIT TRIPS PER YEAR **5.15 million**

The State of Arkansas has over 16,000 miles of highways within its borders. The Arkansas State Highway and Transportation Department (AHTD), along with the members of the Arkansas State Highway Commission, have shared a vision with the people of Arkansas that has shaped those miles of roadway over the past 25 years and also has given the department a firm blueprint for the future.

Meeting the demands of a growing population in the state over these past years has translated into a host of new highway programs created to handle our growing transportation needs.

In 1991, Arkansas' legislature listened to the department's plans for improvements to the state's system of highways and approved two identical proposals that would provide needed additional revenues for a $2.5 billion, 15-year Highway Improvement Program. The program would include highways on new location, widening of highways to four lanes, provide passing lanes, Interstate rehabilitation and bridge improvements, among other things.

Acts 364 and 382 of 1991 raised the gasoline tax five cents per gallon and the diesel tax an additional two cents

per gallon. The action produced an additional $47.4 million annually for the department and about $10.1 million annually for cities and counties. The rest of the funding would come from the four cents per gallon increase in the diesel tax that was included in the weight/distance tax settlement bill passed earlier in the session. It produced approximately $17.7 million annually for the department and $3.7 million for the cities and counties.

With a Highway Improvement Program in place, the department could turn its attention to more specific needs, such as the state's Interstate highway system.

Nowhere was the need for new four-lane highways more obvious 25 years ago than in the fast-growing northwest corner of Arkansas in cities such as Fayetteville, Springdale, Rogers, and Bentonville. As a result, the 1990s saw the relocation and widening to four lanes of the major artery to that area, Highway 71 from Alma to Fayetteville. Upon completion, the new roadway totaling over 40 miles was re-designated Interstate 540. Not only did it provide safer and faster travel to that area, it also included the construction of Arkansas' first highway tunnel, the twin-bore Bobby Hopper Tunnel near Winslow.

Interstate 540 was not Arkansas' only new Interstate highway designated in the 1990s. Highway 65, the major highway leading from Little Rock to Pine Bluff, the largest city in southeast Arkansas, was widened and its 42 miles were officially designated as Interstate 530.

The addition of the two new Interstate routes in 1999 raised the state's Interstate mileage from 542 to 636.

New Interstate miles were well received, but at the same time, the department also began focusing on Arkansas' existing Interstate miles and the need to keep them in the best condition possible. A significant milestone was accomplished by Governor Mike Huckabee, the Arkansas State Highway Commission, the General Assembly and the people of Arkansas in 1999 when the use of bonds to finance highway improvements was approved. The result was the 1999 Interstate Rehabilitation Program which reconstructed nearly 60 percent of Arkansas' Interstates over a six-year period. The Program received numerous national awards. In addition, it gained national attention for its revolutionary use of a new process called rubblization. A construction and engineering technique, rubblization was found to save

time and money by reducing existing roadway concrete into rubble at its existing location and using the broken concrete as a base for the new roadway rather than hauling it away.

Arkansas had now addressed its most serious Interstate needs, and in the process, had gone from having one of the worst Interstate highway systems in the country to having one rated among the best.

With a successful program in place for its Interstates, attention turned to the remaining miles on Arkansas' highway system, its county roads and its city streets.

A one-time infusion of funds from the Arkansas' General Revenue Surplus of 2007 allowed the Department to proceed with a statewide repaving program. The funds allowed for resurfacing projects in all 75 counties of the state over a two year period. In 2007 alone, 43 resurfacing projects totaling over $16 million were undertaken.

The year 2008 brought yet another funding source into play for the AHTD. Acts 4 and 5 of a special legislative session that year raised the severance tax rate on natural gas production. The

state was seeing a boom in gas production in the north central part of the state in an exploration area known as the Fayetteville Shale Play. This provided an additional $30 million earmarked for highway improvements in the state. Funds from the tax, though not as high today as originally expected, are now being utilized for resurfacing highways in the Fayetteville Shale gas exploration area of north central Arkansas.

With all of the progress, Arkansas, like other states in the country, still needed to find new sources of revenue to continue to maintain and improve its highway system. To help in that search, Act 374 of the 2009 Legislative Session created the Arkansas Blue Ribbon Committee on Highway Finance. The purpose of the Committee was to study issues relating to transportation revenues and costs, and to recommend to the Governor, the Legislature and the Highway Commission, the best methods for raising adequate revenues to address Arkansas' constantly growing transportation needs.

The newly formed Committee was composed of six legislators, one Highway Commissioner, one representative from the Municipal League, one representative from the Association of

Arkansas Counties, and 10 members selected from the general public.

Approximately 18 months were spent discussing proposals, reports, concepts, testimony, and comments from a number of sources. In addition, five public hearings were held across the state to gather opinions and ideas from local residents.

In late 2010, a report was presented to the Governor's Office. The interim study found that the current formula of public roadway funding was defective and would not be sustainable in the near term or the long term. The Committee presented a list of viable funding options.

Now, four years later, three of those options have already become a reality.

First, the success of the 1999 Interstate Rehabilitation Program led Arkansas voters to approve a second phase of the program in 2011. Currently underway, the department has scheduled 75 projects in the 2011 program that will improve an additional 458 miles of Interstate miles across the state.

Second, in November 2012, voters in Arkansas approved one of the largest highway construction programs ever undertaken by the AHTD.

Through a constitutional amendment which passed with 58 percent of the vote, the people of Arkansas passed a 10-year, half-cent sales tax to improve highway and infrastructure projects throughout the state.

Known as the Connecting Arkansas Program, the game plan is to expand selected two-lane roadways to four-lane highways and add new lanes to identified interstate highways. It includes 31 projects on 19 corridors around the state and totals 180 miles of improvements.

With passage of the program, the Arkansas state sales tax temporarily increased to 6.5 cents for 10 years, effective July 1, 2013. The increase will result in an estimated $1.8 billion in cash and bond proceeds. The new tax will be abolished in 2023 when the bonds issued to pay for the work are repaid. Today, the first several of those projects are already underway.

Yet a third recommendation of the Blue Ribbon Committee on Highway Finance became a reality in 2011 with passage of the new tax, that being the creation of the State Aid Program for Cities. The program dedicates one cent per gallon of the existing motor fuel tax for improvements to city streets across Arkansas. Incorporated cities and towns may now request funding and utilize it to improve city streets in their area that serve as major or minor arterial and collector routes. A State Aid City Street Committee administers the program. The AHTD provides technical assistance to the Street Committee. For projects approved by the Committee, the AHTD designs the work, procures construction contracts and inspects the funded projects. To date, over 107 miles of municipal streets in Arkansas have been improved. A total of 23 projects have been completed, seven are under construction and 23 more are planned. They represent a much needed infrastructure investment, to this point, of more than $17 million.

Any report of progress on Arkansas' highway system over the past 25 years must include a new landmark in the southeast corner of the state. The AHTD celebrated the opening of a new bridge across the Mississippi River in 2010. The new four-lane structure at Lake Village replaces an original two-lane bridge built in 1940. The new structure took nine years and $341 million to build. The bridge boasts being the longest cable-stayed bridge on the Mississippi River and the third longest in the United States. The new Greenville Bridge was a joint project of the AHTD and the Mississippi Department of Transportation.

Not all of the improvements to Arkansas' highways have been made on roadways and bridges. Great strides have been taken over the past 11 years to make sure motorists traveling the state have inviting, comfortable Welcome Centers available as well.

A study conducted in 1997 indicated the time had come to begin replacing eight of the old Visitor Centers with new facilities that would provide safe and clean locations for travelers to rest, and serve as a tool to promote tourism in Arkansas.

Governor Mike Huckabee and the Legislature passed Act 345 of 2001 that approved the initial phase, to replace four of the centers. In May 2001, the Arkansas State Highway Commission passed a Minute Order approving those projects. At a news conference in the spring of 2002, Governor Huckabee announced plans for the first of the new Centers to be located at Texarkana and construction began soon after.

Act 1145 of 2003 was passed to begin the next round of center improvements.

Since 2002, new facilities have been constructed in Texarkana, Corning, El Dorado, Fort Smith/Van Buren, Lake Village, Blytheville, West Memphis, and Helena–West Helena.

The new centers incorporate design elements such as native stone and large timbers. Each includes more space for travel brochures, sitting areas and special exhibits. They also contain computer kiosks, multi-media space, and picnic areas. A special feature of the Lake Village Welcome Center is a 3,700 square-foot multi-level fishing and observation deck overlooking Lake Chicot.

With all of the improvements taking place on Arkansas' highways, the need arose to keep motorists informed of construction developments as they traveled. The challenge—give motorists a tool that provides helpful information before they hit the road so that they know what to expect and are able to make appropriate travel plans. The solution is *IDriveArkansas.com*, a website providing motorists with up-to-date information on traffic flow, road conditions, lane closure locations, and much more. To accompany the site's launch, an extensive promotion campaign was developed to direct motorists to the site and inform them of information available at their fingertips.

Today at the AHTD, "behind-the-scenes" work is already under way on future improvements. At a public information meeting, our staff is discussing future projects with local residents, at a computer screen our engineers are studying roadway design and on the construction job-site, our crews are building a better highway system for motorists traveling the state of Arkansas. Everyone involved shares the same goal—a safer and more efficient highway system to meet the demands of a growing motoring public.

By Angela Tillotson

CALIFORNIA

California Department of Transportation (Caltrans)

Malcolm Dougherty
Director

YEAR FORMED **1972**

FTE **19,511**

KEY FACTS:
TOTAL STATE ROAD MILES
(OWNED BY STATE HIGHWAY
AGENCY) **15,080**

STATE-OWNED BRIDGES **12,180**

TRANSIT TRIPS PER YEAR
1.37 billion

FREIGHT RAIL ROUTE
MILES **5,200**

The past 100 years brought tremendous growth and change to California and the state's transportation system. In 1914, California's population was between 2 million and 3 million. It is now more than 10 times that. California's first transportation entity—the Bureau of Highways—was created to study highway needs and make recommendations for a 4,500-mile state highway system, a system that now has more than 50,000 lane miles. California's state transportation organization's name and duties changed several times, until 1973 when it became Caltrans—one entity unifying all transportation functions.

Caltrans accomplished many outstanding feats and engineering marvels during the past century, some of them were the nation's first. In 1936, the San Francisco–Oakland Bay Bridge opened and was the longest of its kind at the time. The next year, California's first north–south highway, State Route 1, was completed and served as an important tourist and commercial corridor. California's freeway era kicked off in 1940 with the Arroyo Seco Parkway—the first freeway in the west. Twenty years later, California would be the site of the 1960 Winter Olympics, and this would be the impetus to build Interstate 80, the first all-weather, trans-Sierra Nevada

highway, another major engineering achievement. The 1970s brought the state's first permanent high-occupancy vehicle lane—a toll plaza on the Bay Bridge, the passage of new federal and state environmental laws, and the state's first traffic management center.

The past 25 years, however, significantly changed Caltrans' focus from a highway-centric transportation system to one that acknowledges that people and goods move on more than just highways: airports, rail, seaports, local roads, mass transportation, bicycling, and walking. Caltrans has moved from simply building highways to working to create a safe, integrated, sustainable transportation system now and for future generations.

Earthquake Country

California is the nation's most populated state and the second most earthquake-prone. The state's transportation system is crucial for getting California's residents where they need to go, but it is also critical to the nation's goods movement. The ports of Los Angeles and Long Beach make up the largest port complex in the nation, handling a fourth of the nation's container cargo traffic. Earthquakes in California have caused hundreds of deaths, billions of dollars in

damage to the state highway system, and economic loss.

California's highway system has more than 12,000 state-owned bridges. After the 1971 Sylmar earthquake struck the Los Angeles area and damaged several bridges, Caltrans started its first bridge seismic safety retrofit program. The program focused on bridge expansion joints and was completed in 1989. In October 1989, the Loma Prieta earthquake in the San Francisco Bay region caused significant death and bridge failure. The San Francisco–Oakland Bay Bridge was damaged and major routes were forced closed. That is when Caltrans established its current Seismic Retrofit Programs. After the Loma Prieta earthquake, Caltrans identified 1,039 state-owned bridges needing seismic retrofit. In 1994, the Los Angeles area once again suffered extensive damage and loss of life during the Northridge Earthquake. After that quake, Caltrans identified an additional 1,155 state-owned bridges that needed seismic retrofit.

The current Seismic Retrofit Programs focus on identifying and retrofitting existing bridges statewide and bringing them to the latest seismic safety retrofit standards established to prevent collapse during future earthquakes. Of the 2,203

bridges identified as needing seismic retrofit, Caltrans has achieved seismic safety on all but one, which is scheduled for completion in 2016.

Caltrans Acts Fast

With a population of more than 38 million people, California's transportation system has to be reliable. When repairs are needed—especially in the state's metropolitan areas, highway closures are more than an inconvenience. They can increase congestion and can greatly affect emergency response and the economy. Sometimes Caltrans can plan ahead when it needs to close its highways, but when the unexpected happens, quick response is crucial.

California's Los Angeles and San Francisco Bay regions are some of the state's most densely populated areas. During the 1989 Loma Prieta earthquake the San Francisco–Oakland Bay Bridge was significantly damaged. The Bay Bridge is one of our country's busiest bridges, and the damage greatly affected transportation in the Bay Area. Caltrans' quick response allowed the bridge to reopen in only 30 days. The 1994 Northridge earthquake damaged multiple highways and bridges in the Los Angeles area, including Interstate 5/State Route 14, the Gavan Canyon Bridge, and Interstate

10. Again, Caltrans reconstructed these damaged vital routes in record time.

Caltrans had two unexpected incidents to deal with in 2007—both on heavily traveled routes. In April, a tanker overturned on the Interstate 880 and Interstate 580 approaches to the San Francisco–Oakland Bay Bridge, an area also known as the MacArthur Maze. The truck was carrying thousands of gallons of gasoline that spilled onto the highway and caught fire, causing major damage to the highway. Then in October, a fiery tunnel crash on Interstate 5 near Santa Clarita involved 31 vehicles and killed three people. This key route links Los Angeles and San Francisco. Caltrans cleared and reopened the tunnel in an astonishing three days, and the department's quick action and partnership with the MacArthur Maze contractor allowed that highway to reopen in a record 26 days.

With experience handling emergency transportation situations in the state's most populated areas, Caltrans applied some of the same strategies to planned rehabilitation projects, but it takes partnerships to complete these projects in record time. When Caltrans needed to repair a section of Interstate 5 through downtown Sacramento, the most congested highway section in the Sacramento region, the work needed to be carefully planned. The contractor proposed using around-the-clock work, seven days a week and partnering with Caltrans for intense outreach to keep the public informed. The repairs were completed in just 38 working days—instead of the projected two years—with minimal inconvenience to the public.

Paying for Transportation

Like the Great Depression of the 1930s, the Great Recession of the 2000s brought financial turmoil to the nation, yet Caltrans moved forward with some of the state's most needed and remarkable projects—just as it did during the Great Depression. None of California's impressive transportation system could exist without funding. While fuel taxes have been a primary funding source for the state's transportation system, funds are limited. Even with rising fuel costs, vehicles are becoming more fuel efficient and using less gas, and that means less funding for transportation.

In 2004, California voters approved the Transportation Congestion Improvement Act, also known as Proposition 42, to protect transportation funds. The act limited using transportation funds for nontransportation-related needs. Then in 2006, Californians again cast their votes for transportation by approving Propositions 1A and 1B, which protected the Proposition 42 funds and authorized $19.9 billion in bond sales for a broad range of transportation projects.

When the Great Recession hit America, the American Recovery and Reinvestment Act of 2009 provided Caltrans with $3.64 billion for transportation projects, and California was the first

state to obligate $1.5 billion to projects. These included a $1 billion widening project on Interstate 405, $13.5 million to resurface and repair a 50-year-old section of Interstate 80 in the Bay Area, and $1 billion to replace sections of Doyle Drive in San Francisco. These financial aids have been instrumental to California's transportation system, but the funds have nearly all been used. To continue giving Californians the transportation system they need, Caltrans is challenged with finding a sustainable funding source.

Partnerships Help Bring Projects to Life

In the past 100 years, California's transportation system has moved from open highways to an intricately woven system that includes several multi-level stack interchanges, such as the four-level interchange connecting U.S. Route 101 to State Route 110 in Los Angeles—the world's first stack interchange. To continue giving Californians a world-class transportation system, Caltrans uses innovative financing to move traditional transportation funding to a diversified approach that includes financing concepts developed from both the public and private sectors.

In 1989, California legislation authorized Caltrans to enter into public–private partnership agreements for up to four projects, with up to a 35-year lease on these projects and allowed developers to charge tolls on the privately constructed facilities. Two projects were constructed under this bill: the State Route 91 Express Lanes and the State Route 125 Southbay Expressway. The SR-91 Express Lanes were the nation's first privately funded toll road, the first fully automated toll facility, and the

first to use value pricing. The Orange County Transportation Authority operates the 91 Express Lanes, a four-lane, 10-mile toll road built in the median of SR-91 between the Orange/Riverside County line and SR-55. The State Route 125 Southbay Expressway opened in 2007, preserved 1,000 acres of natural habitat, and is a critical 10-mile, north–south corridor that serves international border crossing.

State law has changed to allow Caltrans and regional transportation agencies to enter into unlimited public–private partnership agreements for transportation projects. The first project under this new legislation is the Doyle Drive/Presidio Parkway Project. Doyle Drive in San Francisco is a high-priority safety project that will replace the facility with a modern, earthquake-safe one. Doyle Drive is the primary highway and transit link through San Francisco between counties to the north and south.

Another of Caltrans' partners is the Self-Help Counties Coalition, an organization of 20 local county transportation agencies delivering voter-approved transportation sales tax measures throughout California. Member agencies provide the authority and the funding to deliver priority transportation projects in the state. The coalition works closely with Caltrans, the California Transportation Commission, elected officials, and other public- and private-sector interests.

Partnering with other states also benefits California. Caltrans entered into a multistate partnership with the departments of transportation from Illinois, Michigan, and Missouri. All four states in this partnership are pooling their resources to purchase rail equipment at lower costs. This allows them to acquire the equipment in high volume under one contract to design, build, and deliver 130 bi-level passenger railcars for regional intercity rail corridors in California and the Midwest.

2013: The Year of Iconic California Structures

In Spring 2013, Caltrans opened the new Tom Lantos Tunnels at Devil's Slide. Located on State Route 1 in San Mateo County, the two parallel 4,200-foot-long tunnels run through San Pedro Mountain and bypass a stretch of highway that suffered frequent storm-related slides and closures. The tunnels were the first new tunnels on the state highway system in almost 50 years. Later that year, Caltrans completed the Caldecott fourth bore to reduce congestion and travel times for Bay Area motorists traveling in the off-peak direction. All three tunnels feature state-of-the-art fire and life safety systems that detect fire and monitor air quality.

The most iconic structure of California's transportation system is the new East Span of the San Francisco–Oakland Bay Bridge. The bridge opened Labor Day weekend 2013 and features a bicycle and pedestrian path. It is the world's largest self-anchored, self-suspension bridge and the largest public infrastructure contract in California's history. The new East Span has been designed to withstand rare seismic events that are expected to occur at the bridge site only once every 1,500 years.

The Next 25 Years: A Sustainable Transportation System

During the past 25 years, Caltrans has become more aware of California's diverse transportation needs and is learning to work with and preserve finite resources by focusing on building a sustainable transportation system— now and for future generations. This requires delicately balancing the planet, people, and prosperity to create a transportation system that everyone can use, whether they drive, take the bus, ride the train, fly, walk, or bicycle. This must be done while protecting the environment, spending wisely, and helping the economy.

Caltrans developed California's extensive highway system as the state's population and economy grew in the 20th century. Today, the population is still growing, but limited funds and space have slowed highway expansion and shifted the focus to using the existing system more efficiently. To achieve a more sustainable transportation system, Caltrans is adopting a "fix-it-first" approach by giving the highest spending priority to preventive maintenance and repairing existing roads. This approach reduces maintenance costs later, creates jobs, and supports business and residential investment in areas already served by transportation infrastructure.

Climate change and diminishing natural resources are a major concern for Caltrans. Balancing transportation needs with protecting the environment can be challenging. Before 1940, Caltrans was required to follow only eight environmental laws. By 2012, the number of environmental laws the department must follow had grown to 91. California's Global Warming Solutions Act of 2006 and Sustainable Communities Strategies of 2008 call for metropolitan planning organizations to create land use and transportation plans that meet regional transportation-sector greenhouse gas reductions and energy, water, and natural resources conservation. Caltrans is partnering with local agencies to better integrate state and local transportation systems and encourage active transportation. This helps regional agencies achieve greenhouse gas reductions, enhance public health, provide a wide range of projects to benefit active transportation users, and ensure that communities can fully share in the benefits of the environment, economy, and social equity.

The next 25 years are uncertain, but what is certain is that Caltrans will continue to give Californians a safe, sustainable, integrated, and efficient transportation system.

COLORADO

Colorado Department of Transportation

Donald E. Hunt
Executive Director

YEAR FORMED **1917**

FTE **2,908**

KEY FACTS
TOTAL STATE ROAD MILES
(OWNED BY STATE HIGHWAY
AGENCY) **9,063**

STATE-OWNED BRIDGES **3,449**

TRANSIT TRIPS PER YEAR
106 million

FREIGHT RAIL ROUTE MILES
2,663

Colorado's majestic mountains, plateaus, canyons, and high plains have made the state a major visitor destination since the 19th century. But the same features that make Colorado America's highest state also pose daunting challenges for the state's various transportation systems.

Colorado traces its state transportation agency roots to 1910, when a three-member Colorado Highway Commission met for the first time and began the task of determining out how to designate certain roads and routes as part of the state's official highway system. The new horseless carriage was in Colorado to stay.

Before many years had passed, auto roads opened over Wolf Creek Pass (1916) and Loveland Pass (1927), replacing previous wagon roads and trails. The first stretch of paved highway in the state was laid in 1921 between Denver and Littleton at a cost of $74,000. The state highway inventory grew to more than 3,000 miles through inclusion of previous private toll roads and county roads that were turned over to state control. By 1921, the Colorado Highway Department had enough road miles in its jurisdiction to create a maintenance division, which by 1928 consisted of 150 two-person patrols located all across the state.

As the decades wore on, surface transportation was increasingly dependent on automobiles and trucks. Railroad lines declined in reach and use. More high pass routes connecting the Front Range with the Western Slope were also opened for motor vehicles, including Berthoud Pass (1938) and Monarch Pass (1939). As populations grew and more vehicles were registered in Colorado, pressure to provide improved roads and to keep them open throughout the year, even in areas where typical winter snows measured 30 feet or more, increased.

The timeframe between widespread concrete and asphalt surfacing of Colorado's state highway system and the advent of urban freeways was relatively short. The first approval of interstate highway routes in Colorado occurred in 1947, and just one year later work began on Colorado's first interstate segment, the Valley Highway (now I-25) in Denver. In 1952, the Denver-Boulder Turnpike, Colorado's first modern era toll road, opened for business.

By the 1960s, freeway construction was ongoing in many parts of Colorado, including west from Denver along I-70.

Much of the current 9,100-mile state highway system had been designated and hard-surfaced for year-around travel. The new interstates took over some of these routes, and in other places followed new rights of way. The terms I-25, I-70, and I-80S (later to become I-76) were familiar to most Coloradans.

I-70 opened east–west through metro Denver in 1965 but could not be pushed on to Colorado's Western Slope until a solution to the problem of crossing the Continental Divide could be reached. That answer came in the form of two tunnel bores, each nearly two miles long, beneath the Divide at an elevation of 11,000 feet almost directly west of Denver. The first bore, the Eisenhower Memorial Tunnel, opened in 1973. Its twin bore, the Johnson Memorial Tunnel, followed in 1979. A new era of transportation ease linking both sides of Colorado had begun.

It would be 13 more years (October, 1992), however, until I-70 was completed through Glenwood Canyon. During its 12 years of construction, this $490 million Final Link project ushered in a new environmental awareness and ethic at the Department of Highways through its careful design, extensive input from local citizens' groups, and a commit-

ment to ensure that the freeway blended into the beautiful canyon environment as much as possible. Numerous national and international awards for design and construction followed.

By 1991, the newly-named Colorado Department of Transportation (CDOT) turned its attention to improvements along the existing corridors to improve safety and capacity. CDOT was now responsible for supporting general aviation in Colorado, as well as coordinating transit, bicycle, pedestrian, and other transportation-related programs. Highway initiatives were focused on improvements on 28 of the state's most strategic transportation corridors, including the US 40 Berthoud Pass Mountain project and a multi-year multi-phase improvement program on US 160 over Wolf Creek Pass.

In 1999, in coordination with the Denver metro-area Regional Transportation District (RTD), CDOT began the largest transportation project in Colorado history. The $1.67 billion Transportation Expansion Project (TREX) on I-25 in the southeast Denver metro area blended several transportation modes into one coordinated interstate corridor. At its opening in 2006, this project offered convenient modal linkages among

highway, traditional transit, light rail, bicycles, and pedestrians in what has become a national model for similar improvements in other metro areas. T-REX involved historic partnerships and was completed well ahead of schedule and under budget. The entire project was conducted alongside and in full view of the traveling public, resulting in high levels of public support and appreciation.

During this era, CDOT also completed I-25 expansion improvements from the Colorado Springs city center to North Academy Boulevard (Colorado Springs Metro Interstate Expansion, or COSMIX) in December 2007, one full year ahead of schedule. The $150 million cost made it the largest transportation project underway in Colorado at that time.

Just a few months after completion of COSMIX, Colorado and CDOT shared the pain of the nation and the world resulting from a massive economic downturn. Funding sources were reduced or disappeared entirely, and CDOT joined other state departments of transportation in dealing with reduced budgets and future funding uncertainty.

CDOT's funding situation was helped temporarily with the passage of the

American Recovery and Reinvestment Act of 2009, signed into law by President Barack Obama at the Museum of Nature & Science in Denver. CDOT received just over $340 million from this legislation and utilized it for 115 needed transportation projects all around the state, including construction on the state highway system, local agency cooperative projects, and transit projects.

Infusion of state funds from the 2009 Funding Advancement for Surface Transportation and Economic Recovery (FASTER) legislation meant that CDOT was able to move forward rapidly on critical bridge projects and other state highway system safety improvements. The Colorado Bridge Enterprise was created within CDOT to administer and establish a bonding program with the purpose of "financing, repairing, reconstructing, and replacing bridges designated as structurally deficient or functionally obsolete, and rated 'poor.'" More than 160 bridges have been addressed under this program as of February 2014. FASTER provided the first permanent, dedicated new funding source for CDOT in more than 20 years.

Due to funding challenges, CDOT increasingly turned its attention to maintaining and improving existing transportation infrastructure rather than trying to increase capacity through new construction for which traditional funding was not available. New emphasis was placed on more efficient capacity management within existing highway infrastructure through use of managed lanes, creation of high demand temporary lanes within existing rights of way, and asking the cooperation of the public to alter travel times to avoid over-capacity "rush hour" type situations at several

locations. A new CDOT Division of Transportation Systems Maintenance & Operations was created in 2013 to manage this important initiative.

CDOT also formulated new ways to do more with less and to accelerate its construction program. One of the most significant examples was the Responsible Acceleration of Maintenance and Partnerships (RAMP) program. Through RAMP, CDOT shifted to an expenditure-based budget approach which makes better use of the agency's cash balance to start projects in the year of expenditure rather than requiring that all funding must be in hand before beginning construction. CDOT also leveraged RAMP funding by accepting applications from public and private agencies willing to enter into project partnerships. In October 2013, the Colorado Transportation Commission approved 44 RAMP partnership projects valued at $580 million, as well as $66 million in additional operations projects.

RAMP also dedicated approximately $750 million to maintain the statewide transportation system, with identified projects in surface treatment, bridges, culverts, tunnels, intelligent transportation systems, and other assets.

New ways of doing business are being explored and implemented by CDOT, including a shift to a risk-based asset management system in conjunction with new requirements from the Moving Ahead for Progress in the 21st Century Act (MAP-21) federal legislation, as well as implementing the state's first public–private partnership. In 2009, the state legislature created the High Performance Transportation Enterprise (HPTE) to explore innovative partnerships and

financing to accelerate much-needed capacity and mobility improvement. The US 36 Denver/Boulder Express Lanes Project is the first of its kind for CDOT. In return for up-front equity from a private partner, CDOT has entered into a concessionaire agreement that allows the partner to assume the risk of the construction portion of the entire project as well as ongoing maintenance and operations of the corridor in return for collecting toll revenues for 50 years. This agreement keeps the ownership of the roadway with the state and also includes revenue sharing should revenues exceed a certain level.

Another significant challenge has been identifying solutions and funding for other heavily congested corridors, especially the I-70 corridor from Denver west to the Continental Divide and beyond. Following years of study, CDOT completed a Record of Decision that recommended a combination of possible roadway and alternative transportation improvements. While funding is sought for the final solution, the first major capacity improvement on I-70 west of Denver in nearly four decades, the expansion of the eastbound Twin Tunnel near Idaho Springs from two lanes to three, was completed in 2013. Expansion of the westbound Twin Tunnel is expected to be completed by the end of 2014. Other interim solutions that include paving shoulders and tolling use of those lanes during peak hours are also being explored.

While much is new at CDOT in the past few years, and much is continually changing, much also remains the same. CDOT's legacy of service was put to an extraordinary test in September 2013, when historic flooding hit much of the

Colorado northern Front Range and northeastern Colorado, as well as the Denver metro area and the Colorado Springs vicinity

The inventory of damage was immense. Hundreds of homes were destroyed; many more were damaged. On the state highways system, 242 miles of roadways were damaged, 27 roads and corridors were closed, and 120 bridges were damaged or destroyed, blocking access to schools, workplaces, and retail services. CDOT lost a major office and maintenance facility in Evans, where state vehicles, equipment, and personal vehicles were destroyed. Eight Coloradans lost their lives.

Recovery and repair activities began while the rain was still falling. Many key access routes from the foothills and adjacent communities to I-25 were reopened within a few days. CDOT fulfilled its goal of reopening all flood damaged highways no later than December 1, 2013, with the final corridor reopening on November 26. The nearly around-the-clock work of CDOT employees from all over the state and our partners in the contracting and U.S. military communities was crucial to this success. So was the work of hundreds more CDOT employees who picked up additional job responsibilities to free their co-workers for crucial flood recovery assignments.

A large banner carried by children of the flood-ravaged Boulder County community of Lyons into a celebration event for the reopening of US 36 from Lyons to Estes Park proclaimed, "Thank you for rebuilding our road home." It was a sentiment felt and expressed by thousands of Coloradans throughout the flood crisis.

Once again, in the latest response to catastrophes that have occurred over the department's 103-year history, CDOT's employees showed that they are always on duty, always near at hand, and always ready to serve—no matter the weather, the circumstances, or the difficulty of the task at hand.

CONNECTICUT

Connecticut Department of Transportation

James P. Redeker
Commissioner

YEAR FORMED **1895**

FTE **3,079**

KEY FACTS
TOTAL STATE ROAD MILES
(OWNED BY STATE HIGHWAY
AGENCY) **3,722**

STATE-OWNED BRIDGES **2,804**

TRANSIT TRIPS PER YEAR
42.6 million

FREIGHT RAIL ROUTE
MILES **330**

In 1895, Connecticut's Governor signed legislation creating a three-member State Highway Commission. At the time, there were some paved streets in every city, but in between, the roads were muddy in wet weather, dusty in dry weather and bumpy everywhere.

Getting out of the mud was serious business. The 1895 law specified that new paving should be macadam, telford, or other stone "that will at all seasons of the year be firm, smooth, and convenient for travel."

By 1901, the Connecticut highway commissioner and the new State Highway Department had proposed a system of "trunk lines" which embraced some 1,400 miles of highways. Formal designation of a trunk line system did not come until 1913 when 14 routes aggregating about 1,000 miles were approved by Connecticut's General Assembly. While heavy commercial use of the state highway system had not yet developed, the period following 1913 saw an insistent demand for more and more miles of hard-surfaced roads.

Making Connecticut's trunk line system passable during New England winters became a goal and a challenge when state forces and equipment were called

upon to remove snow and ice beginning in 1917. Plowing equipment consisted of four- and six-horse teams hitched to non-motorized road graders.

A period of modernization followed, including the removal of railroad grade crossings, the elimination of sharp curves and steep grades, and the widening of high-crowned narrow roads in the interest of safe highway travel. Aesthetics were considered important too, with the creation during 1925 of the Division of Roadside Development which took charge of tree care, roadside stabilization work, and erosion control.

A highlight of Connecticut's modernization program was the 1940 completion of the 38-mile Merritt Parkway built to alleviate traffic congestion on US 1. The Merritt's design was a product of the City Beautiful Movement and included 60 bridges reflecting many different design styles, including neo-classic, neo-gothic, Richardsonian rustic, and art deco. Parkway development in Connecticut was interrupted by World War II and essentially superseded by the planning, design and construction of the Interstate Highway System through the state.

Following World War II, the Connecticut Highway Department gave special

emphasis to highway improvements intended to relieve congestion in compact urban areas. During 1949, the Wilbur Cross Parkway, including the West Rock Tunnel, was completed and opened to traffic.

A high standard of design for the multilane, controlled-access expressway was emphasized as Connecticut was recommending locations for its share of interstate highway mileage. During the mid-1950s, Connecticut continued the improvement of its highway system, including sections on the locations selected for the interstate system. The Connecticut Turnpike, later to be named the John D. Lodge Turnpike, was placed under construction during this same period for its 129 miles. Ultimately, 89 miles of the turnpike were incorporated into the interstate system as Interstate 95. Following its completion in 1958, the Turnpike became the subject of a research paper titled "The Ribbon of Hope."

As Connecticut proceeded to plan, design and construct its 342 miles of interstate highway, a severe shortage of trained engineering personnel developed. This was alleviated with the active recruitment of highway technicians and graduate civil engineers

from technical institutes and colleges throughout New England.

Safety and beautification were not overlooked during the interstate era as Connecticut completed one of the largest programs in the nation for the installation of median barrier rails. It was also the first state highway department in the nation to receive approval of a landscape development project under the 1965 Highway Beautification Act.

The year 1969 marked a transition when the various state-operated transportation modes were made bureaus and placed under a new Connecticut Department of Transportation, 74 years after the creation of the original State Highway Department. In a broad sense, the Connecticut DOT was established to serve and to integrate the overall transportation needs of Connecticut, consistent with the elements of public safety, service and convenience.

In the 1980s, following the collapse of an I-95 bridge in Greenwich, Connecticut embarked on a 10-year, $7 billion program to provide for the repair and rehabilitation of the state's highways, primary and secondary roads, transit

system, state and local bridges, and aviation system. The Transportation Infrastructure Renewal Program provides for not only repair and rehabilitation, but also for their improvement and maintenance. The cost of this program was and is still supported by a Special Transportation Fund.

Since the 1983 bridge collapse, a great deal of emphasis has been placed on bridge maintenance and inspection through the establishment of a bridge safety and evaluation unit. This unit includes field engineers permanently assigned to each of the state's four DOT districts to provide direct supervision and technical expertise to field forces. The program has received special recognition from the Federal Highway Administration.

Another major change in the area of public transportation was the decision to subsidize both bus and rail mass transit services with state dollars. This resulted in the continuance of needed transit services during a period when economic conditions were causing the decline of these services provided by private operators. The New Haven commuter rail line between New Haven and New York City is the busiest commuter rail line in America.

Today, the Connecticut DOT is making major investments in public transportation. Among today's priorities are:

- Establishing higher speed intercity and commuter rail services between New Haven, Hartford, and Springfield, Massachusetts. The new service will begin in 2016 and is expected to make travel more convenient, take cars off congested highways in the corridor, and reduce emissions.

- Upgrading the New Haven Line with new train cars, new catenary, expanded and new rail yards, new and redundant power supply, Positive Train Control, rehabilitated bridges, and expanded parking. The three New Haven Line branches to New Canaan, Danbury and Waterbury, are also being upgraded and more service is being added.

- Adding more service on Shore Line East, the commuter rail line between New Haven and New London.

- Establishing a true bus rapid transit system in central Connecticut to be known as CTfastrak. This service will begin in early 2015 and will serve as a key intermodal corridor linking several bus systems in central, western and southern Connecticut, connecting to the rail line between New Haven and Springfield as well as the Waterbury Branch, and providing connections to Bradley International Airport. CTfastrak will speed commuters to their destinations and reduce traffic congestion.

- Implementing Complete Streets on all projects.

- Planning for and building bicycle and pedestrian trails and including bike/ped options in new construction projects.

- Establishing transit-oriented development at major bus and rail facilities. A major TOD project is now getting underway at the Stamford Transportation Center.

- The department also sponsors and promotes annual campaigns for work zone safety, seat belt use, anti-drunk driving, texting and driving, and motorcycle safety.

Connecticut's airports, including Bradley International Airport in Windsor Locks, were under the aegis of the DOT for many years but are now overseen by the Connecticut Airport Authority.

Over the past five years, the Connecticut DOT has invested billions in rail and bus operations, bus rapid transit, some 4,100 miles of roads, 5,300 bridges, two ferries across the Connecticut River, and the State Pier in New London.

From an agency with a single focus of building, maintaining, and regulating roads, the Connecticut DOT has evolved into a true multi-modal agency with widely diverse transportation responsibilities. Now into its second century, the department's commitment to meeting Connecticut's transportation needs and to solving Connecticut's transportation problems will continue to drive its decision making and policies.

DELAWARE

Delaware Department of Transportation

Shailen P. Bhatt
Secretary

YEAR FORMED **1917**

FTE **1,712**

KEY FACTS
TOTAL STATE ROAD MILES
(OWNED BY STATE HIGHWAY
AGENCY) **5,375**

STATE-OWNED BRIDGES **829**

TRANSIT TRIPS PER YEAR
10 million

FREIGHT RAIL ROUTE MILES
218

DelDOT Reflects on 25 Years of Progress

During the past 25 years, the Delaware Department of Transportation (Del-DOT) has become a more data-driven, efficient, transparent, and multi-modal focused agency. The department now ensures that streets and roads serve pedestrians and bicyclists in addition to motorists. It uses computer software to prioritize projects and spending. And it maintains a constant exchange of information with stakeholders via tools such as social media, live and virtual public workshops, and a smartphone application.

Of course, the former Delaware Highway Department, established in 1917, has continued to evolve throughout its history. Once primarily dedicated to road construction, the department has assumed responsibility for rail, transit, aeronautics, and other modes of transportation. As the population of Delaware has grown, and as technology has developed, DelDOT has grown and developed with it.

The department has worked to improve and evolve through rigorous self eval uation. Under the leadership of current Secretary Shailen Bhatt, DelDOT recently implemented a Performance Management program designed to track and evaluate decisions in relation to the department's mission, vision, and goals. By measuring tangible results, performance management helps the department devise plans and allocate resources more effectively. The process not only gauges how well the department is currently functioning, it also predicts the costs and benefits of future decisions. Performance management tracks internal factors that contribute to employee satisfaction as well as external factors that affect customers' quality of life.

The department recently enhanced the process that develops the six-year Capital Transportation Program. Using computer software, the process now involves a set of criteria to assess the need for, and the feasibility of, each project. As a result, the department is better equipped to make decisions based upon needs of the transportation system. Meanwhile, the public is better able to understand DelDOT's decision-making process, its mission, vision, and goals.

To ensure the public understands its decision-making process, and to learn about community concerns, the department for decades has held public hearings. Public hearings often draw crowds when a proposed project is expected to affect

a densely populated area. But public hearings about relatively small projects in relatively unpopulated areas of the state have drawn only a few people to learn and to comment first-hand. What began initially as a cost-cutting measure, DelDOT experimented with a new approach to holding a public workshop.

When the size and location of a project makes a traditional public workshop impractical, DelDOT may use a virtual workshop. A virtual workshop includes a web page, which provides a description of the project, an audio component, and a link to a video available on the department's YouTube channel. The video provides everything that would be provided in a traditional workshop, including maps and photos, and the project's web page includes surveys and other opportunities for comment. By putting videos and opportunities to comment online, DelDOT provides an opportunity for interested parties to learn and comment at their convenience. Improved technology has allowed the department to participate in transportation planning in ways that were unimaginable when AASHTO celebrated its 75th anniversary.

In fact, improved technology has revolutionized almost every aspect of DelDOT.

Take the department's Transportation Management Center (TMC) for example. Whether a storm covers Delaware roads with ice or a NASCAR race fills Delaware roadways with several thousand out-of-state visitors, DelDOT is able to monitor conditions statewide and respond to dangers and congestion within minutes, 24 hours a day, seven days a week. The TMC is a hub for real-time data about traveling conditions throughout the state. In addition to live feeds from more than 140 cameras placed at key intersections, the TMC also receives constant streams of data about traffic speeds and weather, including air, road, and subsurface temperatures. Such information helps DelDOT decide when to spread salt, where to change the duration of traffic lights, and what information to share with motorists via variable message signs and other means of communication.

DelDOT's own radio station, WTMC 1380 AM, streams and broadcasts commercial-free traffic reports 24 hours a day, seven days a week. WTMC can be streamed onto computers, and smartphones, or heard on car radios.

The DelDOT smartphone application enables users to interact with the department in yet another way. Available

for both Apple and Android phones, the DelDOT App provides users with constant access to travel advisories, streaming live video from key intersections, and color-coded maps that show delays, incidents and travel advisories throughout the First State. Users can also view the variable message signs that are posted at key "bottleneck" areas on Delaware roads.

In addition to WTMC and the DelDOT App, Facebook, and Twitter are among the department's social media tools for providing useful information to customers. The department's Facebook page boasts more than 6,000 page "likes," and its Twitter page boast almost 8,000 "followers." Both pages provide frequent updates about accidents, road closures, snow-removal operations, weather forecasts, and more. These pages allow customers to react to DelDOT news and solicit more information, thus promoting open government.

But not every aspect of DelDOT has changed. Road construction and road maintenance continue to comprise a great deal of the department's work. One of the projects that DelDOT was eagerly anticipating at the time of AASHTO's 75th anniversary was a six-lane controlled-access highway that would provide much needed relief to congested Routes 13 and 113. That project, completed on May 21, 2003, has resulted in State Route 1, which stretches approximately 50 miles, from north of the Chesapeake & Delaware Canal in northern Delaware to south of Dover, the state capital. Route 1 includes the U.S. Senator William V. Roth Jr. Bridge across the C&D Canal. Completed after 2,230 days of construction, the Roth bridge is a 4,650-foot-long cable-stayed bridge.

Another significant project constructed a new Charles W. Cullen Bridge, which opened just prior to Memorial Day in 2012. The Cullen Bridge spans the Indian River Inlet at Delaware's beach resorts and replaces a 1965 steel girder bridge, which had endured decades of harsh winters and heavy tidal currents. The new bridge, a cable-stay bridge, was built to stand for 100 years. It is 2,600 feet long and supported by four 249-foot-tall pylon towers. The bridge roadway in each direction consists of two 12-foot-wide travel lanes, a 10-foot outside shoulder, and a four-foot-wide inside shoulder. Additionally, a 12-foot-wide sidewalk can be accessed from the ocean side of the bridge for pedestrians and cyclists.

Improvements to I-95, the longest stretch of interstate highway to pass through the state, have continued. The I-95 Fifth Lane project added a fifth lane along I-95 in both the northbound and southbound directions for all vehicle use. The was part of a multi-year, multi-project Turnpike Improvement Program that included work at the Churchmans Road/SR 7 intersection and the Churchmans Road Bridge across I-95. The program also included work at the SR-1/I-95 Interchange, a

longtime point of congestion. Construction of elevated flyover ramps in both north and southbound direction, completed in 2013, will allow the safe and smooth flow of vehicles through one of the state's most vital commercial corridors. This was the final major step in the $147 million project, which was financed jointly by state and federal governments.

Another improvement project for I-95 was the addition of highway-speed E-ZPass lanes at the I-95 toll plaza. This $32 million project was fully funded through the American Recovery and Reinvestment Act (ARRA). Construction added two dedicated E-ZPass lanes in each direction with full-width right and left shoulders. It also included the widening of the approach to the northbound cash plaza to create more vehicle storage and improve usage of all plaza lanes, and expansion of the northbound cash plaza to seven lanes.

DelDOT continues to construct and maintain a modern and interconnected transportation system, and in the 21st Century that means providing a variety of transportation options. In 2012, the League of American Bicyclists ranked Delaware as the 10th most Bicycle Friendly State. By 2013, the state had jumped to fifth in the league's rankings. Such progress is the result of policies and initiatives promoting multi-modal transportation.

The Complete Streets Policy, established by an executive order from Delaware Governor Jack Markell, seeks to improve public health and reduce pollution by requiring DelDOT to accommodate as many modes of transportation as possible whenever it builds, or rebuilds,

any road or bridge. The First State Trails and Pathways Initiative, also established by an executive order from Governor Markell, promotes the construction of a network of shared-use trails and pathways that will support non-motorized travel and alternative transportation opportunities for Delawareans and visitors. Statewide, DelDOT is pursuing a rails-to-trails master plan, which would convert abandoned railroad corridors into trails for walking and biking. Altogether, these initiatives, policies, and plans focus on bicycling and walking and providing safe and convenient ways to reach nearby jobs, shops, schools, transit, and recreational sites.

DART First State is Delaware's bus, train and intermodal transportation provider. The Delaware Transit Corporation (DTC), a division of the Delaware Department of Transportation, operates DART First State. Incorporated in 1995, DTC was formed to consolidate five former semi-autonomous agencies into one comprehensive service provider. Today, DART First State services include intercounty, fixed route and seasonal bus routes; Paratransit; contracted SEPTA commuter trains; Operation Lifesaver rail crossing safety program; and RideShare Delaware ridematching program. DART provides fixed route bus service on 70 routes throughout the state offering over 2,700 bus stops, over 270 bus shelters and 81 benches. Of the 224 fixed-route buses, 30 are hybrid electric vehicles. All fixed-route buses have bike racks and are wheelchair accessible. DART also offers Paratransit service to qualified individuals and operates 309 paratransit vehicles throughout the state. DART contracts with SEPTA to provide weekday commuter train service to all four

Delaware stations. Additionally, Ride-Share Delaware, a free public service of DART First State, offers rideshare services for individuals who live or work in the State of Delaware, as well as business support and transportation benefit assistance to employers interested in implementing commuter programs.

The Office of Aeronautics is responsible for planning, coordination, and implementation of improvements to the public use airport system within the state. State law gives the office of Aeronautics jurisdiction over public-use airports only, which may be privately or publically owned, but are open to use by anyone. DelDOT currently oversees ten 10 public-use airports, including the Civil Air Terminal at the Dover Air Force Base. The Civil Air Terminal handles freight, aircraft at the base, and twice annually provides service for Delaware's two NASCAR events. Plans

are underway to expand the parking at the terminal to meet increased demand. Delaware's only commercial use airport is in New Castle County, with service beginning in 2013, from low-cost commercial airline Frontier, serving the airport with flights to Atlanta, Chicago Midway, Denver, Detroit, Fort Myers, Orlando, and Tampa with connections to all parts of the globe.

Of course, like any transportation agency, DelDOT faces significant challenges. The department's Transportation Trust Fund (TTF), a program started in the late 1980s, was designed to provide a dependable source of revenue dedicated to the transportation system. While the TTF program worked well for many years, the program is not sustainable in its current form. Sources of revenue, such as the motor fuel tax, motor vehicle document fees and revenue from toll operation all go into the trust fund, but

have not been able to keep pace with the growing needs of the department's projects. In a time of decreased budgets, and "doing more with less," the department finds itself maintaining more than improving or adding capacity. Governor Markell has proposed increasing the department's capital budget by $500 million over five years. That increase would be funded by $50 million dollars in borrowing each year in addition to another $50 million raised by an increase in the state's motor fuel tax. However, the Delaware General Assembly has yet to take up the proposal. It has, as you might imagine, sparked controversy and conversation on transportation funding.

DelDOT has made many improvements over the past 25 years in the way it serves its residents and those visiting the State of Delaware. It continues to live its mission daily—*Excellence in Transportation.*

DISTRICT OF COLUMBIA

District of Columbia Department of Transportation

Matthew Brown
Interim Director

YEAR FORMED **2002**

FTE **Approx. 1,100**

KEY FACTS
TOTAL STATE ROAD MILES
(OWNED BY STATE HIGHWAY
AGENCY) **1,380**

STATE-OWNED BRIDGES **200**

TRANSIT TRIPS PER YEAR
419 million

Although the story of today's District of Columbia Department of Transportation (DDOT) began in 2002, the agency's foundations were laid in the decades and centuries prior. The ever-changing environment of transportation, and of the District's governance, has shaped the role and responsibilities of the agency. The original council system, the Engineer Commissioners, and the modern council–mayor system all played a critical role in shaping our transportation system.

From the dirt roads and canals of the 1820s and the development of the streetcar system in the 1870s to the rise of the automobile in the 1920s and the inauguration of Metro service in the 1970s, transportation choices have influenced the residential and commercial development of the District for nearly two centuries.

In the early 19th century, roads in the District were largely unpaved and difficult to traverse. People moved along dirt roads by horse-drawn carriages or on foot. Nearly 90 percent of the District's 23,000 residents in 1830 lived in the "Old City" south of Boundary Street (now Florida Avenue) or in Georgetown. The remainder of what is now Washington, DC, was then Washington County, DC, a rural area dotted with estates and farmland. Goods and heavy loads were transported by canals, including the Chesapeake and Ohio (C&O) Canal and the Washington City Canal, which ran along the Mall and connected to the Potomac River near the White House and to the Anacostia River at the Navy Yard.

When the Washington Branch of the Baltimore and Ohio Railroad opened in 1835, the canals had outlived their effectiveness and rail had proven to be a viable transportation alternative. Public transit at the time consisted of horse-drawn omnibuses, first on the dirt roads, then later on rails. Given the uneven conditions of the city's roads and the elevation of outlying parts of the District, this early transit system was limited in its usefulness.

The first major development in transportation in the District came in 1888 with the advent of the electric streetcar. Streetcars running on underground electrical conduits allowed the city to expand beyond its traditional boundary at Florida Avenue into the "streetcar suburbs" like Columbia Heights, Cleveland Park, Brookland, and Anacostia.

Engineer Commissioners

From an early stage, transportation issues were a major focus in District government. In 1878, responsibility for the District's daily affairs was given to a three-member Board of Commissioners. The board consisted of two commissioners appointed by the President and one commissioner from the United States Army Corps of Engineers. The "Engineer Commissioner" was charged with the maintenance and oversight of all of the District's infrastructure projects, including street cleaning, snow removal and maintenance, and paving of roads. The Engineer Commissioner remained in charge of infrastructure projects in the District until the passage of the Home Rule Act in 1973, when the Board of Commissioners was abolished and replaced with an elected mayor and city council.

Under the Engineer Commissioners, the District saw its first street master plan (1893), comprehensive zoning plan (1920) and comprehensive street lighting plan (1923). These plans are largely credited with preserving the Baroque aesthetic character of the city.

Developing the System

During its prime, DC's streetcar system boasted more than 100 miles of track within the District, and connections to the Maryland and Virginia suburbs. Streetcars enjoyed more than six decades as the primary form of transportation in Washington until the automobile revolution of the 1920s. As the internal combustion engine was developed, buses began to replace streetcars, which required regular track maintenance and electrical work. The increasing affordability of cars allowed more people to live further from the urban core and decreased the use and effectiveness of streetcar lines.

Despite marking the beginning of the end for the streetcar, the 1920s and 1930s were very important to transportation in the District. The District's roads struggled to handle the increased traffic caused by the city's exploding population, which had more than doubled over 30 years and grown to more than 400,000. As the federal city, Washington was not eligible for the Federal-Aid Highway Program as states were. The city had insufficient money in its General Fund to finance the road improvements necessary to accommodate the population expansion. In 1924, the Board of Commissioners successfully lobbied Congress to allow the District to institute a two-cent-per-gallon gasoline tax that would be used exclusively for road maintenance. In 1938, the

Federal-Aid Highway Act was amended, allowing the District access to the same pool of highway funds available to other states. As a result, the District's transportation system saw dramatic improvement in a short period of time.

Rapid Progress

Funding from the gas tax and Federal-Aid Highway program allowed both the agency and the system to achieve rapid progress. In 1932, the 19 divisions within the city's "Engineer Department" were reorganized, with DDOT's predecessor, the newly formed Department of Highways, assuming the transportation functions formerly split between eight divisions. Less than half of the District's 544 miles of road were paved with asphalt in 1924: by 1948, there were 980 miles of paved road in Washington. In 1944, the Department introduced a cost analysis system to all of its maintenance and construction projects.

Although auto use was increasing dramatically, alternate modes of transportation were immensely popular in the District in the 1940s. In 1940, one out of every seven District residents commuted to work on foot. In 1948, 38 percent of commute trips were taken by bus. An underground rail system was considered in 1942 but not recommended.

Population Decline and Metro

As World War II wound down and employment and residential centers developed in the Virginia and Maryland suburbs, residents started to move out of the city. The 1950s marked the first of five consecutive decades of population decline in the District. Workers living in the suburbs still needed ways to commute to the city, increasing the number of cars and buses on the District's roads. By the 1960s, it became obvious that the city's street grid could not support the increasing volume of commuter traffic.

At the time, two competing visions for increasing the capacity of the transportation system developed. One camp favored the development of numerous limited access expressways to channel traffic around the city's most congested areas. Planners developed a network of freeways through established neighborhoods across the District, including two additional beltways. Groups opposed to the freeway system advocated a subway transit system to alleviate congestion and preserve community links.

Although construction had already begun on segments of the freeway network, the transit advocates were successful in blocking most of the expressway plans, and in 1965, Congress authorized $431 million for development of an expandable 25-mile subway network. Ground was broken for the system in 1969 and Metrorail service began in 1976, offering a sustainable alternative to single-occupant vehicles and a complement to commuter buses in the District.

DDOT and the Superagency

By the time Metro service began, the Department of Highways had become the District Department of Transportation. In addition to its original responsibilities for planning, developing, and maintaining the District's roadway network, the new Department of Transportation assumed responsibility for coordinating transportation with Metro, inspecting and registering vehicles, licensing motorists, enforcing parking regulations, and planning and implementing a bicycle network.

The first District Department of Transportation operated for only 10 years before being combined into the Department of Public Works (DPW), a new "superagency" formed in 1984 to assume the responsibilities of the Departments of Transportation, General Services and Environmental Services. Unfortunately, the responsibility for providing so many services, coupled with dwindling resources, forced DPW to prioritize its efforts, leaving parts of the District's infrastructure underdeveloped and largely forgotten.

"The organization became increasingly focused on delivering on the responsibilities it had on a day-to-day basis, and that was picking up the trash," recalls Dan Tangherlini, first director of the modern DDOT. "You had lost a focused, accountable attention to the transportation asset" when DPW took over responsibility for transportation. "We did not have a meaningful continuing capital budget to make the kinds of replacements we needed to make." And it showed.

Potholes and Utility Cuts

By the 1990s, the system had deteriorated to the point of crisis. Potholes were rampant to the point of being sadly comical. "It was almost part of the fabric of the expectations of the city that if it were not for the potholes, we were not sure what was going to hold the streets together," half-jokes Tangherlini. Although the potholes were problematic, they were not the biggest inconvenience on District roads.

As the digital age reached full swing, telecommunications companies began to cut trenches in streets to run data cable. Unfortunately, these street cuts were performed with little or no oversight or coordination. One company would come and cut the road to run cable, disrupting traffic along some of the District's busiest thoroughfares. "Two weeks later, another company would come and cut the same route," recalls Tangherlini. The seemingly endless road cuts showed the need for a coordinated, accountable method for managing the public right-of-way.

In 2002, DDOT was remade into a cabinet-level agency with independent funding authority and accountability to the DC Council. "We were driven by this crisis to organize ourselves and then create some meaningful structures and policies around regulating the public right of way, recognizing it is the largest, most valuable asset the city owns, then treating it as an asset that needed to maintained and invested in," says Tangherlini, who was instrumental in the formation of the new DDOT along with then Mayor Anthony Williams and Councilwoman Carol Schwartz.

Exceeding Expectations

"Expectations were incredibly low for the new agency," says Emeka Moneme, DDOT's third director, who also was involved in drafting the agency's charter. Due to the poor condition of the transportation system under DPW, Congress had debated transferring control of the District's roads to the federal government, questioning whether or not the District government could effectively manage such an important asset. "The importance of the provision of the transportation system got lost over time," according to Michelle Pourciau, DDOT's second director. Given these common sentiments, it was clear that the new agency had its work cut out for it.

DDOT responded with excellence. "We wanted to make sure we were thinking beyond what people saw the agency doing traditionally," Moneme says. Addressing the challenges of the District's transportation system would take more than filling potholes and co-ordinating utility cuts. It would require a flexible, adaptable agency with the ability not only to react to changes in the environment of transportation, but also to proactively anticipate changes. "We saw a lot of creativity and public–sector entrepreneurship," says Moneme. "It was in the DNA of the agency from the beginning."

From its formation, DDOT was progressive and creative. "We took new and innovative funding to a whole new level," recalls Pourciau. Within six years, the new agency had repaved more than half of the District's roads, thanks in large part to the financial and organizational structures in place and the agency's unique position as a city and state DOT.

A 21st Century Agency for a 21st Century City

The agency's formation coincided with the beginning of the District's first sustained population increase since the 1940s. Although the region had been growing in population for decades, the 2000s marked the District's first growth in half a century. "Before the formation of DDOT, we were really struggling with how to address the projected population in the region and how to compete for that growth," Pourciau says. "If we couldn't get more people to live in DC, our transportation just couldn't handle all of the long commutes. DC is pretty built-out. There's just no room for more or new highways."

As a result, DDOT had to find ways for the transportation system to accom-modate current users, as well as attract new residents and businesses to the District. "We really tried to tie econom-ic development to everything we did," says Gabe Klein, the agency's fourth Director. Through initiatives like Capital Bikeshare, DC Circulator, Great Streets and the Anacostia Waterfront Initiative, "DDOT was able to really show how in-frastructure could shape communities," according to Moneme.

During its brief history, the agency has made progress that 10 years ago would have seemed impossible. "We were able to elevate transportation as an issue," states Klein. "We showed that DDOT is a world-class transportation agency that can handle mega projects. Few District agencies have done as much for the District as DDOT."

Into the Future

As we progress through the 21st century, DDOT will continue to be a world-class transportation department, and a model agency within the District govern-ment. Our workforce is highly skilled and adept at managing the challenges facing the transportation system and the agency. "We've come a long way in the last ten years," says Terry Bellamy, DDOT's fifth Director. "In my tenure as Director, I've seen significant progress in landmark programs like pay-by-phone parking, Capital Bikeshare and the 11th Street Bridge project. But DDOT isn't done yet. In order to meet the needs of the District into the future, we need to keep working."

Mayor Gray's Vision for a Sustainable DC sets aggressive targets for green-house gas reductions and alternative transportation, and DDOT will play a leading role in helping the District achieve these ambitious goals. We have made transportation improvements in underperforming neighborhoods across the District, but parts of our city still need infrastructure investments to thrive as sustainable, livable communities. Traf-fic-related fatalities are down more than 50 percent since the agency's formation, but we will continue to enhance the safe-ty of our roads, sidewalks and crosswalks until they have reached zero.

DDOT has become known as a go-to agency within the District government and a national leader in innovative transportation programs, and will continue to lead the industry and the District for years to come.

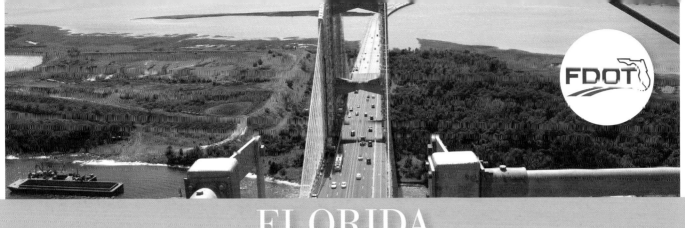

FLORIDA

Florida Department of Transportation

Ananth Prasad
Secretary

YEAR FORMED **1915**

FTE **6,630**

KEY FACTS
TOTAL STATE ROAD MILES
(OWNED BY STATE HIGHWAY
AGENCY) **12,076**

STATE-OWNED BRIDGES **5,441**

TRANSIT TRIPS PER YEAR
268 million

FREIGHT RAIL ROUTE
MILES **2,874**

AASHTO's celebration of its 100 year centennial is also an occasion for the Florida Department of Transportation (FDOT) to reflect on the truly remarkable transportation system developed over those 10 decades and in particular over the past 25 to 50 years in our state and nationally.

In 1910, Florida's population was almost 753,000. Today we have over 19 million people and will soon become the third most populated state in the nation. Fortunately, our transportation system kept pace with that incredible growth. Today Florida has a vast multi-modal transportation system thanks to the legacy of those leaders and visionaries who understood that we had to prepare for and invest in our future.

There is no higher calling for transportation professionals now than to honor the legacy of our predecessors by continuing to build on their legacy.

Florida's transportation legacy is both instructive and inspiring:

- It is a legacy of tremendous investment in which billions of dollars helped to develop a world class system of highways, airports, water

ports, and transit and rail systems— and even space ports.

- It is a legacy of commitment and dedication recognizing that Florida's wonderful quality of life and economic vibrancy required superior mobility for efficiently moving people and goods

- And it is a legacy of partnerships and teamwork—as FDOT's range of strategic alliances expanded continuously over the years to include communities, contractors, metropolitan planning organizations, transportation modal operators, economic development organizations and many other key stakeholders.

- FDOT has truly evolved from a public works agency to a fully integrated major transportation enterprise with an annual budget of over $8 billion. Yes, Florida has a story to tell about leaving a transportation legacy— yesterday, today, and tomorrow.

Where We've Been? …

In the early 20th century, Florida was largely a rural and agrarian state. Today, Florida's economy is highly diverse and comparatively more resilient to economic downturns. Agriculture still plays

a major role in our economy, but over the past five decades Florida's economy has become increasingly varied. Florida ranks high among all states in numerous sectors of the economy including tourism, logistics, emerging technologies, manufacturing and finance.

What role did transportation play in supporting the Florida global gateway? A major role!

- FDOT steadily invested in roads and bridges to link our communities, our farms to markets, and to airports that bring visitors by the millions from around the globe

- The state's investment in transportation infrastructure construction has increased dramatically in the past several decades growing from $836.4 million in FY 91/92 to $2.3 billion in FY 12/13—and a most recently adopted work program that will sharply increase this annual investment from $2.5 billion to $4.8 billion between FY 13/14 and FY 17/18

- Florida's investment in transportation has also grown substantially in terms of an increasing share of

the resources from non-federal sources including major leadership in public–private partnerships (P3). *Engineering News and Record Magazine* recently cited FDOT as a national leader in P3s

- FDOT also invested in its staff— today we have an outstanding smaller workforce that manages a much larger and more complex program

- Over the years, FDOT has been aggressively planning for the future and monitoring our performance against our plans

- In fact, this year we celebrate having achieved all 20 of the performance measures that the Florida Transportation Commission holds the department accountable for, including the following examples that demonstrate our recent past performance journey and its diversity:

FDOT's Performance Legacy— FY 2012/13 Results
All Results Shown Exceed Commission Objectives
- The percentage of the bridges on the state highway system having a

condition rating of either excellent or good—95.1 percent

- The percentage of lane miles on the state highway system having a pavement condition rating of either excellent or good—91.5 percent

- The public transit ridership growth compared to the population growth rate—3.59 percent

- The department's dollar amount of administrative costs as a percent of the total program—0.87 percent

- The number of SunPass transactions as a percentage of total transactions—79.4 percent

Current performance is indicative of past progress as a department. It has been a legacy of not only investing in capacity, but doing an outstanding job of preserving and maintaining our system. It has been a legacy of becoming increasingly multi-modal with transit system usage outpacing population growth. In recent years, it has been a legacy of leveraging technology for greater efficiency and improved transportation operations. And it has been a legacy of outstanding stewardship—making

sure that as many cents on the dollar as possible improve transportation.

Where We Are Now?—The Legacy of a Mission–Oriented FDOT…

Today's legacy building can best be defined as being a mission focused and driven FDOT. Our mission is as follows:

The department will provide a safe transportation system that ensures the mobility of people and goods, enhances economic prosperity, and preserves the quality of our environment and communities.

Let's consider that mission–oriented legacy by reviewing our performance for each component of our mission statement:

Safety
The safety of Florida's highways is a paramount FDOT priority.

- Since 2007, the number of fatalities dropped by 17 percent; the number of serious injuries by 21 percent.

- Fatalities declined 25 percent and 47 percent between 2006 and 2010 for aging road users and teen drivers.

- Fatalities declined 9 percent, 18 percent, and 3 percent between 2006 and 2011 for pedestrians, motorcyclists, and bicyclists.

- At 87 percent, the statewide seat belt usage rate remained high and is three points higher than the national average.

- The number of miles between safety incidents for Florida's transit agencies increased by more than 11 percent between 2004 and 2012.

Mobility and Economic Prosperity
Economic competitiveness and mobility are strategic FDOT priorities. The movement of people and goods supports Florida's economy in many ways.

- The impact of transportation investments is a robust $4.92 in economic benefits for every dollar spent on

transportation improvements—supporting thousands of jobs annually.

- Florida is investing $9.6 billion over five years to improve the state's Strategic Intermodal System of roads, transit facilities, airports, spaceports, seaports, and rail facilities.

- Travel Time Reliability on the State Highway System in 2012 was 94.6 percent, the highest in the eight years this key measure—for both people and goods movement—has been in place.

- Annual vehicle hours of delay on the State Highway System (SHS) has decreased from 387 million hours in 2004 to 215 million hours in 2012.

- In 2012, 2.2 percent of the State Highway System was severely congested—this had been as high as 3.6 percent in 2005.

- Aviation tonnage at Florida public airports was 2.6 million tons in 2012—the highest volume of air cargo in five years in a challenging economy.

- Departure reliability at Florida airports has improved since 2009 (80.3 percent)—by 2012, on time departures stood at 83.5 percent

- Florida's commercial, general aviation and military airports generate $107.8 billion in economic activity—over 8.5 percent of Florida's Gross State Product (GSP)

- Between 2011 and 2012 pedestrian facility mileage on the SHS in urban areas increased from 59.4 percent to

62.8 percent; over the same period bike lane and shoulder mileage increased from 57.6 percent to 58.8 percent on the same system

- Florida is experiencing a steady increase in rail passengers with 1.2 million passengers in 2012—ridership has been increasing every year since 2005

- Average public transportation headway (time between buses) has been decreasing steadily—since a high of 29.2 minutes in 2003 to 20.9 minutes in 2011—helping make public transportation an increasingly attractive mobility option.

Quality of our Environment and Communities

FDOT delivers its transportation program as stewards of financial resources and of our state's many environmental and community assets.

- Over the past decade Florida advanced more than 150 transportation enhancement/transportation alternatives type projects.

- Since 1992 over half a billion dollars have been invested in Florida projects for these transportation enhancement/transportation alternatives categories: bicycle and pedestrian facilities, landscaping, preservation of abandoned railway corridors, rehabilitation/operation of historic transportation facilities, and control and removal of outdoor advertising.

- An April 2013 analysis of MPO transportation planning indicated a wide range of improvements over prior

reviews in areas such as land use, public participation and optimizing the performance of existing facilities.

- All areas within Florida are now air quality attainment areas.

- The department carries out its role as an environmental steward in many ways including increasing the tonnage of recycled pavement from about 570,000tons in 2005 to over 940,000 tons in 2013—an approximately 65 percent increase in less than a decade.

In addition to the above mission–related accomplishments, FDOT in recent years has placed much attention on our customers. Every other year FDOT conducts an extensive customer survey that includes residents and visitors. The results have been very good and show improving customer satisfaction over the years.

- Visitors are satisfied with Florida's overall transportation system—with approximately 90 percent either satisfied or very satisfied over the 2000 to 2011 time period: those indicating being very satisfied increased substantially from 30 percent to 39 percent over that period.

- Three out of every four Florida residents surveyed indicate that travel time between cities and towns is satisfactory—agreement went from 67 percent to 75 percent between 2000 and 2011, with strong agreement increasing from 5 percent to 12 percent.

- Commercial vehicle drivers express satisfaction with Florida intercity

travel time, with the percent satisfied increasing from 68 percent in 2000 to 78 percent in 2011—those commercial drivers indicating being very satisfied increased from 5 percent to 11 percent over the same period.

Where We're Going?— Being Strategic About Our Future, Leaving a Legacy…

FDOT is committed to making sure that transportation bolsters Florida's broader and bigger vision of a state of opportunity and a great quality of life. As such, our future has everything to do with being strategic.

Being strategic starts with Florida's Strategic Intermodal System (SIS). The primary focus for ensuring a strong link between economic requirements and transportation is accomplished through the designated SIS. Created by Florida statute in 2003, the SIS is a statewide network of high-priority transportation facilities, including the largest and most significant commercial service and general aviation reliever airports, spaceports, deep-water seaports, freight rail terminals, passenger rail, and intercity bus terminals, rail corridors, urban-fixed guideway transit corridors, waterways and high-volume highways. The SIS continues to enable the department to focus significant attention and resources on non-highway modes and facilities.

SIS facilities carry more than 99 percent of all commercial air passengers and cargo, virtually all waterborne freight and cruise passengers, all rail freight, and 89 percent of all interregional passengers. The SIS also accounts for more than 70 percent of truck traffic and 54 percent of total traffic on the state highway system. All SIS facilities are eligible for state transportation funding, regardless of mode or ownership. The SIS includes facilities owned by the state as well as regional, local, and private-sector partners. The department's funding for SIS improvements also leverages extensive private and local investment—clearly indicative of the importance of these facilities to communities and business. Each year, FDOT invests about 70 percent of capacity dollars for SIS projects. The department plans to continue to do so well into the future—even exceeding the state legislature's requirement of 50 percent capacity investments for SIS projects.

FDOT also has an ambitious Future Corridors Initiative, which by its very title demonstrates our commitment to being proactive and future focused. With growth in population, visitors, and a resilient economy that is again expanding, FDOT will continue to take a systematic approach to planning our corridors for the future focusing on freight mobility, improved intermodal connectivity and improving transportation operations and efficiency through Intelligent Transportation Systems (ITS) and other means.

Florida will also expand our focus on ports as a true global gateway. This will include strategic investments in our water, air, and space ports as well. As global trade expands and the Panama Canal expands, Florida will be well positioned for sustained economic growth bolstered by a world class transportation system for decades to come.

A Final Word…

FDOT has an invaluable "can-do" culture like other "can-do" states. Our team continues to find new ways to collaborate and innovate. Recently, Secretary Ananth Prasad held a meeting with 1,010 employees using webinar technology. Technology will increasingly be a key component of our future progress.

We are also leading the way in performance management and measurement with Secretary Prasad serving as Chairman of the AASHTO Standing Committee on Performance Management (SCOPM). FDOT has submitted performance reports to Congress for each of the past two years well in advance of the national requirement. State DOTs are performance-oriented and embrace this as a partnership of equals with the federal government.

Not only is FDOT passionate about performance, but we are committed to innovation. Nowhere will this be more important than in how we continue to fund and finance infrastructure investment. Our population will increase by around 7 million by 2040, we will see another 30–40 million visitors annually by that time as well. Freight traffic will increase substantially too. And yet, we have approximately $130 billion in unmet needs on our SIS alone. When a 150-year AASHTO report is published, may it be said of FDOT that it took bold and innovative leadership to:

- Diversify our revenue sources;
- Greatly expand public–private partnerships;
- Continue to combine and leverage federal, state, local, and private-sector funding; and
- Effectively apply tolling alternatives.

The future will demand such a diversified revenue strategy. In the years ahead FDOT will also establish an even broader legacy of partnerships at many levels with other public agencies, the private sector, MPOs, transportation operators of freight and passenger modes, and other states with a common vision such as our neighbor states.

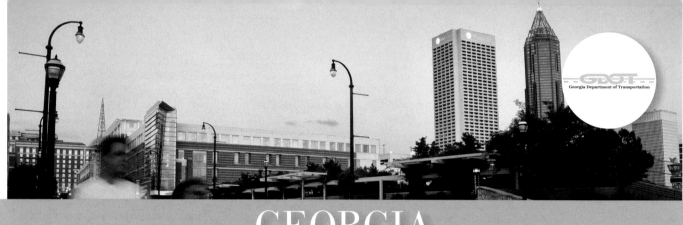

GEORGIA

Georgia Department of Transportation

Keith Golden, P.E.
Commissioner

YEAR FORMED **1916**

FTE **4,131**

KEY FACTS

TOTAL STATE ROAD MILES (OWNED BY STATE HIGHWAY AGENCY) **17,929**

STATE-OWNED BRIDGES **6,632**

TRANSIT TRIPS PER YEAR
169 million

Fourteen state highway engineers met at the swank new Georgian Terrace Hotel in Atlanta in November, 1914, to discuss forming an organization to help "get farmers out of the mud." The following month, that meeting led to the creation of what we now know as the American Association of State Highway and Transportation Officials (AASHTO).

And that battle cry led to the birth two years later of a federal program for continuous financial aid to state highway agencies. Correspondingly in 1916, the Georgia Highway Commission (now the state's Department of Transportation) was created to administer the princely sum of $403,000 in federal funds the state received during the aid program's first two years.

One hundred years later, the Georgian Terrace remains a vibrant, venerated institution; AASHTO celebrates its Centennial; just about all the nation's and Georgia's farmers are out of the mud— at least en route to market if perhaps not always in their fields; and Atlanta has grown by, give or take, five million more people.

Approaching its own Centennial in 2016, the Georgia Department of Transportation has grown as well and played a key role in the growth and transformation of the state throughout the past 98 years. Still largely rural and agrarian at the turn of the 20th Century, Georgia has become a global economic titan—only 27 of the world's 196 countries enjoy greater annual gross domestic products. And Atlanta—in 1914 a city in many ways still recovering from the destruction of The Civil War—has become the ninth largest metropolitan area in the United States and both a destination and key hub for international travel and commerce. Atlanta's airport is the busiest in the world; state ports in Brunswick and Savannah are among the nation's leading and fastest growing in roll-on/roll-off and containerized cargo shipments; and Georgia's 18,000 miles of state highways, including about 1,250 center-line miles of Interstates, are consistently considered among the best-maintained in the country. Together, along with a robust rail network, they have helped make Georgia home to more than 11,000 logistics businesses and the fifth-largest logistics employer in the country.

Every advancement comes at a cost and, like its counterpart state transportation agencies across the nation, Georgia DOT finds itself straining to adequately maintain current assets while growing

for the future. Our greatest challenge continues to be identifying and securing sustainable funding to carry out our mission. Federal aid has grown to more than a billion dollars a year and represents slightly more than half the state's transportation budget. But we believe we cannot continue to rely on state and federal funds tied to the diminishing value of existing fuel taxes. So, while national and state leaders consider alternatives for future transportation funding, the department is focusing on innovative, creative ways to maximize current resources. Our goal is to maintain existing assets; complement them with sustainable new infrastructure where feasible; seek out operational improvements that can provide the greatest "bang for the buck;" and continue always to provide for the safety and mobility of our system's users.

The Georgia Department of Transportation is governed by the State Transportation Board. The Board's 14 members—one representing each of the state's congressional districts—serve staggered, five-year terms. Board members are elected by those state senators and representatives whose legislative districts fall within all or part of the relevant congressional district. The Board, in turn, selects a commissioner to manage the Department's day-to-day activities. Current Commissioner Keith Golden, a professional engineer and long-time department executive, was elected in 2012.

The constant budget pressures on Georgia DOT during recent decades, along with a combination of technological advances, internal efficiencies, broader use of consultants and privatizing some routine activities, have resulted in a continual decline in the department's employee headcount. From more than 9,000 in the mid-1970s, Georgia DOT employees now number approximately 4,400. The department believes this number essentially represents a "right-sized" DOT to fulfill its ever-evolving mission.

A core precept of that mission—indeed, the core precept—is safety. With our federal, state, and local partners, the department has implemented an aggressive Safety Action Plan in recent years focused intently on reducing highway fatalities. Results have been exceptionally gratifying. From 1,748 in 2005, deaths on Georgia roads have declined for eight successive years to 1,186 in 2013—nearly a 33 percent improvement.

We also have worked resolutely to help all of Georgia grow and prosper.

Twenty-five years ago, as AASHTO celebrated its 75th Anniversary, we wrote of a new initiative known as Economic Development Highways designed to place nearly all Georgia cities and residents within reasonable proximity of an Interstate Highway or four-lane road. It came to be known as the Governor's Road Improvement Program (GRIP) and was expanded to include 22 corridors and truck routes representing almost 3,300 miles of new or widened, improved roadway. While work has been completed on nearly 85 percent of the 12 initial corridors, GRIP and the economic development of rural Georgia it represents remains a key department focal point.

By geographic definition, most of Georgia remains rural today; half of the state's population now lives in Metropolitan Atlanta. Balancing the rural versus urban dynamic and crafting a program that is fiscally constrained, sustainable and best for all of Georgia always poses a special challenge for the department.

In the 1980s, the department launched its historic and massive "Freeing the Freeways" program—a $1.5 billion undertaking that doubled Metro Atlanta's Interstate lane miles to more than 1,800 over the following decade-and-a-half and featured the construction of the iconic Tom Moreland Interchange of Interstates 85 and 285.

In September 1990, Atlanta was chosen to host the Summer Olympic Games six year later. So as Freeing the Freeways work continued, Georgia DOT, with stalwart support from the U.S. Department of Transportation and the Federal Highway Administration, began preparations to accommodate the world. Two components of those preparations well served the department and the tens of thousands who visited Atlanta in 1996—the Transportation Management Center (TMC) and the Highway Emergency Response Operators (HERO) program. The active, real-time traffic management of the TMC and incident clearing prowess and motorist assistance services of GDOT HEROs have become templates duplicated by transportation agencies throughout the country and around the world. Both functions have continued to grow and expand their services long after the Olympics and remain today two of the department's most heralded and appreciated services.

As the city continued (and continues still) to grow, its new interstate lanes quickly filled while transportation revenues shrank and construction costs climbed. Georgia DOT and state-elected leaders realized fundamental strategic changes were necessary to continue to maintain mobility, especially in Atlanta's crowded urban setting. One strategy adopted by the Transportation Board and the department in 2007 as central to Metro

mobility and the financial realities of the time was that any new limited access capacity added would be of a managed lanes configuration.

Correspondingly, DOT leaders continued pursuing public–private partnerships to capture the resources and creativity of the private-sector in addressing hugely expensive needs in crowded corridors. First authorized by the Georgia General Assembly in 2004, Public–Private Partnerships, or P3 as it is known here, has been refined and perfected to now be a key component of the department's strategy to maintain mobility in Metro Atlanta. Work is underway on the Northwest Corridor project—an $833.7 million P3 venture to add 30 miles of reversible managed Georgia Express lanes alongside Interstate Highways 75 and 575 on the city's northwest side. The project is scheduled to open in 2018.

The first Georgia Express Lanes opened on Interstate 85 (northeast of downtown) in 2011 and now operates at capacity during morning and evening commute hours. On the Metro south side, design is underway on a Georgia Express Lanes project on Interstate 75 that is set to open in 2016 and an extension of the existing I-85 lanes is expected to be complete in 2017.

Georgia DOT recognizes, however, that P3 projects and tolled express lanes are not applicable in every corridor in Atlanta, let alone the whole of the state. They can be part of an overall strategy but other elements are needed too.

One is to maximize the safety, efficiency and use of both existing and future assets, a strategy reflected in the department's right-sizing of its personnel and also its adoption last year of a Complete Streets policy—a long-term, broad initiative to design and build transportation infrastructure in a way that accommodates and best serves all of its users.

The department is employing a host of other innovative efforts to stretch the most efficiency and use from existing infrastructure and available dollars. Increased use of time-saving design/ build contracts, more HEROs, diverging diamond interchanges, new roundabout intersections, traffic signal synchronization, active management of signals in busy corridors, ramp meters on expressways, flexible shoulder lanes and variable speed limits on Interstates are among the strategies being employed by Georgia DOT.

As we look toward the opportunities and challenges of the next 100 years, we reflect on a 2010 study for the department that showed us what Georgia's future could be if sufficient transportation funding is found and sound strategies followed. It could equal 320,000 new jobs and $515 billion in economic benefits in just the next 30 years.

Fulfilling that promise will require the efforts of more than just this department. But in the meantime, no mobility improvement is too insignificant and no savings too small for Georgia DOT.

HAWAII

Hawaii Department of Transportation

Ford N. Fuchigami
Interim Director

YEAR FORMED **1959**

FTE **2,257**

KEY FACTS
TOTAL STATE ROAD MILES
(OWNED BY STATE HIGHWAY
AGENCY) **949**

STATE-OWNED BRIDGES **719**

TRANSIT TRIPS PER YEAR
75 million

RECENT HIGHLIGHTS:
– President's Award—
  Environment

Overview

The Hawaii Highway Department was organized in 1925 shortly after Congress passed a measure to extend the provisions of certain laws to the territory of Hawaii, including financial support for good roads. Today, the Hawaii Department of Transportation (HDOT), which was formed in 1959 shortly after Hawaii became a state provides, operates, and maintains 11 commercial and four general aviation airports, 10 commercial harbors, and 2,450 lane miles of paved freeways, highways, and roads on the state's six populated islands. HDOT's mission is to provide a safe, efficient, accessible, and inter-modal transportation system that ensures the mobility of people and goods and enhances and/or preserves economic prosperity and the quality of life. The agency is divided into three modal divisions—airports, harbors, and highways—which reflect the primary transportation systems that serve the 1.4 million residents.

As an isolated island chain located nearly 2,400 miles from San Francisco in a tropical climate, Hawaii's transportation system is considerably different than other states. Volcanoes, tidal waves, and heavy rains have dictated major chapters in the state's highway history.

For example, lava from Mauna Loa and Kilauea volcanoes on the big island of Hawaii has periodically overrun highways. Despite its isolation from the lower 48 states, Hawaii has several Interstate routes that are not connected to the rest of the system but are nonetheless part of it. And the state's population and economic growth was driven more by the aviation industry rather than inland waterways, trains, and highways.

Aviation Transforms Hawaii

Because of its isolation, the air travel boom in the 1940s and 1950s transformed Hawaii and helped secure its acceptance as the 50th state in 1959. In 1925, U.S. Navy Commander John Rodgers and his crew attempted the first flight from San Francisco to Hawaii which propelled Hawaii into a new, modern era. Despite running out of fuel 365 miles short of Oahu, the crew made a safe water landing and crafted sails from the wings of their seaplane. They navigated toward Hawaii for 10 days before being picked up near the island of Kauai by a submarine.

Two years later, the John Rodgers Airport was dedicated, opening the skies to commercial air travel from the U.S. mainland, Japan, and locations around the Pacific Rim. Once a remote

location accessible only by ships, Hawaii was gradually transformed by growth of air travel. The John Rodgers Airport became the Honolulu International Airport in 1947. By 1954, it was the fourth busiest airport in the nation, accommodating 255,000 aircraft operations and the largest number of military aircraft movements by any civilian facility.

Today, the 15 state-operated airports serve more than 30 million passengers, 430,000 tons of cargo, and 900,000 takeoffs and landings annually statewide. Since Commander Rodgers' inaugural flight in 1925, Hawaii's population has increased nearly 5.5 times from 256,000 to nearly 1.4 million people.

Because of the importance of aviation to both the state and global economy and day-to-day life in Hawaii, HDOT is carrying out a major airports modernization project to not only enhance the traveler experience and improve efficiency and safety, but also create jobs and stimulate the economy. The ultimate goal of the $2.7 billion modernization program is to transform the state's airports into world-class facilities over the next decade so they can meet the future needs of residents and visitors alike.

Interstate and Defense Highway System Fuels Progress

Long before World War II, Hawaii's strategic location in the Pacific Ocean made it a vital part of the U.S. defense system. Following the war, it became clear that transportation improvements were needed to realize Hawaii's potential as a military asset. Shortly after Hawaii became a state in 1959, special legislation brought it into the Interstate system and authorized construction of 50 miles of interstate highways. On August 29, 1960, three routes were designated for Hawaii. Because they were not connected to any other parts of the Interstate system, the Hawaii routes were identified as H-1, H-2, and H-3. A fourth route, H-201, was added as a signed interstate in July 2004. These three initial interstate routes, which were completed over a 20-year period from 1977 to 1997, helped tie together the multitude of military bases scattered over Oahu with the huge Pearl Harbor naval complex and Hickam Air Force Base. In addition, they helped meet the great and often overwhelming local and civilian tourist traffic on Oahu.

Construction of the Hawaii Interstate System was the biggest public works project in Hawaii's history and assisted the 50th state in its social, economic,

and political development. The new freeway infrastructure also benefited the nation on a global scale by developing a stronger U.S. military presence in the Pacific region.

And just like mainland interstates, Hawaii's interstates are aging and deteriorating which has led to a series of rehabilitation and modernization projects. For example, a segment of the H-1 Freeway in Honolulu is one of the oldest and busiest traffic corridors on Oahu, handling nearly 200,000 vehicles per day. A $42 million federal-aid rehabilitation project, scheduled for completion by the end of 2014, was designed to prolong the roadway surface and address congestion through resurfacing, restoration, and rehabilitation.

Harbor Development Supports Continued Growth

Hawaii's long maritime history was born with the first Polynesian seafarers to set foot on the islands. Given its geographically isolated location in the middle of the Pacific Ocean, Hawaii has always depended on ocean shipping for essential commodities and supplies. More than 80 percent of all goods and materials needed for daily life including food, clothing, building materials, vehicles, fuels, and other consumables are imported into the islands, and more than 98 percent of that total is shipped through the state-operated port system.

As the state continues to grow, commercial harbor development to accommodate cargo shipping growth is a top priority for HDOT. Commercial harbor development projects are planned well in advance to meet projected requirements for the next 20 years and more. Planned improvements include harbor facility upgrades, acquisition and expansion of cargo yard space, installation of utilities, and construction of roads to facilitate movement of goods from harbors.

HDOT currently operates 10 commercial harbors that support economic prosperity and promote the well-being of the state's cargo, fishing, and passenger cruise industries.

Building a Multi-Modal Transportation Future

As an island chain, Hawaii is already confronting the harsh realities of a growing population on limited land space and the impact on transportation systems. Based on the 2010 census, Hawaii is the 40th largest state in terms of population, but ranks 13th in terms of population density with 214 people per square mile.[1] A greater focus on multi-modal transportation alternatives is needed in order to make existing systems more efficient and sustainable and to support projected growth. The state's automobile-centric transportation system of the past century will run out of room as population continues to grow. Alternative means of transportation such as bicycling, walking, rail transit, and buses within and around urban cores are already becoming increasingly important to mitigate

traffic congestion, long commute times, greater fuel consumption, and negative environmental impacts.

The seventh edition of the Hawaii Statewide Transportation Plan addresses development of a multi-modal and inter-modal network, focusing on the importance of making connections among transportation modes and other statewide priorities including protecting the environment, complementing land use, supporting the economy, and improving quality of life.

Major transportation goals for fiscal years 2015–2018 are:
- Ensuring mobility and accessibility;
- Enhancing safety, ensuring security;
- Protecting the state's unique environment;
- Supporting Hawaii's economy and future growth objectives;
- Supporting state energy goals;
- Creating secure, flexible, and sustainable revenues for transportation needs; and

- Implementing a statewide planning process that connects land use and transportation.

Going forward, the plan emphasizes that the state's transposition system will require a mix of modes, means, uses, choices, and types of coming and going to make connections and meet the challenges that lie ahead in this unique transportation environment.[2]

---

[1] *Hawaii Population 2014*, World Population Review, March 2014, accessed at *http://worldpopulationreview.com/states/hawaii-population* on March 10, 2014.

[2] *Hawaii Statewide Transportation Plan: Hawaii's Multi-Modal and Inter-Modal Network*, Hawaii Department of Transportation, 2012, accessed at *http://hidot.hawaii.gov/administration/files/2013/02/hstp2011-volume1-making-connections.pdf*.

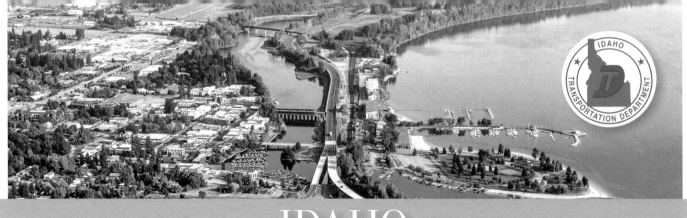

IDAHO

Idaho Transportation Department

Brian W. Ness, P.E.
Director

YEAR FORMED **1913**

FTE **1,655**

KEY FACTS
TOTAL STATE ROAD MILES
(OWNED BY STATE HIGHWAY
AGENCY) **4,979**

STATE-OWNED BRIDGES **1,311**

TRANSIT TRIPS PER YEAR
2.27 million

RECENT HIGHLIGHTS
– Completion of the US 95 Sand Creek
  Byway—a project first discussed in the
  1940s.

– Major reconstruction and expansion
  of the Interstate 84 corridor through
  the Treasure Valley—the state's most
  populous region.

– Major reconstruction and expansion of
  the US 95 corridor in northern Idaho.

– Major reconstruction and expansion
  of US 30 in south-eastern Idaho.

– Realignment of the department's
  organizational structure to reduce
  layers and improve customer service.

The legacy of Idaho's road and bridge builders over the past 100 years is visible throughout the state, written in concrete, steel, and asphalt in places as diverse as Horseshoe Bend Hill and Fourth of July Pass.

A sound transportation system has been and will continue to be the foundation of Idaho's economic development. A good transportation system is the lifeline for commerce and growth. The development of this transportation system has shaped Idaho, its cities and its economy this past century and will continue to define its future.

The first recognition of any territorial responsibility for highways occurred in 1881 with the construction of bridges over the Boise, Payette, and Bear rivers.

A five-member bridge commission directed the projects.

On July 3, 1890, Idaho became a state without a road of its own, as all routes in the state were designated as county roads. For the first 23 years of Idaho's statehood, selection of road projects using state funds required approval of the Legislature. Each project was administered by an individual commission that remained in authority only for the duration of the project.

Fifteen separate commissions were created to supervise road construction, including nine involving bridges. During that 23-year period, $535,000 (an average of approximately $27,500 per year) was spent from bond issues for construction of roads and bridges.

Most resources in the early part of Idaho's statehood were directed toward railroads rather than highways. From 1874 to 1910, when the Utah Northern Railroad first reached Idaho, 20 railroads had constructed lines within the state.

A shift in interest to roads was stimulated by a series of "good roads" meetings held throughout Idaho in 1905. The National Good Roads Association sponsored those meetings.

C.H. Moore, president of the association, led a group of experts who discussed the benefits of good roads and demonstrated construction methods. The meetings aroused much interest, and businesses closed in some cities to allow employees to attend.

In 1913, a five-man State Highway Commission was created and the first State Highway Engineer appointed.

This commission was empowered to lay out, build, and construct state highways any place within the state. The initial funds were obtained from the licensing, on a horsepower basis, of the 2,080 vehicles in operation at that time, and later from bond issues, some of which refused to float.

The first contract under the new commission was awarded December 13, 1913, and covered 5.5 miles of the old Oregon Trail east of Pocatello. In the three years following, about $1 million was expended; then the coming of federal aid brought more orderly procedure and stabilized finances.

The first federal aid project was awarded in October 1917 to construct three steel and 43 concrete bridges in Lemhi and Custer counties on what is now US 93.

Although the Idaho Highway Commission existed for only six years, it was successful in developing the basis for the state highway system, as it exists today. It is significant to note that much of today's system follows closely the lines laid out between 1913 and 1919. This was accomplished despite the financial hardships that existed throughout this period.

On April 1, 1919, the State Highway Commission and the State Engineer's office were abolished and all duties were transferred to the Bureau of Public Works. The Bureau of Highways became a subdivision of that department. The Idaho highway system in 1919 consisted of about 2,200 miles of roadway. Less than 50 miles of that roadway was paved.

It was expanded to 4,500 miles with 1,000 miles of pavement in 1930 and 5,128 miles with 3,600 miles paved in 1950. The search for other sources of income resulted in a three-cent-per-gallon tax on motor fuels in 1923 to finance this growth.

By 1927, registration was up to 101,366 vehicles, but the maintenance of gravel roads was taking an unduly large share of the total income. The decision was made to try bituminous-treated surfacing and 80 miles was applied.

In 1934, only one-third of Idaho's 5,000 miles of road were paved or oiled. Another third was made of crushed rock while the final third were essentially unimproved wagon trails.

Until 1938, there were no markings on Idaho roads to keep traffic separated. That year, the state hired two crews to paint yellow centerlines on hard-surface highways and had begun to install directional road signs in some locations.

Of course, from the very beginning, the posting of highways signs brought inevitable vandalism. Only two signs remained undamaged on a 54-mile stretch of US 93 near Shoshone after the first three months of their installation. During those three months, one sign was hit by 22 rifle or handgun shots and at least one shotgun blast.

As World War II loomed over the next decade, Idaho found itself with a wealth of minerals important to the nation's war making ability. Tungsten, mercury, copper, lead, and phosphates lay in Idaho mines waiting for extraction and transportation to factories.

The Defense Highway Act of 1941 authorized the construction of access roads and strategic network construction. In 1944, Congress passed the Federal Aid Highway Act.

Routes for all states, including those in Idaho, were established on maps; but without a national funding program to actually build the roads, the plan stood idle for the next 12 years until President Eisenhower turned his attention to the nation's highway problems.

Meanwhile, the Idaho Legislature created the Department of Highways in 1950. In 1951, the State Board of Highway Directors was established to oversee the department. The board consisted of three members appointed by the governor and confirmed by the legislature. It was the first time that the state engineer was required to be an Idaho licensed professional engineer.

In November of 1956, the Idaho Department of Highways was reaching out to the motoring public for support. The department published an informational booklet, *Idaho Interstate Highway System: What, Why and How.*

The 28-page publication offered an overview of the federal highway plan and how it would impact Idahoans.

"Travel via the interstate highway will save time because of the reduction in travel distance and higher sustained operating speeds made possible by the elimination of left turns, intersections at grade and traffic signals," the booklet proclaims.

Accompanied by a cover letter addressed to "Dear Mr. Highway User," the booklet portrayed the future of Idaho's interstate system with uncanny accuracy, down to artist's conceptions of what

"diamond" and "trumpet" rural intersections would look like in rural Idaho.

Clearly, the Department of Highways was attempting to garner public support for the project.

"For the first time in 25 years, you will have a highway system matched to the capacity of your modern automobile. You will get the full benefit from the large investment you have in our modern means of transportation," the booklet continued.

At times, the authors resorted to hard-sell tactics:

"When you and your family go for a drive on the Interstate System your chances of being in an accident will drop by two-thirds....You may be one of the 4,000 people who will not die in an auto accident each year after the Interstate System is completed."

Idaho's interstate plan covered 611 miles through the state on four specific routes. The network would serve 17 of the state's 44 counties.

Although Idaho's interstates safely carry passenger and commercial freight traffic, they were designed primarily for U.S. Armed Forces as presidents Franklin D. Roosevelt and, especially, Dwight D. Eisenhower, recognized a critical need to move troops and supplies quickly from one end of America to the other.

"It is a military highway," said Keith Green, a retired State Chief Engineer whose career in Idaho transportation began in 1957 on the interstate near Jerome. "One of the things that determined the height of the overpasses was

the size of the missile that was expected to be towed underneath it."

Because of its geographic location, perched on the western edge of the northern Rocky Mountains, Idaho's interstate was built more as a network of crossroads than a destination in itself. But without the construction of Interstates 84, 90, and 15 in the last half of the 20th Century, America's inland and coastal Northwest would remain mostly isolated from the rest of the country.

As the interstate was in its planning stages, engineers followed the routes of the early western settlers who came through Idaho on the Oregon Trail. These hardy souls with their wagons and livestock by necessity took the path of least resistance over the often harsh conditions they found on the western plains, mountains, and high deserts.

Interstate 15 north of Salt Lake City is the only major connection between the United States and Canada between Seattle and western Minnesota.

Similarly, the Interstate 86/84 route that cuts a swath diagonally between Salt Lake City and Seattle is the only direct route from the interior to the Northwest coast. Without these routes, traffic would have to swing far north to Helena, Montana, or as far south as Sacramento before drivers could set a straight course for the great Northwest port cities.

Interstate 90, enters northern Idaho at the Idaho/Washington state line and runs east through Coeur d'Alene and Wallace before leaving the state at the Montana state line. At about 84 miles, this original part of the Mullan Road was intended to connect the Columbia River on the West Coast with the Missouri River.

The route travels through Post Falls, Coeur d'Alene, then through the mining towns of Wallace, Kellogg, and Mullan before entering Montana.

Idaho has the distinction of having the last traffic signal on Interstate 90. The interstate begins in Seattle and ends in Boston, a distance of 3,020 miles. In 1991, the last stop light on the interstate was removed in Wallace, Idaho.

In 1974, the Department of Highways, Department of Aeronautics and Public Transportation Department were combined to form the Idaho Transportation Department.

The Division of Motor Vehicles was transferred from the Department of Law Enforcement to the transportation department in 1982.

In the past 25 years, substantial upgrades have been to all Idaho highways improving safety and commerce.

In June 2012, the US 95 Sand Creek Byway was completed after first being discussed in the 1940s. To meet the growing traffic needs of the state's major urban center—the Treasure Valley and Boise—major expansion projects were constructed on I-84 and I-184.

From 2006 through 2011, the Idaho Legislature authorized the sale of $857 million in Grant Anticipation Revenue Vehicle (GARVEE) bonds to finance work in the six corridors. GARVEE is a funding program that allows Idaho to plan, design, and build more highway projects in less time than through traditional transportation funding methods.

With this funding, major improvements have been made to I-84, US 95, US 30 and Idaho 16.

The Idaho Transportation Department operates under the direction of the Idaho Transportation Board, a seven-member panel of citizens appointed by the Idaho Governor and confirmed by the Idaho Senate. The transportation board is responsible for establishing department policy and hiring the department's director.

Board members represent each of the state's six transportation districts and serve staggered, six-year terms on a part-time basis. The seventh member, the board chairman, serves at the pleasure of the governor and votes in the event of a tie.

Idaho, the 13th-largest state in land area, is divided into six administrative districts for the construction, maintenance and operation of the state highways. The headquarters of the transportation department is in Boise. District offices are located in Coeur d'Alene, Lewiston, Boise, Shoshone, Pocatello, and Rigby.

The headquarters provides services to the department's six regional offices. The Highway Safety, Aeronautics, Public Transportation, and Motor Vehicle programs are also administered through the headquarters' office.

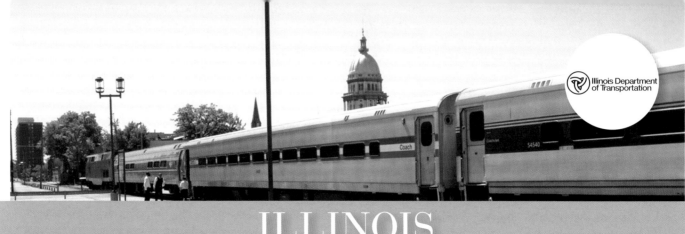

ILLINOIS

Illinois Department of Transportation

Erica Borggren
Acting Secretary

YEAR FORMED **1905**

FTE **5,449**

KEY FACTS
TOTAL STATE ROAD MILES
(OWNED BY STATE HIGHWAY
AGENCY) **15,995**

STATE-OWNED BRIDGES **7,440**

TRANSIT TRIPS PER YEAR
669 million

Heart of the Nation

For as long as there have been automobiles, highways, and air traffic, there have been dedicated transportation agencies. From massive bridges spanning the Mississippi or Illinois Rivers to winding roads eloquently carved into limestone bluffs, from two-lane roads tracing through rural corn and soybean fields to dirt and grass landing strips to the steel and concrete jungle of O'Hare International Airport. And on every mile of interstate and railroad that made Illinois what it is today, the mark of an Illinois transportation agency can be seen and felt.

Over the past century, Illinois businesses, residents and visiting travelers have seen the steady development of one of the largest and most effective multi-modal transportation systems in the nation including roadways, passenger and freight railroads, transit and commuter services, bikeways, airports, waterways and canals, port districts, and inter-modal facilities. During just the past 50 years, Illinois' geographical location near the center of the nation and the diversity of statewide transportation options have made the Illinois multi-modal network a keystone and a vital hub for national and regional travel and freight movement.

The Illinois system supports convenient travel for a state population of 12.9 million, the fifth most in the nation, and more than 100 million visitors to Illinois each year. Motor vehicles traveled more than 104.5 million miles on Illinois roads and bridges last year, about twice the amount of travel 40 years before, when the Illinois Department of Transportation (IDOT) was formed. Inter-city passenger rail services transported more than 1.8 million riders to and from destinations across Illinois in 2013, more than twice the total served just 10 years ago. And last year alone, transit systems throughout the state carried more than 659 million riders, while more than 42 million people flew on commercial airlines using Illinois airports.

While striving to ensure Illinois residents and visitors are properly equipped with transportation options to help them reach their destinations safely and successfully, the state also understands the significance of freight movement within and through Illinois. Illinois' 7,400-mile network of railroads carries more than 300 million tons of freight into and out of Illinois each year. Some 1,100 miles of navigable waterways serve barges carrying more than 120 million tons of freight each year. More than 140,000 miles of state and local

roads and streets, including 16,000 miles of state-owned highways and interstates, and more than 26,500 bridges statewide, serve commercial carriers transporting another 300 million tons of freight annually. Meanwhile, Illinois' regional airport system processes more than 670,000 tons of freight each year.

Breaking Through Boundaries

The nation witnessed many transportation milestones throughout the 20th century, and Illinois continues to boldly push transportation boundaries into the 21st century. Illinois, in 2010, was eager to break ground on one of the most revolutionizing transportation options in the nation—high-speed rail between Chicago and St. Louis. With the goal of establishing more balanced and consistent usage of Illinois' transportation network, once completed, the Chicago to St. Louis high-speed rail corridor will move people throughout the state in a way that improves safety, convenience, connectivity, and accessibility, all while promoting economic development and helping people reach destinations faster and more reliably.

IDOT, in partnership with northeastern Illinois transit agencies Pace and the Regional Transportation Authority, implemented the Bus on Shoulder program, which allows Pace buses to utilize the shoulder and save passengers travel time on selected Chicago-area interstates. This innovative program was created to increase ridership, improve travel times, and relieve congestion.

Planning for the Future

A sturdy transportation plan embraces the concept of enhanced mobility, which can be achieved by offering individuals and businesses a range of choices in modes of transportation for their travel and freight shipment needs. Imagine what our transportation system could be if we strengthened our modal bonds, ultimately reducing congestion, improving accessibility and adding connections. The modern global marketplace requires businesses to adjust rapidly to new product demands, market geographies and on-time transportation delivery issues. For Illinois' industrial and commercial businesses, the reliability of on-time, safe, and damage-free delivery of their products is essential to customer satisfaction and loyalty. To assure reliability, the enhanced planning and development of a multi-modal system will provide additional options for assuring access to markets or for obtaining material inputs for production. A multi-modal system ensures that if one mode experiences capacity challenges, other modes are available to provide additional capacity. The ability of Illinois to assure its industry of an on-time, reliable and flexible transportation system is key to the state's ability to compete in the global economy.

In early 2013, IDOT published the Illinois State Transportation Plan, a long-range plan designed to guide IDOT through the next few decades with a progressive and action-oriented framework. It's IDOT's goal that the action items enable safety for all transportation users, preserve and manage existing infrastructure, accommodate future growth in population and employment, support global economic competitiveness, integrate transportation options for underserved populations, protect the environment, and more.

IDOT is in the early stages of developing a statewide transit plan to ensure that goals identified in the 2013 long-range state transportation plan are met along with the more local needs of communities, large and small. Over the past 25 years, the rural public transportation program in Illinois has grown from 26 grantees serving 44 counties to 41 grantees serving 88 counties. Northeastern Illinois' public transit system continues to be strengthened through investments such as reconstruction of the Chicago Transit Authority's Dan Ryan Red Line, serving South Chicago areas. IDOT, also in accord with the long-range plan, is actively developing a human capital plan that will support the transportation industry by enabling strategies to empower individuals interested in transportation-related careers and inspire younger generations and/or underutilized populations to join the industry.

While moving millions of people and building a foundation for the industry, state railroads, highways, waterways, and airports are moving millions of tons of freight into and out of Illinois each year. In recognition of the importance of freight movement throughout northern Illinois, a first of its kind partnership was formed to invest in freight improvements that already are increasing the efficiency of northeastern Illinois passenger and freight rail carriers and infrastructure. The state of Illinois, city of Chicago, Metra (northeastern Illinois commuter rail provider), Amtrak, the nation's freight railroads, and the U.S. DOT came together early this century and created the Chicago Region Environmental and Transportation Efficiency Program (CREATE). This program is designed to enhance quality of life for the region's residents and visitors and support economic growth.

Safety resides at the heart of the transportation planning. Safety concepts and best practices must be incorporated into every planning element undertaken at IDOT, on IDOT projects, and on the Illinois transportation system. Illinois has the goal of making Illinois' transportation system operate at the highest level of safety performance. And, we can

always strive to be safer—and safer means striving to drive fatalities to zero—across all modes. Every life is important and it is vital that Illinois travelers take part in IDOT's commitment to do all we can to eliminate fatalities on Illinois' transportation infrastructure. The fatality rate on Illinois' highways has declined by almost two-thirds since 1982 despite a steady growth in travel during that period. Yet portions of the transportation system still experience crash rates that exceed public expectations.

With the projected increase in the demand for transportation in the future, keeping the transportation system safe will continue to be a serious challenge. A safe transportation system reduces the tragic human costs from the loss of lives and from suffering due to accidents. People want to be protected from hazardous situations that might endanger or negatively impact their lives, property, economic well-being and/or the lives of their family and friends. IDOT understands we must start with transportation planning to ensure safety is included in the discussion from the beginning and implement the use of performance measures to track our progress.

Maintaining and Strengthening Transportation

Over the past few decades, the state has invested many billions of dollars in the Illinois transportation system. Most recently, thanks to Illinois Jobs Now!, a six-year, $31 billion capital infrastructure program, IDOT, since 2009, has invested $15.1 billion in roads and bridges, $1.7 billion in transit, $800 million in rail, and $420 million in air transportation. This program alone has created or support more than 180,000 jobs.

In partnership with the Missouri Department of Transportation (MoDOT), southern Illinois welcomed a new bridge in late 2003, connecting southern Illinois to Cape Girardeau, Missouri. The new 3,970-foot-long cable-stayed bridge replaced an old 18-foot-wide truss bridge constructed in 1926. Just over 10 years later, in early 2014, IDOT and MoDOT opened the Stan Musial Veterans' Memorial Bridge, the first new bridge to connect Illinois' Metro-East area with St. Louis in some 40 years. Bridges such as these are critical to the transportation needs of the southern Illinois and provide additional travel options for travelers and freight movement.

The discussion around building a third airport in the Chicago metropolitan area dates back to the 1980s, but it was not until early 2002 that IDOT announced the purchase of the first parcel of land for what is now identified as the South Suburban Airport in Will County. In 2013, Governor Pat Quinn signed a law that will give IDOT the authority to build the South Suburban Airport. Another project that was envisioned decades ago is the Illiana Corridor, designed to be an alternate expressway route for motor carriers and other travelers from Northern Illinois to Northern Indiana, and one that will relieve significant freight congestion already existing in the Chicago area. Today, a partnership between IDOT and the Indiana Department of Transportation has identified a recommended Illiana Corridor that extends about 47 miles from I-55 near Wilmington, Illinois, east to I-65 near Cedar Lake, Indiana.

Over the past 30 years, IDOT has been expanding and improving Illinois 13, a primary east–west corridor in southern

Illinois. These improvements, including the construction of a new single point urban interchange at Interstate 57 and Illinois 13, provide access to new areas enabling the potential for new economic development. This regionally important project has been essential for the expansion of commerce in southern Illinois as the potential for future economic growth is dependent on transportation arteries that are safe and free from traffic congestion.

Billions of dollars have been invested in the Illinois Aviation System over the decades. Air travel has gone from dream to the jet-age, literally transforming the way we think about travel and world commerce. Today, aviation is a vital component of the Illinois economy. Illinois is home to the corporate headquarters of aviation giants Boeing and United Airlines, as well as hundreds of other aviation companies. More than 337,000 jobs can be attributed to the aviation industry in Illinois, with a total annual economic impact of $40.9 billion.

All of these investments and projects promote and support quality of life for Illinois residents and visitors. The new bridge connecting the Metro-East with St. Louis has already made a difference by giving travelers and commercial carriers another transportation option to help reach destinations safely and more efficiently. The Illiana and the South Suburban Airport, once completed, will offer one of the nation's fastest growing suburban areas a more well-rounded and connected transportation system. Additionally, through all facets of IDOT's project development and implementation as well as day-to-day operations, the department strives to make certain that IDOT commitments to safety, integrity, diversity, responsiveness, quality, and innovation are incorporated throughout.

Looking Forward

Clearly, Illinois' economic success and quality of life are built on this safe, effective, accessible, and progressive transportation system. IDOT continues to be proactive in transportation planning, maintenance, and project delivery, with ongoing goals to bridge gaps among the transportation modes, strengthen current connections and build new connections that make sense to improve ease of travel, and help build and support communities.

Bridge and pavement maintenance are among the state's top priorities today, along with new or expanded travel services involving passenger rail, transit, and airports. Challenges to the quality and capacity of the Illinois transportation system are extensive and continuous, and IDOT keeps up with the pace by being a national leader in transportation planning, maintenance, and project delivery. This steadfast and reliable attention to service and ongoing improvements will help ensure that Illinois residents, visitors and commercial carriers can easily continue to utilize the state's transportation options to safely and effectively reach their destinations through this century and beyond.

IDOT believes that transportation can enrich the lives of each person who comes in contact with it directly via travel or indirectly via the food on his or her table or the clothes on his or her back. Transportation is a necessity—without it, many of us cannot reach our jobs and schools, and the food and goods we rely on cannot get to us.

INDIANA

Indiana Department of Transportation

Karl B. Browning
Commissioner

YEAR FORMED **1917**

FTE **Approx. 3,579**

KEY FACTS
TOTAL STATE ROAD MILES
(OWNED BY STATE HIGHWAY
AGENCY) **10,982**

STATE-OWNED BRIDGES **5,315**

TRANSIT TRIPS PER YEAR
33.4 million

Overview

The first Indiana State Highway Commission was established by the General Assembly in 1917 to make the state eligible for federal highway funds that became available with the 1916 federal-aid highway bill. However, plans to establish a state system of roads were put on hold when the constitutionality of the first law was challenged in court. Although the Supreme Court eventually upheld the 1917 law, the General Assembly had repealed it and passed an act establishing a new State Highway Commission, effective March 10, 1919. The highway commission remained in place until 1981 when the Indiana Department of Highways was created to consolidate three transportation-related commissions.

The Indiana Department of Transportation (INDOT) was established in 1989 to coordinate all transportation modes within the state. In 1914, when AASHTO was created, the Indiana state highway system consisted of 55 total miles. Today, INDOT maintains more than 11,000 centerline miles and nearly 6,000 bridges across the state. In addition, INDOT regulates nearly 4,500 rail miles and 110 public access and 560 private access airports across the state. It has more than 3,600 employees.

INDOT's mission is to build, maintain, and operate a superior transportation system enhancing safety, mobility, and economic growth. Its current work is guided by a series of goals that focus on

- Maintaining steady improvement in pavement and bridge quality
- Meeting established performance indicators and measures
- Ensuring a commitment to safety throughout the agency
- Implementing a talent management system that links strategy and operations to results
- Establishing a culture of continuous improvement that is consistent with performance of a 21st century organization
- Improving customer satisfaction by providing timely responses with quality products and services

Canals and Railroads Open Freight Corridors

Construction of the National Road in the 1800s along with the development of canals and railroads connected Indiana to markets on the east coast and provided a gateway to the west for thousands of settlers. A system of canals, including the Erie Canal, was instrumental in enabling Hoosiers to import and export goods around the world by shipping them through either the Great Lakes or

down the Ohio and Mississippi Rivers to the Gulf of Mexico. The development of railroads further connected Indiana to both the east and west coasts while improving national access to Indiana raw materials and markets for finished goods.

With its central location and strong water, rail, and road connections, Indiana emerged as a center for transportation in the nation's heartland.

Today, Indiana's freight rail system has three Class I railroads and 39 regional, local, and switching and terminal carriers. CSX and Norfolk Southern have extensive rail networks in the state. Each railroad's principal east–west route passes through Indiana, making the state a critical component for transcontinental traffic and traffic moving between the east and Midwest. The Indiana rail network currently has about 3,884 miles of active rail lines.

Waterborne freight is also a key element of Indiana's multi-modal capacity. The state has significant maritime access to the nation's two major inland waterways-the Great Lakes/St. Lawrence seaways and the Ohio/Missouri/Mississippi watershed. These waterways provide high-capacity routes to major domestic

and export markets. The state's three public marine terminals are managed by Ports of Indiana.

Leading the Nation in Interstate Access

Creation of the Interstate System, beginning in 1956, further expanded Indiana's pivotal transportation position. Interstate highways transformed Indiana into a center of logistics and advanced manufacturing while providing economic opportunity for generations of Hoosiers.

In 1976, Indiana became the first state to complete it mainline Interstate program. Indiana ranks first in the nation for both Interstate highway access with 14 routes and pass-through interstates with eight. Indiana is also within a day's drive of 75 percent of the United States and Canada population which has contributed to its important position in freight movement. Indiana ranks ninth out of 50 states in the amount of freight tons shipped into the state—about three percent of the total amount of U.S. freight tonnage—and 10th in the amount of freight tons shipped out-of-state, also about three percent of total U.S. shipments. As much as one-third of the freight on Indiana's transportation network passes through the state with-

out stopping, making through carriers a significant stakeholder in the Indiana freight system.

Indiana's logistics industry, which is centered on the state's interstate highways, employees about 250,000 workers.

Public–Private Partnerships Support Transportation Investments

Indiana has established itself as a national leader in leveraging private-sector capital and innovation to finance, construct, and maintain transportation infrastructure projects. The 2006 lease of the 157-mile Indiana Toll Road is the cornerstone of creating a new model for transportation investments. Income from the toll-road lease will fund more than $12 billion in state roads and bridge construction and improvement projects over 10 years without an increase in state and federal taxes.

Through 2012, INDOT projects funded by the toll-road lease created thousands of new jobs by completing hundreds of statewide transportation projects. One of the most significant completed projects is 67 miles of new terrain extension of Interstate 69 in southwestern Indiana, the nation's longest contiguous Interstate project and the longest new Interstate segment built in a generation.

By the end of calendar year 2015, more than $11 billion will be invested in new construction and preservation transportation projects. Between 2001 and 2005, the state averaged $750 million for highway construction per year. Backed by toll road lease funding, INDOT averaged more than $1 billion in construction dollars invested in highway projects annually between 2006 and 2012.

Providing Funding for Public Transit

INDOT provides financial and technical assistance to 67 public transit systems across the state which results in support for more than 34 million passenger trips annually. In addition, INDOT provides financial assistance to 100 specialized transportation providers throughout the state. INDOT's role in the state's public transit system is mainly financial, administering millions of dollars through funds including the Public Mass Transportation Fund Rural Transit Program, Commuter Rail Service Fund, and the Specialized Transit Fund. Yet that financial support is essential to ensuring a multi-modal system that supports transportation options, eases congestion, and supports energy conservation goals.

A Commitment to Innovation Through Research

Indiana has a long history of supporting collaborative research to advance transportation goals. The Indiana Joint Transportation Research Program (JRTP) facilitates collaboration between INDOT, higher education institutions, and industry to implement innovations that result in continuous improvement in the planning, design, construction, operation, management, and economic efficiency of the Indiana transportation infrastructure. JRTP grew out of the Joint Highway Research Project, a partnership established in 1937 between what was then the Indiana Highway Commission and Purdue University. The Joint Highway Research Project, led by Professor K.B. Woods, head of the School of Civil Engineering at Purdue University, played a key role in administering the AASHO Road Test from 1955 to 1961.

JTRP has produced more than 1,500 technical reports and provided experienced-based educational opportunities to thousands of students. Between 2010 and 2014, for example, more than 500 students participated in transportation research projects that helped agencies find cheaper, faster, better, and safer ways to manage their infrastructure.

As part of the shared commitment to research, INDOT and JTRP annually sponsor the Purdue Road School which attracts more than 2,000 local and state officials, consultants, and suppliers to explore a range of transportation issues over several days. The Road School, originally called the Civil Engineering Conference, was began in 1914 when participants in the engineering conference passed a resolution calling for a provision in the laws of Indiana that there be a yearly School for Good Roads. That commitment to collaborative learning has continued for 100 years.

Looking Ahead

Key challenges that lie ahead for both Indiana's transportation system and the nation as a whole:

- Identifying and securing long-term sustainable funding resources needed to preserve, maintain, and operate public infrastructure and build needed new infrastructure to meet changing needs
- Continuing to invest in research and development to create and deploy new technologies and innovations
- Raising public awareness of the need to invest in transportation infrastructure.

Of particular concern in Indiana is serving the growing demand for the movement of goods in and through the state. INDOT is working continuously to understand the issues and concerns of the freight community and to effectively plan for freight movement in and through Indiana.

IOWA

Iowa Department of Transportation

Paul Trombino III, P.E.
Director

YEAR FORMED **1913**

FTE **Approx. 2,744**

KEY FACTS
TOTAL STATE ROAD MILES
(OWNED BY STATE HIGHWAY
AGENCY) **8,894**

STATE-OWNED BRIDGES **4,071**

TRANSIT TRIPS PER YEAR
21.3 million

Congratulations to AASHTO on its 100th Anniversary. The Iowa Department of Transportation (Iowa DOT) recently wrapped up its own centennial celebration. We have taken the opportunity to look back at the development of transportation in Iowa, as well as looking towards the future.

Agriculture Drives Transportation Needs in Early Iowa History

At the turn of the 20th century, Iowa was facing the impending automobile age and a boom in mechanized agriculture with a 19th-century transportation infrastructure. The state was home to more than 9,000 miles of active passenger and freight rail track, 100,000 miles of roads and streets, and thousands of bridges to move people and goods over Iowa's rolling prairie terrain.

Automobiles made their first Iowa appearance at the 1899 Linn County Fair, but most were shipped in by train. Iowa's 100,000 miles of road were still dirt. On rainy days, that meant a wagon-miring, hoof-sucking, axle-deep gumbo of mud, which made road travel nearly impossible.

As agriculture made the shift from animal and human power to combustion power, Iowa's farmers were able to move beyond farming for subsistence and began to produce for the marketplace. To seize this opportunity, farmers needed to get their crops to towns and trains. Mud roads were not the only impediment; wooden bridges built with few standards in the late 1800s added a potentially fatal hazard for the heavy loads of farm implements. Bridge collapses under tractors and traction engines were common in the first decades of the 20th century.

Organizing a State Agency Charged with Transportation Oversight

In 1904, the Iowa Legislature took its first step towards a modern road system by creating an advisory highway commission, based at Iowa State College (Iowa State University today). The first commissioners would travel the state by rail coach and horseback to conduct road schools, showcasing the most modern road and bridge building materials and techniques to municipal and county officials and engineers. However, this commission had no enforceable powers, and modernization was slow. The legislature, seeing the lack of progress, upgraded the commission in 1914.

The Iowa State Highway Commission (ISHC) became a state governmental body on April 9, 1913, with the power

to set road and bridge construction and material standards. (The Iowa State Highway Commission, and its offices in Ames, became the Iowa Department of Transportation in 1974, and we date our centennial back to 1913.)

The automobile had proven so popular with Iowans that by 1914 there were 147,000 registered, giving Iowa the most cars per person of any state in the Union.

Primary Road System Development

Over the coming decades, the ISHC and the Iowa DOT, applying the best scientific and engineering principle to road and bridge building, would make lasting impacts on the transportation infrastructure of Iowa and the nation.

Starting at home, the ISHC began an ambitious program of paving Iowa's primary roads, the roads and highways that connect the state capitol in Des Moines to county seats and population centers, and would carry the bulk of passenger and freight traffic.

In 1918, when the above picture (the most famous in the Iowa DOT collection) was taken on the Lincoln Highway east of the ISHC headquarters, Iowa had just 12 miles of concrete pavement in the entire state, and no section more

than a mile long. By 1930, 3,272 miles of 7,274 primary roadway miles had been paved, and another 2,863 miles graveled. Even during the Depression decade, Iowa continued to pave, adding another 2,600 miles of concrete or blacktop to the Primary Road System. The ISHC had brought Iowa "out of the mud."

Notable Iowans and Iowa Innovations in Transportation

A number of ISHC personnel and inventions had national impacts on transportation. In 1919, Thomas H. MacDonald left the ISHC, where he was a leading engineer, for Washington, D.C. to join the Bureau of Public Roads. MacDonald would serve as the nations' chief road engineer until 1953.

ISHC employees Jimmy Whitmore Johnson, Rudy Schroeder, and Willis Elbert began work on a slipform paver prototype in 1947. The first slipform model would produce a continuous ribbon of concrete 18 inches wide and 3 inches thick. A 1948 prototype was able to produce a 4-feet-wide, 6-inch-thick ribbon of continuous paving. Finally, in 1949, a full size model was produced, capable of creating a ten-feet-wide, highway-grade lane of concrete. On September 28, 1949, the first lane of public road created with a slipform pav-

er was laid in Primghar, Iowa. Slip form pavers went into commercial production in Iowa by 1955.

A key benefit of the slipform paver was time savings. Under the previous method of paving, fixed forms were erected prior to pouring concrete and a crew could pave approximately 1,000 feet per day. The first slipform paver improved that daily rate to 5,000 feet. This dramatic increase in efficiency came just in time for the building of the Interstate System.

Besides construction, Iowa also made national contributions to highway safety. Now known as sign W14-3 in the *Manual of Uniform Traffic Control Devices for Streets and Highways* (MUTCD), the "No Passing Zone" pennant was first developed in Iowa in 1958 and 1959. The No Passing Pennant became a state standard soon after and a national standard in the 1978 edition of the MUTCD.

The Iowa DOT has also made important contributions to mitigating the social impacts of infrastructure construction. Archaeologists estimate at one time Iowa had more than 50,000 Native burial mounds; sites sacred to native Iowans. Over the decades of Euro-American development the number of sites declined to approximately 10,000. In the course of building Iowa's roads, some of these burial mounds were dug up and paved over, with the artifacts and bones sent on to museums. This pattern was repeating itself in a 1971 construction project along US 34. A number of graves were impacted by the project. The remains of 26 Euro-Americans were re-interred in a nearby cemetery, while the remains of a Native woman and child were sent to the state archaeologist for study.

Maria Pearson—or Running Moccasins—learned the details of the burial issue from her husband John, an ISHC district engineer, and protested this unequal treatment to then-Governor Robert Ray. Pearson's advocacy for Native American burial rights led to a 1976 change in the Iowa Burial Code, providing protection for Native American graves, and repatriation of human remains in Native American cemeteries. Iowa was the first state in the nation to enact such a law, which laid the groundwork for the 1990 federal Native American Graves Protection and Repatriation Act.

Iowa Responds to Changing Environmental Needs

Mitigating negative impacts on the natural environment, while providing a robust transportation infrastructure can seem daunting, unless an agency is willing to stretch beyond the boundaries of the tried and true. The Iowa DOT faced such a challenge when it came to the widening of U.S. Highway 20 in 2000, connecting the cities of Dubuque, Waterloo, Fort Dodge, and Sioux City. The plan to widen US 20 from two lanes to four had been in the ISHC plans since the 1960s. However, US 20 crosses the Iowa River Green Belt in Hardin County, a protected old-growth woodland,

home to endangered species, and site of archaeological wonders. The DOT needed a plan to bridge the Iowa River while doing mitigating damage to the natural environment.

First, the Iowa DOT planned to reroute US 20, so that only 10 acres of Greenbelt land would be impacted. Then engineers chose to build twin 1,500 foot spans of the bridge using an innovative technique known as "launching." In essence, the steel I-girder support structure for the cement highway deck was built, in 300-foot-long sections, in a launching pit near the bridge, with strictly controlled water run-off, to avoid polluting the habitat. The girder assemblies were pushed into place (launched) atop the piers using a giant screw. Then the next 300 feet were welded on the first section, and the process repeated, until all 1,500 feet of steel was moving at the same time. Concrete was carefully poured into place and finished.

This type of bridge building, designed specifically to minimize environmental impact, was the first large-scale I-girder bridge launched in the United States. The Iowa DOT was honored with the 2002 FHWA Environmental Quality Award for its environmentally friendly construction of the US 20 Iowa River Bridge.

The Evolution of Transportation Disaster Planning and Response

One hundred years ago, many Iowa roads and bridges would wash-out due to "normal flooding." Since the days of the ISHC, Iowans have been improving construction standards to make these disruptions less frequent. Even with all the innovations, Iowa has recently experienced several major flooding events, which have washed out roads of

all descriptions, including interstates. The Iowa DOT has adjusted its own list to anticipate and respond to significant infrastructure disruption.

In 2011, the Missouri River flooded near Council Bluffs, damaging I-680 from I-29 to the Missouri River Bridge. As the flood waters receded, the Iowa DOT pushed to have I-680 traffic restored as quickly as possible. Using a number of incentives, and crews working around the clock, the total reconstruction of three miles of interstate was completed in 34 days.

Innovation Is a Normal Business Practice at the Iowa DOT

Iowa has more than 24,000 bridges, and regular maintenance and replacement can cause big disruptions to traffic and commerce in the best of times. In 2011, Iowa became a proving ground for accelerated bridge construction (ABC). Working with the Transportation Research Board's Strategic Highway Research Program 2 (SHRP2), the Iowa DOT replaced the US 6 bridge over Keg Creek using ABC methods. Rather than the typical six months of traffic detours, the ABC method meant traffic was diverted for only two weeks, and is serving as a model for bridge building in the modern era.

In addition to innovations in construction methods, the Iowa DOT has launched innovations to help Iowa travelers during harsh winter conditions. During the winter of 2013–2014, the Iowa DOT introduced a winter driving web page that allowed travelers to see where snow plows were active using real-time data from snow plows. When paired with Iowa's 511 website for road conditions, travelers were able to make more informed decisions about winter driving.

Further, the Iowa DOT is developing a TEXT L8R cell phone application which will disable text and phone capabilities at set parameters. In addition the app would have a portal that would record unsafe behaviors by drivers. The TEXT L8R app would help teens and others comply with existing Iowa laws, create opportunities for conversation on driving behaviors, particularly between parents and teens, and create a safer driving environment for all.

Looking Down the Road at Iowa Transportation Needs

One hundred years ago Iowa's citizens preferred modes of travel were the passenger train, animal-powered wagons, or walking. Automobiles were only available for the privileged few. By the middle of the 20th century, the car was king, passenger rail travel had all but disappeared, and the built infrastructure became less pedestrian-friendly.

In recent decades, Iowans have been looking for alternatives to individual automobiles. Further, as we continue to live longer, healthier, active lives, we need other mobility solutions. All 99 Iowa counties, we are proud to note, are served by mass transit. Iowa has a love for the bicycle going back to the late 1800s, evidenced by the four decades of the Registers Annual Great Bike Ride Across Iowa (RAGBRAI), and continuing into our Rails to Trails conversions. Iowa is now home to more than 1,700 miles of bicycle and multi-use trails, with that number set to grow for years to come.

Over the past 100 years, through hard work, good engineering, and constant innovation the Iowa DOT and its employees have built a transportation infrastructure that has come to touch nearly every aspect of life, leisure, and commerce in Iowa.

Once again we congratulate AASHTO on its 100th anniversary. We look forward to working and innovating together with you over the next 100 years.

KANSAS

Kansas Department of Transportation

Mike King
Secretary

YEAR FORMED **1929**

FTE **Approximately 2,790**

KEY FACTS
TOTAL PUBLIC ROAD
MILES **10,338**

STATE-OWNED BRIDGES **4,976**

TRANSIT TRIPS PER YEAR
7.5 million

RECENT HIGHLIGHTS:

– T-WORKS transportation funding
program (10 years) passed in 2010

– Kansas Turnpike Authority, the
state's only tolling agency, placed
under the direction of the Secretary
of Transportation in 2013

– First major design-build project
begins in 2014

Kansans Committed to World-Class Transportation

Over the past quarter century, Kansans may be unmatched in their commitment to improving transportation.

In 1989, when the majority of the state's highways were in poor condition, Kansans and their leaders made the difficult decision to change that. The Kansas Legislature passed the Comprehensive Highway Program (CHP) and by the end of the program eight years later, 80 percent of the state's 10,000-mile highway system was in good condition.

The program's success demonstrated the safety and economic benefits of investing in transportation. And today, Kansas is in the midst of its third consecutive major funding program. The state consistently places high in rankings of state road systems, and, in 2010, a *Reader's Digest* magazine study rated the Kansas system the nation's best.

While the rankings provide outside validation, Kansans already know that a well-maintained, multi-modal transportation network is good for their families and economy, and it positions the state to compete in a global economy.

Without a doubt, the three programs have enhanced the quality of life of Kansans and, in short, have made Kansas a better place to live.

A *Very* Brief History

A successful 21st century Kansas is rooted in an early recognition that economic growth is inextricably linked to efficiently moving people and goods from one point to another.

While the state's earliest inhabitants traveled by foot on primitive trails or took out across the vast prairie itself, the early settlers of the 19th century moved through Kansas on a series of corridors such as the Santa Fe Trail, Oregon Trail, California Trail, and many others. In time, the extension of the nation's rail system into the heartland helped the state grow and develop into one of the world's great producers of wheat. Some ventures, such as the Pony Express, have survived more as romantic notions than practical solutions to cover long distances in as little time as possible. Route 66, the highway from Chicago to Los Angeles that captured the imagination of Americans, stretched only a few miles through the state but is fondly remembered and commemorated in Southeast Kansas today.

Kansas' early leaders who divided the state into 105 counties recognized that an extensive road network was necessary to connect farmers and ranchers to points from which they could get their products to market. That, along with the fact that there are few geographic barriers to building roads, left a legacy of some 140,000 miles of streets, roads and highways in Kansas today—the nation's third largest public roads network.

As the number of automobiles continued to grow nationally and in Kansas in the early 20th century, there became a necessity for roads that could be navigated in all weather conditions. By 1936, there were nearly 8,000 miles of hard-surface roads in the state. A national road-building milestone was achieved in 1956 when Kansas became the first state to open a section of interstate highway.

While automobiles and trains were the predominate forms of transportation in early 20th century Kansas, an aviation industry was developing in Wichita. Successful Wichita companies including Beechcraft, Cessna, and Stearman, and later Boeing, Learjet, and Spirit AeroSystems, led to the city becoming known as the "Air Capital of the World."

T-WORKS
When the Kansas Legislature passed the 10-year funding program Transportation Works for Kansas (T-WORKS) in the spring of 2010, it not only made a commitment to preserve and improve the state's transportation system, it committed to jobs for Kansans as well.

3 Decades of Commitment
The Kansas Legislature has authorized three major transportation funding programs since 1989. Below are the construction-only dollars.

Comprehensive Highway Program
1989–1997
$3.1 billion

Comprehensive Transportation Program
1999–2009
$5.6 billion

T-WORKS
2010–2020
$6 billion

T-WORKS, the third major transportation program passed in Kansas since 1989, includes $2.7 billion in new revenues over 10 years. It is expected to create or sustain 175,000 jobs during that time.

T-WORKS' primary areas of focus are:
- Preservation of the highway system.
- A multi-modal approach to meeting the state's transportation needs.
- Strategic leveraging of transportation funds to further the state's economic goals.

Project Selection
One of the most significant changes to Kansas transportation under T-WORKS is how major projects are selected. Under the 1989 and 1999 programs, project selection was based mainly on engineering factors. Under T-WORKS, the economic impact of a project and local input become considerations, as well.

Preservation and Modes
Under T-WORKS, 100 percent of the state highway system's preservation needs are met. In addition, investment in transit, aviation, and rail is increased. And at least $8 million is invested in each of the state's 105 counties during the program.

Economic Development
Transportation creates jobs and stimulates the economy of Kansas in both the short and long term. During construction, there are construction jobs and increased spending in local businesses.

In the long run, improvements make it possible for companies to locate or expand in the state, creating more jobs.

During the 1989 Comprehensive Highway Program, more than 117,000 jobs were created or sustained at a time when Kansas badly needed them. In 1992, just three years into the program, *U.S. News & World Report* published an article commending Kansas for having a transportation program that did not bust the state's budget:

"Anyone who doubts that infrastructure spending can jump-start an economy should visit the Jayhawk State, where a highway program has created 3,400 construction jobs since August 1991 and helped trim the unemployment rate to 4 percent, fourth-lowest in the nation."

For the first time, under the 2010 T-WORKS program, economic impact was used as one of the criteria in the selection of major expansion projects. Kansas Department of Transportation (KDOT) analysts used an economic modeling tool to estimate the economic impact of each project proposal. Over the course of the T-WORKS program, the $1.8 billion invested in expansion and modernization projects is estimated to have a long-term economic impact of $10 billion.

The agency also restructured its economic development program, which provides smaller awards to communities for transportation projects tied to economic opportunities. The changes allow program managers to make quicker, more strategic decisions when business opportunities emerge. As the program designers said, the program changes give a government agency the ability to make funding decisions "at the speed of business."

Safety
Underlying all of KDOT's work is one central concern: the safety of travelers. That concern is reflected in the projects, initiatives and legislation the agency has advanced over the years to reduce traffic fatalities and injuries.

KDOT has improved hills, curves, roadside safety, and upgraded two-lane roads to multilane roads, improving safety and mobility throughout the state.

Kansas has seen improvement in every category of seat belt usage and child safety protection; texting is no longer allowed while behind the wheel; and a comprehensive graduated driver's licensing law is in place. Annual safety campaigns address occupant protection, distracted driving, impaired driving and work zone safety.

KDOT provides funds to the Kansas Highway Patrol (KHP) and local law enforcement agencies to conduct sobriety checkpoints and saturation patrols. The KHP is paid to provide extra patrolling in selected work zones on heavily-traveled roads.

Though drivers traveling at 60 miles per hour may not think about it, there are many safety features engineered into every highway in the state. The use of rumble strips is becoming a standard feature on certain categories of road; hundreds of miles of shoulders have been improved and widened under the state's three consecutive funding programs; and intelligent transportation systems have allowed traffic experts to manage the flow of vehicles in heavily travelled areas. Advance traveler information can be obtained by phone, Internet and social media, and dynamic message signs along the roadside provide important information to drivers that improve the flow of traffic and enhance safety.

The improvements and initiatives have spared untold numbers of families the heartbreak of disabling injuries and deaths due to traffic crashes. A general downward trend in fatalities since the latter part of the 20th century led to an all-time low in fatalities (349) in 2013.

Multi-Modal Approach
While roads will probably always be the king in Kansas transportation, other modes of transportation play an important role in the development of the state and are increasingly important to the health and well-being of Kansans.

Railroads helped open Kansas and the West to development and today they are essential to the success of Kansas in the global marketplace. Class I railroads such as BNSF Railway and the Union Pacific Railroad carry Kansas grain and other products to ports for shipping throughout the world. Vital to Kansas farmers are some 2,000 miles of short line rail—about 40 percent of the nearly 4,800 miles of rail in the state. Since 2000, millions of dollars have been invested in the Rail Rehabilitation Program to improve more than a thousand miles of short line track. The development of Logistics Park Kansas City Intermodal Facility by BNSF in eastern Kansas will help to accommodate the growing demands of multi-modal freight rail transportation in the Kansas City region and throughout the Midwest.

State investment in aviation since 2000 has funded more than 400 projects at the state's 140 public use airports. The projects have improved safety and generated new economic development opportunities for communities. Thanks to investments made during the 10-year 1999 Comprehensive Transportation Program, the average condition of Kansas runways improved from fair to very good, giving most communities ready access to air ambulance services for the first time. Runway and general conditions at all the state airports have been improved to the point that new projects under the current T-WORKS program will be selected on how they fit into the strategic plan for the Kansas aviation network. Kansas airports annually support more than 47,000 jobs, generate $2.3 billion in payroll and produce $10.4 billion in economic activity.

During the 10-year, 1999 Comprehensive Transportation Program, KDOT's transit program went from providing 2 million rides to 8 million rides a year. For some Kansans, public transportation provides an environmentally friendly and cost-effective way to get to work. For others, it is the only means by which they can access medical care, trips to the store, and reach other vital services. As the state's rural population ages, transit allows older Kansans to remain independent and involved in their communities. Because not every county in Kansas has transit service, KDOT has implemented a regional transit approach to expand and improve delivery of rural transit service.

Vital to that approach is the effort to increase coordination between transit providers and increase the efficiency of the transit network in Kansas. Investment in transit has increased by 90 percent under the 2010 T-WORKS funding program.

Kansas Turnpike Authority

There is a well-known 1956 *Life* magazine photo that shows the just-completed Kansas Turnpike coming to an abrupt end at an Oklahoma oat field. The skeptics who dubbed Kansas' first and only toll road a "Super Cow Trail" were probably feeling smug when they saw the photo. But, not surprisingly, they did not get the last laugh.

Oklahoma eventually allocated the money to connect to the 236-mile Kansas road that now comprises sections of Interstates 35, 335, and 70. The turnpike, which one legislator has called the "crown jewel" of the Kansas highway system, links the state's aviation center in Wichita, the state capital in Topeka and the state's economic center in Kansas City. Sixty-one percent of the state's population lives within 20 miles of the Kansas Turnpike, and there are 94,000 businesses and 770,000 employees in the corridor.

Kansas Turnpike
Length
236 miles from Kansas City to the Oklahoma border south of Wichita

Traffic (2013)
36 million vehicles

Net Toll Revenue (2012)
$87.5 million

Opened to Traffic
October 25, 1956

Average Passenger Trip
38 miles

Average Commercial Trip
63 miles

When the turnpike was proposed in the early 1950s, there was pushback from rural and western Kansas legislators who did not think their constituents should have to pay for a highway they would seldom use. Out of political necessity, the road was proposed as a privately-funded, no-tax-revenue toll road. That helped push through the authorizing legislation in 1953. For about $160 million, the road was constructed beginning in 1954 and opened in only 22 months.

While the Kansas Turnpike Authority (KTA) and KDOT partnered on projects over the years, they had no formal operational relationship. But eventually, at the urging of Governor Sam Brownback, there was legislative support to formalize the partnership. In 2013, Kansas lawmakers passed a bill to make the Secretary of Transportation the director of the Kansas Turnpike Authority. Creating a single voice for transportation creates consistency, operational efficiency and resource sharing, which will produce savings and more service for every toll and tax dollar.

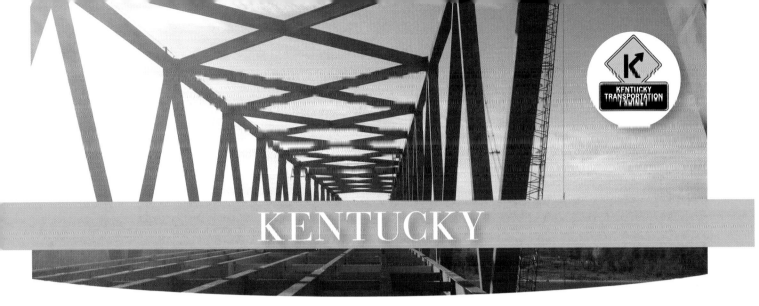

KENTUCKY

Kentucky Transportation Cabinet

Michael W. Hancock, P.E.
Secretary

YEAR FORMED **1912**

FTE **Approx. 4,730**

KEY FACTS:
TOTAL STATE ROAD MILES (OWNED BY STATE HIGHWAY AGENCY) **27,625**

STATE-OWNED BRIDGES **8,975**

TRANSIT TRIPS PER YEAR **25.49 million**

Originally known as the Department of Public Roads, Kentucky's transportation agency was a founding member of AASHTO. The Kentucky Transportation Cabinet (KYTC) celebrated its centennial in 2012 and has now embarked on a second century of service.

Since AASHTO's 75th anniversary report, a number of innovative and large-scale transportation projects have been undertaken—reinforcing KYTC's mission of providing a safe, efficient, environmentally sound, and fiscally responsible transportation system. Some highlights:

1991
- Construction of the Cumberland Gap Tunnel began on June 21. The tunnel carries US 25E under the Cumberland Gap National Historical Park at the Kentucky, Tennessee, and Virginia borders.
- Two 4,600-foot tunnels were simultaneously bored from both sides of the mountain. The tunnels linked-up on July 9, 1992.
- The $285 million project opened to traffic on October 18, 1996.

1993
- Reconstruction of the Clay's Ferry Bridge, which carries I-75 high above the Kentucky River, began.
- The $32 million replacement project is completed in 1998.

1996
- The first section of the project to widen Paris Pike, an icon of central Kentucky's famed thoroughbred farms, is let to construction. Widening 12.5 miles of US 27/US 68 between Lexington and Paris from two to four lanes poses a number of challenges due to the many farms and historic features along the route.
- The $69 million dollar project is completed in 2003. The project was a case study for Context Sensitive Design issues.

1997
- Construction on the William H. Harsha Bridge—Kentucky's first cable stayed bridge—began in April.
- The 2,108-foot-long bridge connects Maysville, Ky., and Aberdeen, Ohio.
- The $37 million structure was dedicated on October 9, 2000.

1998
- Construction on the William H. Natcher Bridge at Owensboro began in January.
- The 4,505-foot-long bridge costs $55.5 million and opened to traffic on October 21, 2002.

- In 2002, the Natcher Bridge was named one of the top 10 bridges in America by *Roads and Bridges Magazine*.

1999
- US 23, the first and only four-lane roadway from state line to state line in Eastern Kentucky, is completed in October.

2003
- The FHWA issues a Record of Decision approving construction of two new Ohio River bridges linking Louisville and Southern Indiana, and reconstructing the Kennedy interchange, where I-65, I-71, and I-64 converge near downtown Louisville.
- Ground is broken for the $2.3 billion project in 2013.

2011
- A 38-mile section of the Western Kentucky Parkway, together with 17 miles of Interstate 24, was designated Interstate 69—Kentucky's newest Interstate highway. Eventually I-69 will extend from the Ohio River at Henderson to the Tennessee border at Fulton.

2012
- A 322-foot span of the Eggners Ferry Bridge on Kentucky Lake was destroyed when the bridge is struck

by a large cargo vessel.
- The bridge, which carried US 68 and Kentucky 80 is repaired and reopens to traffic in 121 days.
- The US 68 Double Crossover Diamond interchange in Lexington won the Mid-America Region Innovation/Small Project category of the 2012 America's Transportation Awards competition.
- The $5.5 million project transformed a congestion-prone interchange on one of Lexington's busiest thoroughfares into a modern interchange with improved traffic flow and safety.

2013
- KYTC received a Project Preservation Award for its role in the Rockcastle River Bridge rehabilitation.
- The bridge, which carries KY 490 between Laurel and Rockcastle counties, is a Pennsylvania Petit Steel Truss structure.
- The 205-foot-long bridge was originally designated for replacement, but an area resident championed its restoration.
- Once it was determined that the bridge would meet present and future needs of the routes it served, the structure was cleaned of old paint, failed steel was replaced, and the bridge was repainted.
- The cost of rehabbing the Rockcastle

River Bridge was $465,000—far less than the estimated $1.8 million cost of replacement.
- The award-winning Rockcastle River Bridge project illustrates KYTC's efforts to maintain Kentucky's historical structures while minimizing costs.

2014
- Replacement of the Milton-Madison Bridge, which carries US 421 between Milton, Kentucky, and Madison, Indiana, is completed.
- The original 84-year-old bridge truss was demolished and the existing piers were strengthened and reused.
- A new 2,400-foot-long bridge was slid from temporary piers to the original piers.
- This innovative multi-step process of bridge replacement has allowed the Milton-Madison Bridge to remain open during construction.
- Otherwise, Kentucky and Indiana may have been without a US 421 bridge for more than a year.
- The Milton–Madison Bridge Project has received numerous awards, including being named one of the top 10 bridge projects in the country for 2012 by *Roads & Bridges Magazine*.

LOUISIANA

Louisiana Department of Transportation and Development

Sherri LeBas, P.E.
Secretary

YEAR FORMED **1921**

FTE **3,791**

KEY FACTS
TOTAL STATE ROAD MILES (OWNED BY STATE HIGHWAY AGENCY) **16,694**

STATE-OWNED BRIDGES **7,877**

TRANSIT TRIPS PER YEAR **35.47 million**

The traveling public of Louisiana has seen many advancements to Louisiana's infrastructure since the Louisiana Highway Commission was established in 1921 under Gov. John M. Parker, who was pushing for more gravel roads throughout the state.

Since that time, the Louisiana Department of Transportation and Development (DOTD) has moved well past the days of gravel works. DOTD has been committed to delivering transportation and public works systems that enhance the quality of life and facilitate economic growth. In addition to more than 16,600 miles of roadway, including over 930 miles of interstate and 13,000 bridges, DOTD supports the development of the state's aviation, marine, port, public transportation, and rail infrastructures. Through this work, we are able to facilitate economic development, create job opportunities, improve vital evacuation routes, and make critical freight corridors safer and more efficient.

Through work aimed at recovery efforts from Hurricanes Katrina and Rita, and programs such as Transportation Infrastructure Model for Economic Development, Geaux Wider and the ongoing construction of the I-49 corridor, DOTD has undertaken numerous and varied projects for improving Louisiana's infrastructure and creating opportunities for economic development.

Construction of the Interstate Highway System in Louisiana began in 1957. By the spring of 1975, I-10 had been opened across Louisiana, with the exception of a 5.5-mile section between Gonzales and Sorrento that was not completed for another three years. The current configuration of I-12, from Baton Rouge to Slidell, was also completed in the 1970s. Construction of I-49 between Lafayette and Shreveport commenced in the early 1980s, and was opened in the mid-90s.

Today, the efforts to improve travel in Louisiana continue with interstate expansion across the state, including the advancement of I-49 projects along with the widening of I-10 and I-12 in the Baton Rouge area.

I-49 North and South
I-49 North
The entire I-49 North project spans 36 miles from north of Shreveport to the Arkansas border. The completion of this corridor will open a vital north–south connector, helping goods to move more quickly across the country and statewide. Currently, 28.9 miles are

completed and open to drivers, and another 10 miles were opened to local traffic in March 2014. The remaining northern sections will open when Arkansas completes their portion of I-49.

DOTD broke ground on the first I-49 North project in Fall 2006. Since then, four segments have been completed, and six others are under construction. The $670 million project is estimated for completion in 2016/2017.

I-49 South

The I-49 South project will convert US 90 from Lafayette to New Orleans into an interstate-quality roadway enhancing travel between the two cities, and ultimately statewide and nationwide once the project is completed. The total I-49 South corridor includes approximately 160 miles of roadway, of which more than 100 miles have been completed or are currently under construction.

Once complete, the extension of I-49 will provide:

- A direct access of Midwest industries to the ports of south Louisiana
- A bypass around Baton Rouge for traffic on I-10
- A connection between oil industry suppliers and manufacturers from New Orleans to Houston.

In early 2014, DOTD announced a $57.1 million contract for a design-build project to widen a two-mile segment of I-49 South from north of Ambassador Caffery Parkway to Albertsons Parkway in Lafayette Parish. The project is expected to be complete in early 2017.

Geaux Wider

The $341 million Geaux Wider Program is a multi-year construction initiative designed to increase capacity, improve safety and enhance mobility along a combined total of over 20 miles of Interstates 10 and 12 in East Baton Rouge and Livingston parishes. Under the program to date, six interstate segments will be widened from four to six lanes.

To date, five segments have been completed and one is underway. Work on current projects in the Geaux Wider Program began in January 2009, with completion scheduled for March 2015.

TIMED

The Transportation Infrastructure Model for Economic Development (TIMED) Program is the single largest transportation infrastructure improvement program in Louisiana's history. Projects in the $5.2 billion program included

widening 536 miles of state highways, constructing the John James Audubon Bridge over the Mississippi Bridge, and widening the Huey P. Long Bridge over the Mississippi River in Jefferson Parish. It also included improvements to both the Port of New Orleans and Louis Armstrong International Airport. The program was funded with a dedicated four-cents-per-gallon gas tax approved in 1989 by the State Legislature and voters.

The widened roadways, new bridges, and expanded ports created by the Louisiana TIMED Program benefit the residents of Louisiana by creating economic development opportunities for business, improving vital evacuation routes, and making critical freight corridors safer and more efficient.

The $1.2 billion Huey P. Long Bridge Widening Project was completed in June 2013, approximately four months ahead of schedule. Expansion of the 1930s era bridge began in April 2006, shortly after Hurricane Katrina and is the largest transportation construction project in the history of Louisiana. The widening project expanded the bridge to three lanes in each direction with shoulders, and more than doubled the driving surfaces from 18 feet wide to 43 feet wide.

The completed bridge is able to carry over 100,000 vehicles per day, more than twice the amount of traffic as it could prior to the widening. This increased capacity makes it a greatly improved evacuation route in emergency situations like hurricanes and flooding.

The John James Audubon Bridge is the longest cable-stayed bridge in the Western Hemisphere and is also the first design-build project undertaken by the department. The new Mississippi River bridge includes almost 12 miles of new roadways and connects Point Coupee and West Feliciana parishes.

Construction on the $409 million bridge began in May 2006. DOTD expedited the opening of the new bridge in May 2011 due to flooding on the Mississippi River. The new bridge improves freight and commerce efficiency for major industries.

Recovery Efforts from Hurricane Katrina

Hurricane Katrina (followed by Hurricane Rita a few weeks later) remains the most costly natural disaster in United States history and one of the five deadliest hurricanes to ever strike the nation. Since 2005, DOTD and the State of Louisiana have overcome unprecedented challenges in the rebuilding and reconstruction of the South Louisiana region. Through programs such as Submerged Roads, Paths to Progress, and construction of the I-10 Twin Spans Bridge, DOTD has taken an active role in rebuilding the region's infrastructure.

Twin Span Bridge

In August 2005, the I–10 Twin Span Bridge, comprised of two parallel

structures spanning Lake Pontchartrain between New Orleans and Slidell, was severely damaged by storm surge. Damage assessment teams from DOTD, supported by consultants, went to work as soon as the winds began to subside. Temporary repairs restored two lanes of traffic (one eastbound and one westbound) within 46 days of the storm, and within 130 days of the storm, additional repairs opened the damaged bridge to four travel lanes.

Work began in August 2006 to build a new Twin Span Bridge. With a total price tag of over $800 million and fully funded by the Federal Highway Administration, the new bridge is one of the largest public works projects in Louisiana history.

The new bridge replaces a four-lane structure (two eastbound and two westbound travel lanes) that was placed in service in 1965. Taller, wider, and more robust than its predecessor, it stands 30 feet above the water and includes a high-rise navigational segment that provides 80 feet of vertical clearance for marine traffic. The mainline sections of the bridge are 21 feet taller than the original Twin Span Bridge, making it less vulnerable to storm surge in the event of a future hurricane.

Additionally, designed for a 100-year lifespan, it is the first bridge in Louisiana constructed of high-performance concrete that's stronger, denser, and less porous than typical concrete, making it more resistant to saltwater-induced corrosion. The bridge features reinforced concrete walls, which act as saddles to prevent the bridge girders from moving laterally. They also increase the bridge's ability to

withstand both storm surge and marine vessel collisions.

The new Twin Span Bridge includes an electrical power system and state-of-the-art fiber optic technology to support Intelligent Transportation System (ITS) tools such as video cameras and dynamic message boards. The ITS tools allow DOTD personnel to rapidly and efficiently monitor and manage traffic conditions on the bridge.

Submerged Roads and Paths to Progress

The $118 million South Louisiana Submerged Roads Program is a comprehensive road rehabilitation program that repaired and resurfaced more than 50 roadway segments damaged as a result of Hurricanes Katrina and Rita. Many of the roadways were submerged in storm water for weeks and were then used as major haul routes for post-storm recovery operations.

The program, which began in July 2007 and was completed in March 2012, was funded by the Emergency Relief Program of the Federal Highway Administration, and administered by the DOTD.

Paths to Progress, which began in April 2012, is a transportation improvement program that continued the work that began with under the Submerged Roads Program. With a combined investment of over $90 million, the program is in the process of rehabilitating, restoring and enhancing more than 60 roadway segments in Orleans and Jefferson parishes. It is a collaborative effort between the Federal Highway Administration, DOTD, New Orleans Regional Planning Commission (i.e., the MPO), and the City of New Orleans.

La. 1 Expressway

The La. 1 corridor through Port Fourchon services approximately 18 percent of the nation's entire supply of oil and natural gas. It serves as the sole evacuation route for lower Lafourche Parish and the barrier island of Grand Isle, and is also the only access route to Port Fourchon, the nation's premier intermodal energy port, and the Louisiana Offshore Oil Port, the nation's only offshore oil port.

This area of our state's sensitive wetlands has been featured nationally as being the victim of coastal erosion and ground subsidence, with portions of the La. 1 highway literally sinking. Each year, tropical storms pose more of a threat to this highway, which is often flooded in low-level storms, and strands many of our coastal residents, tourists and oil industry workers in Port Fourchon as it's a primary access to Gulf operations.

To date, in order to prevent flooding, DOTD has completed three projects to elevate the lowest part of La. 1 from the Gulf of Mexico to Port Fourchon in Leeville. These projects will eventually be part of the La. 1 Expressway, a 19-mile elevated road from Golden Meadow to the Gulf of Mexico.

The 4.4-mile La. 1 Bridge over Bayou Lafourche at Leeville was completed in July 2009 at a cost of $161 million. This fixed-span, high-level two-lane bridge replaced the old La. 1 moveable bridge.

The $137.5 million La. 1 Expressway from the Gulf to Leeville was completed in December 2011. The 5.4-mile project built a two-lane elevated highway to replace the previous La. 1.

This project has vastly improved access and safety for the residents and industry partners in lower Lafourche Parish and the barrier island of Grand Isle. In addition, they have ensured the continued national economic significance and regional viability of La. 1.

Intermodal

DOTD's Intermodal Division consists of Aviation, Ports, Marine and Rail, and Public Transit, and includes over 580 active projects. The Aviation Section averages over 150 active projects at any one time and serves Louisiana's 69 airports, conducting annual airport and heliport safety inspections at 74 public-use facilities and over 780 private-use facilities around the state. The Ports Section averages about 30 active projects at any given time, using funds from the Ports Priority Program. DOTD's Marine and Rail Section continues to work very closely with the ports, Corps of Engineers, and Congressional Delegation on some very significant projects, such as the deepening of the Mississippi River to 50 feet. Through the Public Transit Section, DOTD provides approximately $16.6 million in funding each year to support 155 transit agencies and eight Metropolitan Planning Organizations' public transportation efforts.

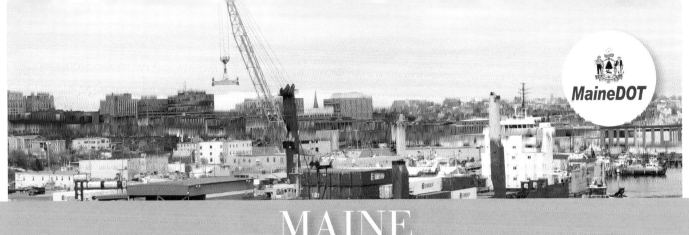

MAINE

Maine Department of Transportation

David Bernhardt, P.E.
Commissioner

YEAR FORMED **1913**

FTE **Approx. 2,100**

KEY FACTS
TOTAL STATE ROAD MILES
(OWNED BY STATE HIGHWAY
AGENCY) **8,393**

STATE-OWNED BRIDGES **1,965**

TRANSIT TRIPS PER YEAR
4.62 million

RECENT HIGHLIGHTS
– Downeaster Expansion

MaineDOT History

More than 100 years ago, in 1913, the Maine State Legislature created the three-member Maine State Highway Commission. The Commission was charged with building a "system of connected main highways throughout the state." This ambitious endeavor was undertaken by the Commission's 12 employees—a chief engineer, five assistant engineers, four stenographers, an accountant and a book keeper. In 1913, the revenue from auto registration and driver license fees, established two years earlier, were used to finance the first highway bond issued for $2 million.

One of the most transformative programs for Maine travel was the evolution of an efficient snow and ice control plan. Serious interest in keeping Maine roads open all winter began in the 1920s. Until that time, motorists jacked up the family car after the first snowfall and impatiently waited for the season to end. During the winter of 1925–1926, an effort was made to keep the road open from Kittery to Bangor. A committee was formed to organize this work and solicit funds from municipalities that were unable to undertake this responsibility.

As the department's fleet of snow fighting equipment grew, procedures were developed to keep Maine roads safe and passable. In 1953–54, a "night patrol" was established to monitor road conditions and report back to headquarters via radio. Today, MaineDOT boasts 400 plow trucks plowing 8,300 lane-miles of road during Maine's rugged winter months.

In 1972, the Maine Department of Transportation (MaineDOT) was established by the Maine State Legislature. MaineDOT retained the Maine State Highway Commission's responsibilities for highways and bridges, but it assumed added responsibilities for air, rail, public transportation, ports, and marine transportation including operation of the Maine State Ferry Service.

The 1980s were marked by the completion of Maine's 365-mile interstate system including 312 miles of I-95 and shorter sections of I-195, I-295, I-395, and the designation of part of the independent Maine Turnpike as I-495.

In 1991, Maine voters decided not to widen the Maine Turnpike and to establish the Maine Sensible Transportation Policy Act, significantly changing the way MaineDOT approaches major

capital improvement projects. The act provides grass-roots advisory group input in the department's process for planning future transportation improvements and places additional emphasis on the examination on non-highway alternatives for solving transportation problems.

The Northern New England Passenger Rail Authority was formed in 1995 to support ongoing MaineDOT efforts to bring Amtrak passenger service to Maine. In 2014, Amtrak has six stations in Maine, providing daily service between Boston and Brunswick.

With more than 3,500 miles of rocky coast, MaineDOT recognized the state's location provides strategic value in an emerging global economy. In the late 1970s, it adopted a "three-port strategy" which preserves coastal resources while encouraging needed cargo port development. Over the years, MaineDOT has invested significantly in each of the three ports to help promote this growth. In Eastport, a $20 million facility was completed in 1998. In Searsport, a $20 million public–private partnership investment resulted in a new terminal being completed in 2003. And in Portland, improvements to the International Marine Terminal, such as the purchase

of a new container crane and additional land, resulted in recruitment of Iceland's largest steamship line, Eimskip, in 2013. It is the first new container service between Europe and Maine since the 1980s. As a result, MaineDOT is further expanding the shipping-container terminal to more than double its current size and linking it directly with a rail line, allowing Portland's terminal to be even more competitive.

MaineDOT also serves as a vital link to Maine island residents as well as tourists. The new Rockland Ferry Terminal opened in 1996 and, today, MaineDOT manages seven ferry boats.

In 1997, MaineDOT's first website went "on line." Now the website serves as an essential communications resource, along with social media like Facebook and Twitter.

Challenges Along the Way
Waldo-Hancock Bridge and the Penobscot Narrows Bridge and Observatory
Built in 1930–1931, the Waldo Hancock Bridge, was designed to carry the increasing numbers of northbound travelers on the coastal Route 1 and connect inland Maine with the international maritime trade along the

coast. Designed by David B. Steinman of New York, the suspension bridge soon became a historical and economic landmark as word of the magnificent steel structure began to spread. Visitors from across the state and New England came to admire the engineering marvel which fostered the growth of tourism in the region.

In 2003, MaineDOT was partway through a major rehabilitation of the historic 71-year-old bridge when engineers discovered severe corrosion of the cables, previously hidden by protective sheathing. Engineers agreed the cables were too corroded to save and the bridge would need to be replaced as soon as possible.

During Fall 2003, community workshop participants suggested a "granite" theme to honor Maine's rugged, no-nonsense nature and the local quarry which had provided some of the stone used in the Washington Monument. This led to the idea of modeling the main support towers of the new bridge after the shape of the monument, even including an observatory on the top to enjoy the magnificent 360-degree views. The community quickly realized the tourism appeal of this concept and supported the overall

design of the bridge, despite their long term love and sentiment for the earlier structure. MaineDOT broke ground for the new bridge in December 2003. And so began an unprecedented partnership—among MaineDOT, Figg Engineering Group, and Cianbro/Reed & Reed LLC—which rose to the challenge of building a unique $85 million bridge in record-breaking time. Most bridge projects of this magnitude take at least a decade to plan and construct. But the Penobscot Narrows Bridge and Observatory took just 42 months to complete from concept to opening.

The Penobscot Narrows Bridge is one of only four bridges in the world with an observatory at the top of the pylon. The observatory, at 420-feet elevation, is the tallest occupied structure in Maine and the highest bridge observatory in the world. The structure has won multiple awards and draws residents and tourists from around the world to enjoy the spectacular view.

Full Closure of I-295

When MaineDOT announced a bold strategy to close southbound lanes of an 18-mile stretch of I-295 during the height of Maine's $10 billion tourism season, the public and media outcry was swift and strong. The busy segment of concrete highway is an integral part of I-295 which stretches between Portland, Maine's largest city, and Augusta, the capital city. MaineDOT determined the full closure was the safest, most efficient and cost-effective way to rehabilitate the crumbling highway. This was an unprecedented full-road closure that spanned the summer of 2008 during the height of the summer tourist season. The ambitious project included putting down 181,000 tons of asphalt, rebuilding five bridges and installing seven miles of guardrail.

A significant media and community outreach campaign was undertaken to reach residents, visitors, local businesses, and others to address concerns and drastically change their perceptions. More than 200 articles and comprehensive broadcast segments helped changed the tone from negative and wary, to positive and supportive. The project was completed 20 days ahead of schedule thanks to 16-hour workdays and a 7-day-a-week schedule including holidays. There were no injuries on the job site and no reported crashes along the busy detour route.

In addition to winning national and state communication awards, the project received accolades in national trade publications including the magazines *Roads & Bridges*, *New England Construction*, and *Hot Mix Asphalt Technology*. Because of the success of the 2008 project, the department undertook the same work heading northbound in 2009.

Today's MaineDOT may surprise the 1913 three-member Maine State Highway Commission. The first female chief engineer, Joyce Taylor, was appointed by Commissioner Bernhardt in 2013. Unimaginable technologies enhance today's public outreach, signage, planning and snow fighting capabilities. The department employs 1,900 individuals, and is responsible for nearly 8,900 miles of state highway, more than 2,900 bridges, three seaports, and 553 miles of state owned track.

Yet MaineDOT's core values of integrity, competence, and service combined with its mission "to responsibly provide our customers the safest, most reliable transportation system possible, given available resources" would likely still ring true to the highway commissioners of 100 years ago.

MARYLAND

Maryland Department of Transportation

James T. Smith, Jr.
Secretary

YEAR FORMED **1971**

FTE **Approx. 8,129**

KEY FACTS
TOTAL STATE ROAD MILES
(OWNED BY STATE HIGHWAY
AGENCY) **5,160**

STATE-OWNED BRIDGES **2,560**

TRANSIT TRIPS PER YEAR
144.8 million

Maryland's transportation system is vital to the productivity and economic competitiveness of the state, as well as an important part in supporting the high quality of life enjoyed by Maryland residents. The importance of a strong transportation network was evident as early as 1666 when Maryland's first road law was enacted to create roads passable by horse and foot. Over the next 300 years, Maryland's transportation system grew to encompass distinct agencies responsible for aviation, highway, marine, mass transit, motor vehicle, railroad, and toll facilities. In 1971, the Maryland Department of Transportation (MDOT) was formed to consolidate these independent state agencies into one cohesive organization to facilitate the safe and efficient movement of people, goods, and services across multiple transportation modes throughout the state. This consolidated approach required a unique funding mechanism and thus, the Transportation Trust Fund was established to support all operating and capital programs for all modes of transportation.

Today, MDOT consists of a headquarters unit and six modal administrations, including: the Maryland Aviation Administration; the Maryland Port Administration; the Maryland Transit Administration; the Motor Vehicle Administration; the Maryland Transportation Authority; and the State Highway Administration. MDOT also is home to the Office of Minority Business Enterprise, which is the official certification agency of the State of Maryland. Firms meeting the standards set forth in state and federal law are eligible for Minority Business Enterprise, Disadvantaged Business Enterprise, Small Business Enterprise and/or Airport Concessions Disadvantaged Business Enterprise certification. With 9,000 employees, MDOT works closely with citizens, elected officials, businesses, communities, governmental agencies and stakeholders to ensure that transportation investments move the state's economy forward by creating jobs and expanding opportunity for all Marylanders.

At the national level, Maryland is one of the few states to include all transportation modes under a centralized department with a consolidated funding approach, which makes it possible to quickly deploy resources to meet Maryland's diverse transportation needs. Transportation revenues are allocated throughout MDOT and applied to areas where the greatest needs exist. The department's six-year Consolidated Transportation Program addresses all

revenues and modal administrations' priorities and provides the basis for funding decisions. Maryland's ability to address unmet transportation needs was greatly enhanced in 2013 thanks to the leadership of Governor Martin O'Malley, Lieutenant Governor Anthony Brown, Maryland Senate President Thomas V. "Mike" Miller, Jr., Maryland House Speaker Michael E. Busch, and members of the Maryland General Assembly in passing the Transportation Infrastructure Investment Act of 2013. In the next six years alone, this act will provide $4.4 billion in new projects that will make a real difference in the state's economic competitiveness by rebuilding and expanding Maryland's interconnected transportation network. It also will provide a sustainable transportation funding source for years to come.

Along with the passage of that act, Maryland also passed a Public–Private Partnership (P3) law in 2013 to create an enhanced framework for future P3s that will attract private investment to help build new infrastructure. Championed by Lieutenant Governor Brown and signed into law by Governor O'Malley on April 9, 2013, the new legislation provides the private sector with a stronger, more predictable and streamlined process, protects public assets, ensures a

strong workforce, requires competitive bidding for all projects, and allows the private sector to submit new unsolicited concepts to address Maryland's infrastructure needs. MDOT has successfully completed two P3 projects, including an agreement with Ports America Chesapeake to enlarge the Seagirt Marine Terminal at the Port of Baltimore to attract some of the largest cargo container ships in the world. Under the agreement, Ports America Chesapeake funded the construction of a new 50-foot deep container berth and four supersized cranes that are needed to handle the very large ships. Another P3 has provided for the design and reconstruction of two Maryland Travel Plazas along the heavily-traveled I-95 corridor. With regulations in place, MDOT is pursuing an innovative P3 approach for the Purple Line, a new light rail transit line in the Washington, D.C. region, by soliciting a single private partner who will be responsible for designing, constructing, operating, maintaining, and providing a portion of the financing for the project.

As Maryland embarks on a new era in transportation resurgence and innovation, the men and women of MDOT look forward to building a safe, modern, interconnected transportation system, while being ever mindful of our re-

sponsibility to protect and preserve the environment.

MDOT At-a-Glance
Maryland Aviation Administration

The Maryland Aviation Administration (MAA) owns and operates Baltimore/Washington International Thurgood Marshall Airport (BWI Marshall) and Martin State Airport, and supports public-use airports across the state of Maryland. At the MAA, the core mission is the operation and support of airports in Maryland to provide residents, businesses, and travelers with the highest levels of service, safety, and economic benefit. BWI Marshall is the 22nd busiest airport in the United States and serves more than 22 million passengers per year. Air service includes an average of more than 600 daily commercial flights and nonstop service to 73 domestic and international destinations. BWI Marshall is a major transportation resource and economic development engine for the State of Maryland region, creating and supporting almost 94,000 regional jobs and more than $5 billion in business revenue.

Maryland Port Administration

The Port of Baltimore is ranked as the top port among 360 U.S. ports for handling autos and light trucks, farm and construction machinery, imported forest products, imported sugar, imported aluminum and imported gypsum. Baltimore ranks second in the United States for exported coal. Overall, Baltimore is ranked ninth for the total dollar value of international cargo and 14th for international cargo tonnage. Business at the Port of Baltimore generates about 14,630 direct jobs, while about 108,000 jobs in Maryland are linked to port activities. The Port is responsible for $3 billion in personal wages and salary and more than $300 million in state and local taxes.

Maryland Transit Administration

The Maryland Transit Administration (MTA) is the 13th largest public transit organization in the United States operating local bus, commuter bus, light rail, metro subway, Maryland Area Regional Commuter (MARC) rail system, mobility and paratransit services in the Baltimore metropolitan region. MTA also supports accessible transit systems throughout the state of Maryland. The MTA provides 24-hour daily service, including holidays and weekends, and operates more than 1,350 vehicles during peak periods. With the teamwork of 3,300 employees, which includes a nationally accredited police department, the MTA transported more than 107 million riders in Fiscal Year 2013 and delivered more than 55 million revenue miles of service.

Motor Vehicle Administration

The Maryland Motor Vehicle Administration (MVA) ensures the safe enjoyment of Maryland's transportation infrastructure by providing efficient, courteous and accurate driver-related services, including licensing and registration, to Maryland citizens and safeguarding personal information. With approximately 1,700 employees working at 24 offices and 18 Vehicle Emission Inspection Program stations throughout the state, MVA processes more than 12 million core transactions each year and manages more than 10 million driver and vehicle records. Serving as home to the Maryland Highway Safety Office, MVA also is a key agency responsible for highway safety initiatives and campaigns in Maryland.

Maryland Transportation Authority

Financed by toll revenue, the Maryland Transportation Authority (MDTA) was established in 1971 by the Maryland General Assembly to finance, construct, operate, preserve, and improve the state's toll facilities, as well as to finance new revenue-producing transportation projects for MDOT. The MDTA is responsible for eight toll facilities—two turnpikes, two tunnels, and four bridges. The MDTA's revenues are separate from the state's General Fund and Transportation Trust Fund and are reinvested into its facilities for maintenance and operations. The agency's strong bond ratings secure its position to finance transportation solutions for Maryland's citizens. This year, the MDTA received underlying affirmed "AA" ratings from all three bond-rating agencies—the highest rating possible for a toll agency.

State Highway Administration

The Maryland State Highway Administration (SHA) operates, maintains, and rebuilds the numbered, non-toll routes in Maryland's 23 counties—more than 17,000 lane-miles and 2,572 bridges. SHA roads carry 66 percent of the state's traffic and 85 percent of its truck freight, providing economic opportunity, mobility and access for people, goods and service throughout Maryland. SHA delivers more than $1 billion of work annually that is competitively awarded to private entities, sustaining thousands of jobs in the highway industry for contractors, suppliers, engineering firms, and small and minority businesses.

MASSACHUSETTS

Massachusetts Department of Transportation

Richard A. Davey
Secretary and CEO

YEAR FORMED **2009**

FTE **Approx. 10,000**

KEY FACTS
TOTAL STATE ROAD MILES
(OWNED BY STATE HIGHWAY
AGENCY) **3,016**

STATE-OWNED BRIDGES **3,459**

TRANSIT TRIPS PER YEAR
408 million

In June 2009, Governor Deval Patrick signed "An Act Modernizing the Transportation Systems of the Commonwealth of Massachusetts." This landmark transportation reform legislation required the Commonwealth to integrate five separate transportation agencies and authorities into a new, multi-modal, streamlined Massachusetts Department of Transportation (MassDOT). Formally established on November 1, 2009, MassDOT has become a single, unified transportation organization focused on customer service and safety, with a vision to be a national leader in transportation excellence.

The creation of MassDOT is just the latest event in the long history of transportation stewardship in Massachusetts that stretches back to the creation of the Massachusetts Highway Commission in 1893, which was the first organized highway commission in America. In 1897, America's first subway was constructed between the Park Street and Boylston Street stations in downtown Boston. This half-mile section of track is still in full service today as part of the Massachusetts Bay Transportation Authority (MBTA) system, making the MBTA the oldest continuously operating subway system in the country.

Health, Sustainability, and Multi-Modalism

The transportation reform law that created MassDOT also included the creation of the Healthy Transportation Compact. Co-chaired by the Secretary of Transportation and the Secretary of Health and Human Services, this inter-agency initiative is designed to facilitate transportation decisions that balance the needs of all transportation users, expand mobility, improve public health, support a cleaner environment, and create stronger communities. The efforts of this new Compact have a firm foundation in the *MassDOT Project Development and Design Guide* (2006). This guide serves as a national model for developing context-sensitive, community-friendly road and bridge projects. With partnerships across state government, MassDOT is working cooperatively to achieve a healthier, more environmentally friendly Massachusetts through smart transportation policies and investments.

On June 2, 2010, MassDOT launched GreenDOT, a comprehensive environmental responsibility and sustainability initiative that will make MassDOT a national leader in "greening" the state transportation system. GreenDOT is driven by the three primary goals to:

(1) reduce greenhouse gas emissions; (2) promote the healthy transportation options of walking, bicycling, and public transit; and (3) support smart growth development.

GreenDOT calls for MassDOT to incorporate sustainability into all of its activities; from strategic planning to project design and construction to system operation. As part of GreenDOT and Transportation Secretary Richard Davey's Healthy Transportation Directive, Massachusetts now has a "mode shift" goal (the first of its kind for any state) to triple walking, biking, and transit travel by 2030. Massachusetts already has some significantly higher non-automobile mode shares than the nation as a whole: 7.6 percent transit vs. 2.3 percent nationally, and 19 percent walking compared to 10.4 percent (the total share of travel by bicycle is roughly the same at around one percent).

"Massachusetts Car-Free Week" enhances the GreenDOT mission by encouraging customers to leave their cars in the driveway and try bicycling, walking, public transit, carpooling, or vanpooling, for one week in September. This global event takes place annually in over 1,000 cities in 40 countries in an effort to showcase the community and environmental benefits of reducing the number of vehicles on the road, and also promotes the financial, community, and health benefits of using public transportation, carpooling, bicycling, and walking.

Massachusetts contains nearly 600 miles of "shared-use" paths, suitable for recreational or commuting purposes. Primarily for bicycle and pedestrian use, these facilities are a combination off-road and on-road routes, some as exclusive paths and some with dedicated lanes on existing roadways. MassDOT promotes the "Bay State Greenway," a proposed long-distance bicycle network of 788 miles in seven corridors, to create a cohesive network of bicycle facilities across the commonwealth.

Other bicycle-centered initiatives include the Bay State Bike Week—an annual springtime celebration of bicycling in Massachusetts, "Same Roads, Same Rules," a campaign to provide safety tips for motorists and bicyclists on how to safely share the road; and "Moving Together," the state's annual bicycling and walking conference that brings together professionals from state and local government, advocates and design professionals to advance bicycle and walking transportation.

Another major effort focused on alternative transportation is the Massachusetts Safe Routes to School (SRTS) program, which creates safe, convenient, and engaging opportunities for children to walk and bicycle to and from school. The program goals include increasing children's physical activity, improving air quality, reducing traffic congestion, and fostering the continued growth of safe and sustainable communities. More than 640 elementary and middle schools—43 percent of all such schools in the commonwealth—are partnered with the federally-funded SRTS program (the nationwide average is 15 percent).

The Central Artery/Tunnel Project
While the organization MassDOT and its stated vision may be relatively new, Massachusetts has been no stranger to innovation. The most visible example of this commitment to innovation over the past 25 years was the completion of the Central Artery/Third Harbor Tunnel Project. Commonly referred to as the "Big Dig," this project has been recognized as the largest, most complex, and technologically challenging highway project in the history of the United States. The project significantly reduced traffic congestion and improved mobility in downtown Boston, one of America's

oldest and most congested major cities. In addition, it helped improve the environment, and established the groundwork for continued economic growth for Massachusetts and all of New England.

Reaching substantial completion in 2006, the project replaced Boston's deteriorating six-lane elevated Central Artery (I-93) with an eight-to-ten lane state-of-the-art underground highway, constructed two new bridges over the Charles River, extended I-90 to Boston's Logan International Airport and Route 1A, constructed the Massachusetts Bay Transportation Authority Silver Line which serves the South Boston waterfront and Logan Airport, created more than 300 acres of open land and reconnected the urban fabric of downtown Boston.

The project included several key pieces of new infrastructure which have become vital components of the urban highway network in downtown Boston. One of the key components of the project was the construction of the Ted Williams Tunnel beneath Boston Harbor. Named for the legendary Boston Red Sox baseball player, the tunnel opened in 1995, doubling Boston's cross-harbor tunnel capacity from four lanes to eight. On the East Boston side of the tunnel, the land-based approach and the underwater portion is 90 feet below the surface of Boston Harbor, the deepest such connection in North America. This connection was built using a dozen steel tube sections, each longer than a football field, that were sunk into a trench on the Boston Harbor floor and connected together.

Another key piece of infrastructure is the Leonard P. Zakim Bunker Hill Bridge. Opened in 2005, the Zakim

Bridge is the widest cable-stayed bridge in the world, and also the first "hybrid" cable-stayed bridge in the United States, using both steel and concrete in its frame. The main span consists of a steel box girder and steel floor beams, while the back spans contain post-tensioned concrete. The project required the largest use of segmental bridge construction and the largest application of steel box girders in the United States.

The CA/T Project created more than 300 acres of new parks and open space, including the Rose Fitzgerald Kennedy Greenway which sits on 27 acres where the existing elevated highway stood, 105 acres at Spectacle Island in Boston Harbor, 40 acres along the Charles River, and 7 acres as part of an expanded Memorial Stadium Park in East Boston.

The Accelerated Bridge Program

While the Big Dig is Massachusetts' most renowned project, Massachusetts continues to be at the forefront of transportation innovation with considerable national recognition for various efforts to better meet customer needs.

In 2008, the Commonwealth of Massachusetts faced the troubling problem, shared by many states, that its roads and bridges—most over 60 years old—were showing the effects of age and deferred maintenance. In fact, of Massachusetts' 4,516 bridges, many were near the end of their design life and 543 were structurally deficient. Without much-needed investment, by 2016, nearly 700 bridges would have become structurally deficient.

To solve these problems, the Massachusetts Legislature authorized the Accelerated Bridge Program (ABP), which began in August 2008. The program had

six goals: to reduce the number of structurally deficient bridges, to stimulate the economy, to save money by completing projects sooner, to apply innovation, to provide access and opportunity for women and minorities, and to be transparent and accountable in all aspects of the program.

The Fast 14

The ABP program became Massachusetts' laboratory of innovation as it served as a proving ground for successful practices and technologies. Exemplifying the transformative aspects of the program, MassDOT's I-93 "Fast 14" Project replaced 14 bridge superstructures along Interstate 93 in Medford in just ten 55-hour work weekends. Called the most ambitious project in the nation by FHWA Administrator Victor Mendez, this award-winning project used accelerated bridge construction techniques, including prefabricated units and rapid-setting concrete. These techniques ensured that the project was completed on-budget and ahead of schedule in a single construction season without impacting rush-hour traffic. Using conventional methods and materials, it would have taken four years to replace all 14 bridges.

This customer service-driven project used several innovations to be successful. The project's innovative management practices included design/build; a single field office shared by MassDOT and the contractor; a shared mobile command center for emergency response and traffic management; electronic submittals and use of shared databases. Communications strategies were diverse and included first-in-the-nation technology to provide real time traffic conditions to the public.

As U.S. Department of Transportation Secretary LaHood wrote in his blog, this project proved that "America is ready, willing, and able to dream big and build big." This project has achieved a remarkable degree of public satisfaction, which MassDOT measured with a formal survey supported by FHWA. Results were outstanding—93 percent of respondents indicated that they were satisfied with the project, with an equal percentage satisfied with the information they received about it.

Phillipston Bridge

MassDOT's first "heavy lift" bridge replacement was a resounding success. In just 121 hours, workers demolished and replaced the bridge that carries busy Route 2 over Route 2A in the town of Phillipston. The project was hailed by the community and stakeholders and won five awards for its mobility-driven use of innovation. The project team constructed the 310-ton concrete-and-steel replacement superstructure just north of the bridge on temporary shoring towers. Self-propelled, modular transporters lifted the new superstructure into place in less than five hours, despite poor weather conditions.

Rail and Transit

Regardless of the capacity increases and successes of projects like the Big Dig and the Fast 14, Massachusetts' railways and transit service will always be critical in ensuring the long-term success of the transportation system in the Commonwealth. The MBTA—the main arm of MassDOT's Rail and Transit Division—serves greater Boston along with much of eastern Massachusetts, and is the fifth largest transit system in the country in

terms of daily ridership. Between the MBTA and other regional transportation authorities across the state, roughly half a million public transportation customers are served, making nearly 1.4 million individual transit trips on a typical weekday. The MBTA maintains 183 bus and trackless trolley routes, four heavy rail, five light rail, 13 commuter rail routes, and three commuter boat routes to carry out its mission. Recently, the MBTA has enhanced service on many key bus routes to better serve their customers.

In the past few decades, the MTBA has substantially extended commuter rail service (over one-quarter of nearly 400 route miles added). This included re-establishing service on lines that ceased operations back in the 1950s (the Old Colony Railroad), extending existing lines out to cities well beyond Boston (Worcester, Newburyport, Providence, Rhode Island) and even establishing summer weekend service from Boston to Cape Cod. More expansions are planned, including the South Coast Rail Project, which will promote transit-oriented development along a new line, and provide more economic opportunities for the cities of Fall River and New Bedford by connecting them to the rail system.

The Silver Line

The most significant transit expansion has been the addition of the "Silver Line"—the first bus rapid transit (BRT) service in the commonwealth. Silver Line service began in 2002 with a connection from Dudley Square to Downtown Boston in an at-grade alignment, operating mostly in a combined bus and right-turn only lane but also in mixed

traffic and a short segment of exclusive contraflow lane. In 2003, the MBTA introduced its first ever articulated buses for this route. They are low floor for accessibility and run on compressed natural gas.

In a 2005 report, the Federal Transit Administration evaluated the new service and found that the Silver Line Washington Street "is an example of how a comprehensive systems approach to BRT implementation can result in the achievement of a broad array of system performance objectives—including higher ridership, reduced travel time, enhanced safety and security, and higher customer satisfaction."

A phase II of the project opened in 2005, connecting South Station to Logan International Airport. The tunneled section extending east of South Station was constructed in conjunction with the Central Artery Project. Tunnel sections were fabricated in a nearby, World War II–era dry dock and floated into place. This tunnel section is exclusively a transit way, allowing for rapid transit service in this corridor. Moreover, at certain intersections along its at-grade section, there are interfaces with city traffic controllers to provide traffic signal priority to buses as needed.

These projects and initiatives are proof that Massachusetts is constantly evolving to better serve its customers, improve safety, reliability, economic strength, and quality of life. As a single, multi-modal agency, MassDOT continues to improve and innovate to achieve national leadership in transportation excellence.

MICHIGAN

Michigan Department of Transportation

Kirk T. Steudle, P.E.
Director

YEAR FORMED **1905**

FTE **Approx. 2,500**

KEY FACTS:

TOTAL STATE ROAD MILES
(OWNED BY STATE HIGHWAY
AGENCY) **9,654**

STATE-OWNED BRIDGES **4,410**

TRANSIT TRIPS PER YEAR
101 million

RECENT HIGHLIGHTS:

- Hosted 2014 Intelligent Transportation Systems World Congress

- Developed extensive network of environmental sensor stations

- Piloted safety program with connected vehicle technology in Ann Arbor

- State ranked 12th in the nation for bicycle friendliness

Charting a Course

The first Michigan road map was published in 1826—with only three roads on it. But it was not until 1905 that the state felt the need to create a highway department. By then, there were 2,700 automobiles in Michigan and about 68,000 miles of roads. Fewer than 8,000 miles were improved: 7,700 with gravel and 245 with stone or macadam.

This tiny highway agency, tasked primarily with distributing road improvement funds to counties, grew into today's Michigan Department of Transportation (MDOT).

Over the past 11 decades, Michigan's roads have gone from mud to macadam and beyond. Along the way, the state has had to answer tough questions about funding, the environment, safety, roadside service, signs, road design and materials. Travel on the state's highway system has grown along with the principal industry—automobile manufacturing. As a result, our state became a transportation pioneer. Motorists around the world have benefited from ideas first tried in Michigan. Here's a brief tour of some of MDOT's historical milestones.

Early 20th Century

From its very beginning, MDOT was a forerunner in the development of good roads and the innovations that made transportation progress possible. As Michigan's economic base changed from agricultural to industrial in the early 20th century, citizens and the new auto industry demanded better roads. Under the leadership of its first director, Horatio "Good Roads" Earle, the fledgling Michigan highway department responded.

Earle declared war on the "mighty monarch mud, who rules the road to the exclusion of everyone." In 1909, under his administration, the nation's first mile of rural concrete highway was paved on (M-1) Woodward Avenue between Six and Seven Mile roads in Detroit. The route was completed in less than three months at a cost of $13,537. The short stretch of road became a tourist attraction.

During the following decade, the state worked to bolster road safety. Michigan became the first state to paint center lines between lanes of opposing traffic—one of the most important safety devices in the history of auto transportation. A new "crow's nest" platform allowed a police officer to direct traffic at intersections.

The growing number of roads inspired an effort to help motorists find their way. Colored bands were placed on telephone poles to mark important travel routes, like the Chicago Trail or the Central Michigan Pike. This was the forerunner to the national system of highway numbers and signs.

The 1920s: New Technology

In the 1920s, transportation and technology began to surge. Synchronized traffic signals replaced the "crow's nest." The nation's first snowplow started clearing Michigan roads. This plow rode on sled runners and had wooden wings to push the snow from the road. It was simple, but it answered citizen's demand for year-round travel.

The years between 1923 and 1927 saw the construction of the nation's first intercity "super highway," an eight-lane divided thoroughfare running 18 miles from Detroit to Pontiac. The state's first gas tax in 1925—two cents per gallon—helped to support road construction during the decade.

By the end of the 1920s, 1.2 million automobiles and 176,000 commercial vehicles were registered in the state. The total had increased nearly 500 percent in a decade.

1930s and 40s: Tourism and War Spur Growth

The Great Depression put the brakes on road construction. The Michigan Legislature reallocated millions of dollars in highway revenues to distressed local governments. The state constitution was amended in 1938 to prevent further diversions of highway money.

It was a time of change, nonetheless. In the years before the United States entered World War II, state roads carried more tourists. To serve them, the state built a Welcome Center at New Buffalo on old US-12. It was the first permanent travel information center in the country.

More traffic required more and better signs. New "Do Not Pass" and "Pass With Care" signs helped make roads safer.

During World War II, roads became critical for moving bombs and workers. The nation's first four-lane divided highway helped 42,000 workers get to a bomber factory in Ypsilanti.

The 1950s: A Decade of Thinking Big

The upsurge in auto production and the growth of the domestic economy after World War II sparked a demand for better roads.

The 1950s were a decade of big improvements. The very biggest (in every way) was a modern engineering marvel, the Mackinac Bridge. "The Mighty Mac" linked the state's two peninsulas. At its completion in 1957, it held the record as the world's longest suspension bridge between anchorages. It still holds that record for bridges in the Western Hemisphere. Today, the Mackinac Bridge carries nearly five million motorists per year.

It was also the era of the Interstate System. The largest road-building program in Michigan history began in 1957, when the state's freeway network grew from 100 miles to 1,230 miles in just seven years. For a time, the state led the nation in building its share of the Interstate System.

On the safety front, Michigan pioneered a new kind of five-lane highway, with left-turn lanes at the center. These reduced rear-end collisions and kept traffic moving freely.

The 1960s and 70s: Building and Integrating

The booming economy spurred even more road building during the 1960s. Michigan became the first state to complete a border-to-border interstate, I-94, which ran 205 miles from Detroit to New Buffalo. Later, it would be extended northeast to Port Huron, linking an international border directly to the state's highway system.

With all this traveling came congestion. Michigan became the first state to study traffic using TV monitors. This study, along M-10, was the forerunner of today's Intelligent Transportation Systems.

The transportation picture started to change in the 1970s under the pressure of an international oil crisis and the pressing need to better integrate all transportation systems. In 1973, the department took over jurisdiction of all state programs for all transportation modes.

Michigan's highway trust fund was opened for spending on public transportation, railroads, and port development. State funds purchased nearly 900 miles of freight railroads which otherwise would have been abandoned, allowing service to continue over wide areas of the state.

The 1980s and 1990s

The 1980s continued MDOT's deep involvement in multi-modal transportation. Through the mid-1980s, state subsidies supported the operations of shortline railroads, paid for track improvements and supported Amtrak rail passenger services in southern Michigan. Bus service also received critical financial support, with public bus transportation operating in 82 of the state's 83 counties by the end of the decade.

The state also began to play a stronger role in supporting air transportation, particularly to smaller cities struggling

to retain service under the nationwide deregulation of commercial airlines. Air passenger totals in the state climbed to new highs.

After several years of severe underfunding during the recession of the early 1980s, Michigan's highway system began a comeback. In 1983, backed by new federal and state revenues, the department launched a program to repair highways faster than they were wearing out.

In the final decades of the 20th century, MDOT began to find new ways to protect Michigan's environment and save money. The department began recycling old highways by reusing the original building materials. MDOT encouraged lower emissions by building carpool lots and developing a ridesharing program.

The MDOT Adopt-A-Highway program was created in 1990, and since then volunteers have removed more than 1.4 million bags of trash from state roadsides. Today, approximately 2,600 citizen volunteer groups pick up trash three times a year on nearly 6,000 miles of state highways.

The 21st Century

Moving forward into the new century, MDOT is embracing a transportation future where the flow of data may be nearly as important as the flow of vehicles.

The department is developing an extensive network of environmental sensor stations (ESS). In addition to keeping track of bridge and road conditions, this monitoring system uses weather sensors to transmit data to road maintenance workers, allowing timely and more cost-effective decisions on when to plow, salt, or sand roads.

On another high-tech front, MDOT is working to integrate Intelligent Transportation Systems (ITS) technology connected vehicles, autonomous vehicles and the systems that will support them into Michigan's transportation systems in a sustainable way. The goal: to improve safety, mobility and reliability for customers.

Connected and automated vehicle technology is now an emerging industry in Michigan. It is rapidly being acknowledged as the biggest change in transportation since the inception of the Interstate System.

Just as in the earliest days of the auto industry, Michigan is once again in the forefront. The U.S. DOT is currently sponsoring a pilot safety program of connected vehicle technology in Ann Arbor, using nearly 3,000 cars, buses, trucks, and motorcycles outfitted with short-range radio devices to test the effectiveness of vehicle-to-vehicle and vehicle-to-infrastructure communications. The National Transportation Safety Board formally recommended last year that the technology be installed on all newly manufactured vehicles.

MDOT Director Kirk T. Steudle said that the future of vehicle-to-vehicle and vehicle-to-infrastructure communications, coupled with advances in automated vehicle technology, will have a revolutionary impact on transportation safety. The technology could bring significant benefits for state DOT operations, providing real time information on things like pavement condition, traffic incidents, and congestion cheaper and more efficiently than is possible today. MDOT's unique position at the hub of automotive development provides

Michigan with the opportunity to be at the forefront of using this technology. In 2014, MDOT will host a cutting-edge showcase of intelligent vehicle technology at the Intelligent Transportation Systems World Congress in Detroit.

Even as it pioneers new technology, MDOT and its partners in law enforcement, emergency response, and education continue to focus on safety, trying to drive down accident and fatality rates across the state.

Michigan developed its Strategic Highway Safety Plan long before it became a federal requirement, contributing to a significant improvement in highway traffic safety in Michigan. By 2012, the rate of traffic fatalities in the state had fallen to one death per 100 million vehicle miles. Serious injuries fell by 37 percent from 2002 to 2012. Michigan continually ranks among the top performing states in seat belt use—94 percent in 2011.

New investments in safety infrastructure, such as deployment of centerline and shoulder rumble strips along non-freeway routes and investments in median cable guardrails, will continue to reduce the rate of fatalities and serious injuries. And MDOT is building more roundabouts, which improve safety by reducing fatal or serious injury crashes while at the same time decreasing idling time and vehicle emissions.

MDOT has long employed Context Sensitive Solutions (CSS) as its primary way to interact with stakeholders on projects. Now, CSS incorporates Complete Streets requirements signed into law in 2010. The Complete Streets approach means that roadways will be planned, designed, and constructed for all legal users.

But 21st century transportation is not just about what's happening on the streets. Today, MDOT is truly a multi-modal transportation organization.

MDOT worked with the U.S. Army Corps of Engineers and other Great Lakes states to secure a federal commitment to build a new lock in Sault Ste. Marie. Nearly 70 percent of the U.S. waterborne cargo capacity in the Great Lakes must use the Poe Lock—the largest of the Soo Locks. The new lock, to be built at full federal expense, broke ground on its first construction phase in 2009.

Michigan is all aboard with the national push for more transportation options, especially more passenger rail travel opportunities. In less than a decade, Michigan has gone from making incremental speed changes in its high-speed rail corridor to updating or providing passenger rail stations and adding new passenger rail services.

In 2013, the League of American Bicyclists ranked Michigan 12th in the nation for bicycle friendliness. It is a solid expression of the success of MDOT partnerships with state and local agencies, nonprofits and citizen activists to improve cycling conditions in Michigan.

Michigan's large commercial airports are supported by a significant network of general aviation airports throughout the state, which handle flights for business, agriculture, training, recreation, and even the military. MDOT worked with its airport partners over the past decade to build new runways or extensions to existing runways at many Michigan airports, and repaired pavements at many others. In addition, MDOT assisted in the development or renovation of terminal buildings and helped airports acquire new airport rescue and firefighting or snow removal equipment.

In 2014, Michigan's highway, road, and street system totals nearly 256,000 lane miles. The system includes 11,000 bridges and supports nearly 100 million transit trips per year. Today's MDOT is responsible not only for the 9,651 route miles of state trunkline but also for state programs dealing with all modes of transportation—ranging from aeronautics to bus systems, to rail freight, to bicycle paths. The state system includes 4,683 highway, railroad and pedestrian bridges; 244 carpool parking lots; 665 miles of state-owned railroad; and four state-owned airports.

MDOT also provides financial and/or technical assistance for portions of the transportation system owned and operated by others, including local transit systems, airports, intercity bus, and non-motorized trails.

MDOT has traveled a long way in its first 100 years and is accelerating into the next century.

MINNESOTA

Minnesota Department of Transportation

Charles Zelle
Commissioner

YEAR FORMED **1917**

FTE **Approx. 4,864**

KEY FACTS

TOTAL STATE ROAD MILES
(OWNED BY STATE HIGHWAY
AGENCY) **11,856**

STATE-OWNED BRIDGES **3,615**

TRANSIT TRIPS PER YEAR
101.7 million

Although it is known as the Land of 10,000 Lakes, Minnesota also has quite a few roads. Within its borders, the North Star State has 141,000 miles of state, county, and city highways, roads, and streets. At last count, there are about 20,000 bridges, 10 feet or longer, on that system of roads. The Minnesota Department of Transportation (MnDOT) manages about 12,000 miles of state roads (8.5 percent of the total), which includes approximately 5,000 bridges. The state system carries about 60 percent of the vehicle miles traveled in the Minnesota. In addition to building and maintaining roads and bridges, MnDOT develops and implements policies, plans, and programs for aeronautics, freight and passenger carriers, ports and waterways, public transit, railroads, bicycles, and pedestrians.

Building a Transportation Network

The Minnesota Legislature began passing laws directing the townships and counties in road and bridge building matters dating from Minnesota's early days of statehood in 1858. Although a constitutional amendment passed in 1898 finally allowed state government to participate directly in road development, the state did not begin building roads and bridges until after the State Highway Commission was created in

1905. The Commission lasted until 1917, when the legislature created the Department of Highways.

Transportation work started in earnest in 1920 when a constitutional amendment was adopted that created a system of 70 trunk highways across the state. The next year, the Minnesota Legislature gave the State Highways Department authority to acquire land, plan and build roadways, and use state funding to pay for builders, equipment, and material. Later in the 1920s, an amendment to the state constitution allowed the use of taxes on gasoline solely to build and maintain roads.

And the timing was right. In 1903, there were 920 motor vehicles registered; by 1920, there were 324,166, and 10 years later, that number more than doubled to 775,000. Road surfaces were initially gravel everywhere but in major cities. As autos and auto travel increased, so did the desire for paved roads. By 1950, the state owned and maintained 36,000 miles of paved roads in greater Minnesota

Two things happened in 1956 that pushed transportation along at an even faster pace. First, U.S. President Dwight Eisenhower signed legislation that

established the National System of Interstate and Defense Highways, otherwise known as the Interstate System. And a Minnesota constitutional amendment established a road funding distribution formula that provided money to the state, counties and cities so each could maintain their own systems.

As the years progressed, so did Minnesota's transportation system. In greater Minnesota, the Interstate System was built in pieces. Interstate 94 cuts diagonally from the southeast to the northwest; I-35 connects communities from north to south on the eastern side of the state; and I-90 spans the southern half of the state, from Wisconsin to South Dakota. In the Twin Cities of Minneapolis and St. Paul, a ring of interstate roads —I-394, I-494, and I-694— were built around the metro area.

By 1979, most of the rural interstates were completed. Work on the urban interstates continued until the 1990s because of the complexity of designing and building roads in densely populated areas.

Following the completion of the interstate system, road expansion turned to adding capacity to busy roads. Much-used two-lane roads in rural Minnesota,

such as Highway 53 on the Iron Range, were expanded to four-lane. And lanes were added at various points to the system throughout the Twin Cities.

Using Innovation to Deliver Projects Faster

Keeping up with the ever-growing transportation needs in a tight economy has triggered MnDOT to find opportunities for innovative ways to deliver roadwork projects. In the early 2000s, for example, MnDOT began using a design-build procurement process to deliver projects. The design-build approach means a project starts with about 30 percent of it designed. The contractor bids a flat fee and time of completion. As the project is built, the design continues. This allows contractors to figure out different ways of dealing with construction issues that can save money and time.

MnDOT used design build effectively to fund the rebuild of Highway 52 through Rochester, the new alignment of Highway 212 in the southwestern part of the Minneapolis–St. Paul area and for the construction of the new I-35W bridge in Minneapolis.

MnDOT has also used other innovations to speed construction and lessen interference with traffic. In

2012, MnDOT constructed a highway overpass bridge adjacent to the actual bridge site in St. Paul. Once the spans were completed, the contractor used a self-propelled tractor that was able to lift the span and transport it down several hundred yards of freeway to the installation site. Using this approach, the Maryland Avenue project reduced road closure times by about two months and created a safer work zone for both construction crews and motorists.

The agency did something similar that same year with the Highway 61 bridge in Hastings. The span was constructed at a site upstream from the actual crossing point. When the span was complete, it was rolled onto barges, floated downstream to the installation site, and lifted into place. This approach saved time, was safer for the workers and reduced traffic impacts.

Since 1972, MnDOT has used electronic technology to manage the freeway system, particularly in the Twin Cities area. The agency today operates 600 ramp meters, 5,500 loop detectors embedded in highway pavement and 230 electronic vehicle detectors mounted along the side of roads to count traffic. MnDOT also has traffic signals on highway entrance ramps that manage the rate at which traffic is allowed onto the highway. These tools are controlled at MnDOT's Regional Transportation Management Center in the Twin Cities (RTMC). The RTMC manages traffic flow, dispatches help to remove traffic impediments and collects traffic data on the metropolitan Interstate System.

MnDOT's use of intelligent transportation systems has improved traffic flow and helped make roads safer. And Minnesota has built high occupancy toll roads, named MnPASS, on several metro freeways to make better use of road capacity. It has constructed 296 miles of bus-only shoulder lanes in the Twin Cities that speed transit along during rush hours.

Making the System Safe

In 2014, MnDOT will oversee a $1.1 billion construction program that includes work on more than 300 projects statewide to improve roads and bridges, railroad crossings, runways, and terminals at regional airports, outstate transit facilities, and ports and waterways. This means a lot of work zones across the state and the need to ensure the safety of both the traveling public and construction crews.

MnDOT promotes highway safety through the Toward Zero Deaths initiative, Minnesota's cornerstone traffic safety program that integrates the use of engineering, enforcement, emergency medical and trauma services, and education to reduce traffic fatalities and injuries. MnDOT does this in partnership with a number of state and local agencies. The state has seen a dramatic drop in traffic deaths in the 11 years the program has been in existence. In 2003, there were more than 650 traffic deaths

on Minnesota roads. By 2012, the state had reached 388 fatalities, after seeing a low of 368 deaths in 2011

Some of the engineering solutions MnDOT uses to reduce traffic fatalities include cable median barriers, rumble strips, and enhanced pavement markings. Cable media barriers, for example, can reduce fatal crashes by as much as 90 percent, and centerline rumble strips have reduced fatal and injury crashes on rural two-lane roads by 12 percent since 2012.

Facing Challenges

On August 1, 2007, the I-35W bridge in Minneapolis collapsed into the Mississippi River, killing 13 and injuring more than 100 people. The National Transportation Safety Board cited an error in the original design of the gusset plates of the 40-year-old steel-truss bridge as the probable cause of the collapse. The gusset plates failed under a combination of substantial increases in the weight of the bridge resulting from previous modifications, and traffic and concentrated construction loads on the bridge on the day of the collapse. The tragedy focused national attention on bridge safety, and drove several improvements in state transportation department bridge programs across the country.

Notable changes in MnDOT's bridge program since 2007 include:

- Major bridges now require a formal independent peer review during design to minimize the risk of a critical design error. MnDOT hires separate engineering firms to conduct the reviews.
- MnDOT has conducted research into advanced bridge monitoring techniques, such as acoustic emissions monitoring and infrared

thermography. The department uses these techniques where appropriate, but still considers traditional visual and physical inspection as the foundation of condition assessment.

- MnDOT has changed its bridge construction specifications to limit equipment and material stockpiles on bridges.
- Specific performance measures have been instituted for bridge inspection and maintenance. These measures place performance targets on timeliness of inspections and maintenance accomplishments.
- MnDOT has developed a customized, state-of-the-art Structure Information Management System. Within the system, bridge inspection and maintenance actions are integrated to identify condition, plan and prioritize maintenance need, document and report on accomplishments, and assess benefit of maintenance activities.

In addition, the 2008 legislature provided $2.5 billion in new funding over 10 years to replace or repair the state's fracture critical and structurally deficient bridges. Of the 172 bridges identified and funded by the program, an estimated 120 bridges will be under contract to be replaced or rehabilitated by June 30, 2018. The remaining bridges were either under construction at the time the program was established; classified as lower priority and not required to be funded as part of the program; or privately owned or needing no work other than routine maintenance until after 2018.

Reaching Out to the Public

Over the past decade, MnDOT has worked hard to understand what the public wants in its transportation system through market research and public outreach. In 2009, MnDOT established an "online community" to supplement other methods of gathering public input. The online community is a group of 400 Minnesota residents selected to demographically reflect Minnesota's population. The group is asked weekly to respond to transportation-related questions. Community members participate in online discussions, brainstorming sessions, surveys and chats on a multitude of transportation issues, such as work zone safety, pot holes, safety signage and public meetings. This tool allows MnDOT to gather vital public opinion in a short period of time. The agency uses the data to assist with various programming and project selection decisions.

In the past five years, the agency has also beefed up its social media presence to broaden its public reach. MnDOT is on Facebook, Twitter, and YouTube, and has an active research blog in partnership with the University of Minnesota's Center for Transportation Studies.

Looking to the Future

In 2011, MnDOT published Minnesota Go: A Collaborative Vision for Transportation. It was a statewide effort to engage Minnesotans to from all walks of life in developing a 50-year vision for transportation. Done in conjunction with the University of Minnesota and the Citizens League, Minnesota Go aligns the transportation system with what Minnesotans expect for their quality of life, economy, and natural environment.

In 2013, Charlie Zelle became MnDOT's current commissioner of transportation. Under his tenure, MnDOT adopted the

Minnesota Go vision statement as its own: "Minnesota's multi-modal transportation system maximizes the health of people, the environment, and our economy." He has increased attention on financial management within the agency as a chief goal. MnDOT is ensuring that it is getting the highest return on its investments. Zelle is leading MnDOT to be more efficient and effective with transportation spending. And he is ensuring that the agency stays transparent in its work.

As Minnesota's transportation system has grown during the past century, so have the challenges for finding long-term, stable funding sources. In its most recent State Highway Investment Plan, MnDOT notes that over the next 20 years, the state will face increasing funding challenges. In the plan's first 10 years, the agency will expand the

system in some places and do enhancements and preservation work. In the second decade, MnDOT will only do preservation work. In the past few years, MnDOT has seen an 8.5-cent increase in its fuel tax, which provided for some significant work and periodic infusions of state and federal funding. But inflation and the increasing age of the system are revealing a growing need to address funding in the long term.

The next few decades will likely see great advancements in transportation technology and likely ongoing funding challenges. But one thing remains certain, travelers will still need to get from point A to point B and transportation will continue to be important to Minnesotans. MnDOT remains committed to take care of the state's transportation system using innovation and inspiration.

MISSISSIPPI

Mississippi Department of Transportation

Melinda L. McGrath, P.E.
Executive Director

YEAR FORMED **1916**

FTE **Approx. 3,264**

KEY FACTS
TOTAL STATE ROAD MILES
(OWNED BY STATE HIGHWAY
AGENCY) **10,834**

STATE-OWNED BRIDGES **5,716**

TRANSIT TRIPS PER YEAR
1.57 million

The Mississippi State Highway Commission was formed by the Mississippi Legislature in 1916 with the purpose to act in a supervisory capacity in the administration of federal funds allotted to the state and to work with the Federal Bureau of Public Roads in the planning of a system of highways. In 1930, the Mississippi Legislature enacted the Stansel Act creating the first effective highway department and highway system in the state. This act created a three-member elected Highway Commission with full and general supervisory responsibility over all highway matters and the authority to appoint an executive director with responsibility over the day-to-day operation of the agency. In July 1992, the State Highway Commission and Highway Department were reorganized into the Mississippi Department of

Transportation (MDOT), which is governed by the Mississippi Transportation Commission—similar to the previous Highway Commission.

The State of Mississippi vests oversight of its transportation resources and operations in a three-member elected commission representing three geographic areas in the state (Central, Northern, and Southern districts). In accordance with state law, the commissioners have the authority and responsibility for the supervision of all modes of transportation in the state dealing with aeronautics, highways, public transit, ports, and rail safety. The Transportation Commission is authorized to appoint an executive director of MDOT responsible for administering the policies of the commission and exercising day-to-day

RECENT HIGHLIGHTS

- U.S. Highway 82 Mississippi River Bridge—3.8 miles connects the MS Delta to I-55, U.S. Highway 61 and U.S. Highway 65; completed in 2010

- Biloxi Bay Bridge—95-feet-high, 1.4 miles long, six 12-foot-wide lanes completed in 2007

- I-269—26 mile section of I-269 that will bypass Memphis from Tennessee to Mississippi; begun in 2011

- Bay Saint Louis Bridge—85-feet-high, 1.7 miles long, four 12-foot-wide-lanes completed in 2006

- Split Diamond Project—reconstruction of section of I-55 in central Mississippi; begun in 2012

- State Route 9—9.5 miles of new four lane highway, 10 bridges, and one interchange begun in 2011

- The Stack—multilevel interchange of I-20, I-55, and Highway 49 completed in 2009

- I-55 Reconstruction in Hinds County—widening and reconstruction of I-55 from Byram to McDowell Road; began in 2013

- I-20 Rehabilitation in Scott County—restoration of I-20 from SR 481 to the Scott/Newton County Line; completed in 2013

supervision over administrative and technical matters relating to airport and port development, highway construction and maintenance, weight enforcement, public transit, and rail safety. Today, the organization has expanded to over 3,400 employees with 35 divisions and six districts.

In 1987, the Mississippi Legislature passed a long-range highway program, which was one of the most comprehensive in the country. The development of Mississippi's transportation system over the past 25 years has grown in large part thanks to the provisions of this act, which came to be known as the 1987 Four-Lane Highway Program or Advocating Highways for Economic Advancement and Development (A.H.E.A.D.). This program was designed as a means to fund the effort of moving Mississippi's citizens and goods through a shared vision among legislative leaders and grassroots advocates. The 1987 Four-Lane Highway Program, or A.H.E.A.D., contained four major provisions that set it apart from other construction programs. First, the program established priorities as to which corridors should be constructed first. Second, it set tangible long-range goals. Third, it used a "pay as you go" funding philosophy. Finally, it dedicated

all highway-user revenues to highways. The legislation also allows MDOT the flexibility to maximize the use of federal funding by allowing the substitution of federal funds for state funds on gaming and maintenance projects.

The program called for highways to be built in phases based on vehicle count and road capacity. Three phases were established with each having a mileage goal and an estimated cost. The original drafters of the 1987 program intended that the work be completed in phases that over-lapped each other with most of the work being conducted in Phase II. Highway user revenues were dedicated to build the system. In 1998, MDOT was given the authority to borrow $200 million through revenue bonds if funding resources dictated. Among sources designated to pay for the program were a motor fuel tax, a $5 vehicle registration (car tag fee), a highway contractor's tax, federal aid, and proceeds from the revenue bonds. Phase IV was then incorporated into Vision 21, a needs-based highway program, during the 2002 Legislative Session.

MDOT's goal at the inception of the 1987 Program was that every Mississippian would be linked to a four-lane highway within 30 miles or

30 minutes. MDOT continues to make great strides toward reaching that goal. Mississippians have already realized the increase in economic activity and safety that four-lane highways bring. As of June 30, 2013, 1,077.1 miles of new four-lane highway are in use by the public.

One of MDOT's top priorities has been to replace Mississippi's deficient bridges. This has been an ongoing process throughout the state. The Bridge Replacement and Rehabilitation Program provided funding assistance for any bridge on a state designated road. Federal law allowed between 15 and 35 percent of the funds to be used on the local level. In 2004, MDOT reported a total of 5,481 bridges on the state maintained highway system. Of that figure, 1,223 (or 22 percent of the bridges) were considered structurally deficient or functionally obsolete. In other words, the structures were sound but were no longer able to function at peak capacity. There were also 10,928 bridges on the non-state maintained system of which 3,378 (or 31 percent of the bridges) were considered structurally deficient or functionally obsolete in 2004. With these figures in mind, progress towards bridge replacement and rehabilitation has been pushed by transportation leadership in Mississippi. According to the Federal Highway Administration (FHWA), Mississippi has built some of the most cost-efficient bridges in the southeastern portion of the United States for many years now. MDOT has been recognized by FHWA as a leader in the Southeast in the total number of newly constructed bridges on the Federal-Aid System.

Hurricane Katrina hit the Gulf Coast on August 29, 2005 unleashing un-precedented damage to Mississippi's transportation infrastructure. Due to Katrina's powerful winds and storm surge, massive four-lane concrete plates were lifted from the pilings of both the Bay Saint Louis Bridge and the Biloxi Bay Bridge. The damage to both bridg-es was crippling and beyond repair. Following the devastation caused by Hurricane Katrina, the need to repair the Bay Saint Louis Bridge and the Biloxi Bay Bridge became a top priority of the state.

MDOT funded all Katrina repair and clean up from August 2005 through January 2006 with the exception of $10 million made available by U.S. Secretary of Transportation Norman Mineta and FHWA Administrator Richard Capka. With much left to be accomplished, MDOT was out of funds. $1.1 billion in FHWA Emergency Relief Funds was made available to MDOT on January 23, 2006. A great deal of effort was put forth to gain the confidence of Congress and the President had been put forth by MDOT Commissioners, the Executive Director and staff members. The $1.1 billion in federal funding was a vali-dation of MDOT and FWHA's plans, leadership, and efforts, and allowed the state to tackle the extensive process of

rebuilding Katrina-damaged transporta-tion infrastructure on the coast.

In February 2006, MDOT evaluated design-build proposals for the Bay Saint Louis Bridge. The proposal for the Bay Saint Louis Bridge was $266.9 million with a milestone of opening two lanes to traffic by May 16, 2007. Failing to meet the milestone would result in a $100,000 penalty each day until two-way traffic was complete. Given the almost impossible task, the contractor succeeded in achieving the May mile-stone. On May 17, 2006, MDOT cele-brated the restoration of two-way traffic on the Bay Saint Louis Bridge. The bridge is 85 feet high, 1.7 miles long, 150 feet north of the old bridge and has four 12-foot-wide lanes, an eight-foot-wide inside shoulder, a 10-foot-wide outside shoulder, a 12-foot-wide pe-destrian lane and 22 pieces of artwork along the pedestrian walkway.

MDOT replaced the Biloxi Bay Bridge with a new high-level bridge using the design-build project delivery method, which allowed the designing, engineer-ing, permitting, and construction ac-tivities to be conducted simultaneously. This method was critical in getting the new bridge built quickly. On November 1, 2007, MDOT opened the newly con-structed Biloxi Bay Bridge. The 1.6-mile long bridge carries U.S. Highway 90 directly over the Biloxi Bay connecting Biloxi and Ocean Springs. The bridge is 95 feet high, 1.4 miles long, has six 12-foot-wide lanes, a 12-foot-wide pedestrian lane and 22 pieces of artwork by local artists incorporated into the railing along the pedestrian walkway.

The dedicated and focused efforts of MDOT, FHWA and the design-build

team assured the record rebuild of Katrina-damaged transportation infra-structure. The new bridges are higher, wider and longer than the structures they replaced. Furthermore, Gulf Coast communities are now stronger and their future is brighter.

With the replacement of the Bay Saint Louis Bridge and the Biloxi Bay Bridge, the state was able to focus on other bridge projects including the U.S. Highway 82 Mississippi River Bridge that links Mississippi and Arkansas. This structure originally replaced a narrow 1940s bridge (formerly known as the Benjamin G. Humphreys Bridge) that had weathered the wrath of the Missis-sippi River and ever-increasing volumes of highway and river traffic. Since 1972, according to government statistics, the old bridge had sustained more barge collisions than any other bridge on the Mississippi River and even had an airplane crash into it in 1953. MDOT had begun designs for the replacement bridge in 1995, and in 2005, the Missis-sippi Approach Contract was let at an estimated cost of $86.1 million followed by the Arkansas Approach Contract that was let at an estimated cost of $52.4 million.

On July 28, 2010, MDOT celebrated the grand opening of the new $336 million U.S. Highway 82 Mississippi River Bridge. The bridge connects the Mississippi Delta to Interstate 55 and other four-lane highways such as U.S. Highway 61 and U.S. Highway 65 in Arkansas. Each lane is 12-feet wide with 12-foot outside shoulders and 8-foot inside shoulders to further enhance safety and traffic flow. The entire bridge deck is 2.5 miles long and the total project length is more than 3.8 miles.

The main span portion of the new bridge included four deep river piers anchored 20 feet into the riverbed, two concrete towers soaring 425 feet above the Mississippi River and a spectacular cable-stayed span supported by four fans of pre-stressing strand steel cable. The 378-foot center-span is the longest cable-stayed span in the continental United States. Because the new bridge was constructed in a straight section of the river, it is also much less susceptible to collisions from barge traffic.

Less than a year later, MDOT broke ground on a three-mile section of I-269 in DeSoto County on June 23, 2011. This project kicked off what will eventually be a 26-mile stretch of highway that will bypass Memphis from Tennessee to Mississippi. Not only will the route relieve congestion on the I-69/I-55 corridor and efficiently connect I-40 and I-55 through North Mississippi, but I-269 will also promote local and regional mobility, linking Highways 61, 72, and 78.

In July 2011, 9.5 miles of four-lane construction began on State Route 9 in Pontotoc County to improve the existing transportation infrastructure and to accommodate future growth and economic development in the area. These needs became necessary after Toyota's decision to locate a production plant in Belden. Safer and more durable roads with better access to the west and southwest areas of the plant were needed. On August 16, 2012, MDOT

held a ribbon-cutting ceremony for the new State Route 9. In addition to the 9.5 miles of new four-lane highway constructed, road work also included 7 million cubic yards of earthwork, approximately 170,000 tons of asphalt, 10 bridges and one interchange. The State Route 9 construction was an invaluable investment to help support the growth and economic development throughout the community.

Another project to help accommodate the growth of the central region of the state began the following year. On May 10, 2012, MDOT began construction of the Split Diamond Project in Madison. The project reconstructed a section of I-55 from Old Agency Road in Ridgeland to State Route 463 in Madison while constructing a split diamond interchange between Madison Avenue and the proposed Colony Park Boulevard. The project also called for the addition of two lanes to I-55 in each direction for a total of eight lanes, the addition of frontage roads to the interstate between the Old Agency Interchange and Madison Avenue, the widening of a portion of Madison Avenue to five lanes and building a portion of the new Colony Park Boulevard. Once complete, this project will provide transportation infrastructure to improve the safety of the traveling public and support future economic development in the area.

Another program established by the Mississippi Legislature was the

Multi-Modal Transportation Improvement Program in 2002, which was established to provide funds for high-priority improvement projects to airports, ports, railroads, and transit systems for which funds are not otherwise available. By annually providing $10 million to support the Multi-Modal Transportation Improvement Program, MDOT is further sustaining an efficient and effective intermodal system by balancing modal investments. This program remains a valuable resource for leveraging strategic investments throughout the state.

Although Mississippi has managed to develop a robust transportation system, funding continues to fall short of the state's infrastructure needs. While road construction costs have increased 300 percent in Mississippi, state and federal dedicated transportation revenues have remained flat for the past decade and long-term funding remains uncertain. MDOT has been forced to shift to a maintenance-only approach and focus on system preservation first and foremost. In 2013, the majority of MDOT's budget was spent on infrastructure repair and routine maintenance. However, MDOT remains committed to providing a robust transportation system for the state. With limited resources, MDOT will continue working to find innovative solutions to ensure the preservation of the transportation network. Transportation is the driving force of a strong economy.

MISSOURI

Missouri Department of Transportation

David B. Nichols, P.E.
Director

YEAR FORMED **1913**

FTE **Approx. 4,994**

KEY FACTS
TOTAL HIGHWAY MILES **33,884**

NUMBER OF STATE BRIDGES
AND CULVERTS **10,372**

ANNUAL TRANSIT TRIPS
63.6 million

TONS OF FREIGHT MOVED
More than 30 million

RECENT HIGHLIGHTS

– Kansas City and St. Louis are the second and third largest freight rail hubs in the United States.

– 124 public use airports and 11.7 million enplanements per year

– Maintains an 85 percent customer satisfaction rating.

– Projects averaged 5 percent under budget in the past 10 years.

Missouri serves as a transportation crossroads for the entire nation. After 100 years of keeping people and goods moving, the Missouri Department of Transportation (MoDOT) is known as a leader in innovation, quality and efficient use of funds with an 85 percent customer satisfaction rating. MoDOT plans, designs, constructs and maintains the nation's seventh largest state highway system with 33,884 miles. Missouri also has more major river bridges, 53, than any other state. Missouri ranks 40th nationally in revenue per mile with one of the lowest fuel taxes in the country.

History
On March 22, 1913, the Missouri General Assembly created the Missouri State Highway Department. In 1917, a bipartisan State Highway Board, now called the Missouri Highways and Transportation Commission, was created.

In 1920, the Missouri General Assembly passed a bonding issue to "get Missouri out of the mud." By 1939, the state system had grown to 15,571 miles. The biggest jump in the size of the system came in the 1950s. Missouri took over 12,000 miles of supplementary roads from counties and other local agencies. With this transfer, 95 percent of Missourians in rural areas had access to a state-maintained road two miles from their homes.

Missouri led the nation with the start of the Interstate System in the United States. On August 2, 1956, the first interstate contract was awarded for 13 miles of Interstate 44 in Laclede County. On August 13, 1956, construction began on the first Interstate project to build 2.6 miles of Interstate 70 in St. Charles County.

The State Highway Department merged with the Transportation Department to create the Missouri Highway and Transportation Department in 1980. Another transformation occurred in 1996 when the agency was renamed the Missouri Department of Transportation (MoDOT).

Safety
Safety on Missouri's system is the top priority. In 2004, a partnership of Missouri safety advocates, including law enforcement agencies, health care providers, courts, government agencies, advocacy groups, planning organizations, and concerned citizens banded together to form the Missouri Coalition for Roadway Safety. They implemented a strategic highway safety plan titled Missouri's Blueprint for Safer Roadways and

began the Arrive Alive campaign, setting a goal to reduce roadway fatalities. Missouri met its goal of 850 or fewer fatalities in 2010—two years ahead of the goal of by 2012!

Overall since 2005, due to the combined efforts of the Missouri Coalition for Roadway Safety, 1,538 lives have been saved on Missouri roadways, a decrease of 35 percent.

The coalition attributes its success to the four E's—education, emergency medical services, enforcement, and engineering. Enforcement and education focus heavily on addressing high-risk driver behaviors such as impaired driving, failure to use safety belts and child safety seats, speeding, and distracted driving. Some of Missouri's engineering efforts to improve safety include the addition of cable barrier along all rural interstates. Missouri also has rumble strips along its highway edge lines, and rural roads include a rumble center stripe. Shoulders have been added to many of Missouri's rural roads giving drivers more room to maneuver. Design innovations including roundabouts and j-turns focus on improving intersection safety.

Since the original safety goal has been reached, the group now aims to reduce

the number of traffic fatalities to 700 or fewer by 2016, with the ultimate goal of zero.

Innovations

Missouri is a leader in transportation innovation, pursuing quality work with a cost-effective use of limited transportation funds while serving its customers.

Practical Design

Practical Design challenges traditional standards to develop efficient solutions for today's system needs. Missouri's goal of Practical Design is to build "good" projects, not "great" projects, to achieve a great system. Through Practical Design, engineers properly define the scope by focusing on achieving the project purpose and need while considering the surroundings of each project. A project's design must be sensitive to where it is located, such as rural or in a city, and whether it is an Interstate or a letter route. The surrounding context helps determine the design criteria. Missouri's goal is to get the best value for the least cost. Life-cycle costs also must be considered. For example, in order to meet top standards, MoDOT previously would have built a wide bridge with full shoulders on a rural narrow road. Now the bridge width more closely matches the existing pavement. It is slightly wid-

er and also a brand new bridge, which is an improvement in overall conditions. Missouri has shared its Practical Design approach across the country as all state transportation departments struggle with increasing infrastructure needs with declining available revenue.

Smooth Roads Initiative

In 2005, MoDOT implemented a plan to improve the driving condition and smoothness of its roads. The Smooth Roads Initiative brought the busiest 2,200 miles of Missouri roads up to good condition in just two years. Three-fourths of these roads were in fair to poor condition before the program. Although these roads comprised just six percent of Missouri's system, they carried 60 percent of the vehicle miles traveled and 86 percent of all Missourians live within 10 miles of one of these improved roads. The effort involved 223 contracts, which came in $12 million under the $400 million budget.

Design–Build

Many states have used the Design-Build contracting process to streamline the design and construction of major projects. In 2004, the Missouri General Assembly gave permission for MoDOT to complete three Design-Build contracts. Missouri took an innovative approach and created a proposal process based on a fixed cost, adjustable scope competition. Missouri asked contractors to bring their creativity to maximize the scope and reduce the timeframe within the available budget. The Design-Build teams were allowed to propose other state approved standards as well. It resulted in the successful completion of three major projects—I-64 in St. Louis, I-29/I-35 kcICON project in Kansas City, and Safe and Sound bridges statewide—all completed under budget and ahead of schedule. The General Assembly has since passed additional legislation allowing Missouri to use Design-Build for up to two percent of its total number of projects. Five more Design-Build contracts are underway or will be under contract in Missouri in 2014.

Safe and Sound Bridges
There are 10,364 bridges on the Missouri state highway system—7th largest in the nation.

Approximately 1,100 of them were in poor to serious condition. Beginning in 2008, the Safe & Sound Bridge Improvement Program was an aggressive initiative to address more than 800 of the worst ones in Missouri.

Traditional contracting was used to repair 250 of those bridges. The remaining 554 bridges were accomplished through a single Design-Build contract. In total, the $685 million Safe & Sound Bridge Improvement Program replaced 802 bridges in slightly more than three and half years instead of the expected five years. As a result of that program, MoDOT reversed the recent trend that showed a growing percentage of deficient bridges. Now, 79 percent of Missouri's bridges are in good

condition. Missourians in every county of the state are driving across new and improved bridges.

Diverging Diamond Interchange
In 2009, MoDOT was the first DOT to build a diverging diamond interchange. The design helps relieve congestion in a tight area and is a quicker, cheaper reconstruction than more conventional interchange projects. Construction is shortened because the existing interchange bridge and ramps can be used, with some modifications. There are shorter time periods for traffic disruptions and it is cheaper to build since the existing infrastructure is reused. The diverging diamond interchange design reduces traffic congestion up to 50 percent. It improves safety by eliminating left-turn crashes and reducing the chance of rear-end crashes. Many other states have since adopted the diverging diamond design.

Winter Weather
In our ongoing efforts to more efficiently fight winter weather, a MoDOT employee designed a way to plow multiple lanes with one piece of equipment. The result was the patented TowPlow, a trailer snowplow pulled behind a truck already equipped with a traditional front-mounted snowplow. It can cut a 30-foot swath or 2.5 lanes of pavement. MoDOT has 79 TowPlows in its fleet and many other states use them now as well. MoDOT treatment innovations include using combinations of salt brine and beet juice to maximize the efficiency of materials depending on temperature and type of precipitation.

Customer Service
In 1996, MoDOT created a statewide Customer Service Center with a toll-free

number for citizens to call and discuss their concerns with a live person. After nearly 20 years of providing this service to the public, MoDOT has an 85 percent customer satisfaction rating based on an annual statewide phone survey. An average week results in more than 5,300 calls to our centers, which are located across the state in our seven district offices. On a peak winter weather week, we handle more than 12,000 calls. Callers reach a live person 24 hours a day, 7 days per week. In 2005, MoDOT also developed an interactive online tool for customers, the Traveler Information Map. The map provides weather road conditions, flooding road closures, construction lane restrictions, and access to MoDOT's traffic cameras. In 2013, the website had nearly one million visitors.

Multi-modal Operations
Over the past 100 years, MoDOT has managed to keep Missouri moving. From trails to rivers to railroads to automobiles to airplanes, Missouri is a leader in transportation. If you are trying to get goods from one side of the country to the other, it is likely they'll pass them through Missouri.

- **Aviation**—Missouri has 124 public-use airports and 34 business-capable airports.

- **Railroads**—Missouri has 4,822 miles of mainline railroad track. Kansas City and St. Louis are the nation's second- and third-largest freight rail hubs. In 2012, 438 million tons of freight traveled by rail in Missouri (fourth in the nation).

- **Waterways**—Missouri has 14 public river ports, including St. Louis, which is the third largest inland port in the U.S. Barge traffic in Missouri moves more than 30 million tons of freight through public ports and terminals each year.

- **Public Transit**—More than 70 million annual public transit trips are made by Missourians.

- **Bicycle and Pedestrian**—MoDOT has approximately 600 miles of shared-use paths on the state system and works with planning partners to create facilities that accommodate non-motorized travel.

- **Motor Carrier Services**—MoDOT helps commercial motor carriers get the information, credentials and permits they need to conduct business in Missouri.

National Involvement
Missouri works closely with AASHTO to plan America's transportation system. MoDOT has been a part of the association for most of its existence with MoDOT employees actively serving. Four Missourians have served as president of AASHTO, including C. W. Brown in 1949, Rex Whitton in 1956, Robert Hunter in 1979, and Pete Rahn in 2008. Countless Missourians have served and continue to serve on AASHTO subcommittees working together as a nation of transportation providers.

In recent years, the state has won the AASHTO America's Transportation Award Grand Prize for the I-64 reconstruction in 2010 and the People's Choice Award for the Safe and Sound Bridge program in 2013. Also in 2013, MoDOT's innovative design for a shared four-lane project on Route 5 was awarded in the AASHTO Midwest regional competition. Several other projects have been recognized as top projects in the Midwest AASHTO region in recent years.

Future
In 2013, MoDOT's centennial year, the department launched an extensive public engagement effort to develop a long-range plan of what Missourians want in their transportation system. Staff visited every corner of the state and received more than 12,000 suggestions from MoDOT's planning partners and the general public. The four goal areas of the completed plan include:

take care of the transportation system and services we enjoy today; keep all travelers safe, no matter the mode of transportation; invest in projects that spur economic growth and create jobs; and give Missourians better transportation choices. In early 2014, the Missouri Highways and Transportation Commission adopted these strategies as its new Long-Range Transportation Plan—"A Vision for Missouri's Transportation Future." However, the stark reality is that MoDOT has little chance of delivering that vision in its current funding environment. With fuel tax revenue declining, uncertainty at the federal level and increasing costs of doing business, MoDOT's construction budget is on a steep decline. By 2017, it will be insufficient to maintain the current condition of Missouri's system of roads and bridges.

Despite these funding challenges, the Show-Me state is committed to retaining its position as the crossroads of the United States. MoDOT will be here for another 100 years, leading the nation in innovation, efficiency, and customer service.

MONTANA

Montana Department of Transportation

Michael T. Tooley
Director

YEAR FORMED **1913**

FTE **Approx. 2,242**

KEY FACTS
TOTAL STATE ROAD MILES
(OWNED BY STATE HIGHWAY
AGENCY) **11,003**

STATE-OWNED BRIDGES **2,488**

TRANSIT TRIPS PER YEAR
2 million

"Years ago wild game and Indians made the trails in Montana. Now high-powered engineers and contractors are responsible. These scientific gents have built about 5,000 miles of oiled arterial system and draped it over the landscape where it will do the most good.…These new highways are safe, direct and dustless. You will enjoy driving them."

– *Montana Highway Department, Montana High, Wide and Handsome (1940)*

In 2013, the Montana Department of Transportation (MDT) celebrated its 100th birthday. The commemoration of that important milestone gave the agency a chance to reflect on how far it had come since 1913 and where it is going in the future. Like many great endeavors, the improvement of Montana's highways was not only an enormous undertaking, but also a team effort by those who planned, surveyed, designed, built, and maintained the facilities. It also involved cooperation between the MDT and the Federal Highway Administration—with contributions by AASHTO. While the statement above, written in 1940, may be somewhat dated, the sentiments behind it are still relevant today. Road-building in Montana has certainly been an adventure.

Montana's First Roads

Montana's highways are based on aboriginal trails established hundreds of years ago by North America's first people. The Lewis and Clark Expedition described many of those trails on their journey in 1805 across what would later become Montana. American and Canadian fur traders and trappers in the decades that followed also, for the most part, utilized those ancient trails. In 1860, John Mullan of the U.S. Corps of Topographical Engineers built the first engineered road in the Pacific Northwest and northern Rocky Mountains. The 624-mile wagon road connected Walla Walla, Washington, to Fort Benton at the head of navigation on the upper Missouri River in Montana. For much of the road's length, Mullan used already existing Indian trails, improving grades and widening them for use by wagons. The discovery of gold in southwestern Montana in 1862 drew thousands of miners, freighters, and others to the remote northern Rockies. Many of those pilgrims came here on the Mullan Road.

The stampede to the gold mines caused the establishment of other roads, none of which were engineered, but just kind of grew from use. These included Fisk's overland route from Minnesota, the

Utah–Montana Road, and the famed Bozeman Trail. Within a short time, those primary routes were connected by a tangle of toll roads licensed by the territorial legislature beginning in 1864. Eight years later, in 1872, the legislature abolished the toll road system and put the counties in charge of the roads. The territorial legislature enacted laws that enabled the counties to build and maintain their roads. When Montana became a state in 1889, the roads established during the territorial days and the methods used to finance and maintain them became the basis of the state's modern highway system.

Getting Montana Out of the Mud

After many years of lobbying by good roads groups, the Thirteenth Montana Legislature created the Montana State Highway Commission in March 1913. The commission functioned as an advisory body to the counties, offering advice and direction on how to build proper roads. It also oversaw the use of convict labor as demonstration projects for the counties. In 1915, the highway commission standardized bridge designs and began supervision of the bidding process for bridge projects for Montana's counties. Two years later in 1917, the legislature reorganized the

highway commission to administer the funds made available to the state through the Federal Aid Road Act of 1916. Federal and state legislation gave the highway commission more control over the highway design and construction process, but not of the finances; that remained with the counties. When the Federal Aid Highway Act of 1921 established the Seven Percent System, Montana claimed a Federal Aid Primary system of 4,700 miles. Shortfalls in state matching funds led to the passage of the Good Roads Law by Montana's voters in 1926. It specified that a three-cent per gallon gasoline tax be used only on the improvement of Montana's federal aid highway system. The passage of the law allowed the Montana State Highway Commission to take full control of the road-building process in the state and it truly began to get Montana out of the mud. Yet, despite the monumental effort to improve the state's highways, by 1930 Montana reputedly had the worst roads in the United States.

The 1930s saw the greatest improvements in Montana's highway system up to that point. While Montana may have had the worst roads in the United States in 1930, the state had one of the most modern highway systems in the

country within that decade. Beginning in 1933 with the New Deal, the Montana Highway Department built nearly 5,000 miles of roads on better alignments on easier grades, surfaced 4,500 miles of that system with bituminous oil, established a secondary road system, built nearly 700 bridges and railroad grade separation structures, and initiated an ambitious program to draw tourists to the state from all over the United States and Canada to "enjoy…her highways and byways." Shortfalls in gasoline tax revenue through most of the decade seriously jeopardized the state's ability to match federal funds. To provide those funds for federal allocations, the Montana legislature approved unsecured bonds so that the Highway Department could accomplish its ambitious program. Although Montanans were particularly hard hit by the economic depression, popular support for better roads remained high for most of the decade. By World War II, the Montana Highway Department had achieved most of its goals and publicized the state's modern road system nationwide.

The Post-War Years

War and peace had a significant impact on the Montana Highway Department between 1942 and 1956. During the war, many employees left the department to serve in the armed forces or to work in the war industries. Because there was no federal aid forthcoming to the state for road work during the national emergency, the highway system the department worked so hard to improve in the 1930s, and for which it was justifiably proud, deteriorated during World War II. Before the war was over, however, the federal government began planning for an expanded post-war construction program. Beginning in 1944, Congress passed a series of biennial highway acts that provided more and more federal aid to the states to compensate for the lack of work during the war and to modernize the nation's highway system. That federal funding peaked in June 1956 when President Dwight Eisenhower signed the Federal-Aid Highway Act of 1956 that created the modern Interstate System.

During the years after the war, the commission expanded its programs to best utilize the increased federal funding that characterized the post-war years. That involved the construction of expensive bridges over the state's main rivers, an expanded tourism program, and continued improvements to over 4,700 miles of Montana's primary, secondary, and urban highways, including the resurfacing of those highways to the tune of $46 million. While World War II gave the highway commission time to catch its breath after the heady years of the Great Depression, the post-war years were much more demanding as the Highway Department worked hard to build a modern highway system that would meet the needs of the traveling public for many years to come. Beginning in 1956, however, the planning, design, and construction on an Inter-state highway system would dominate the department's programs.

The Interstate Highway Program

Building the Interstates was a challenge, but one the Montana Highway Department readily accepted and, according to some of the engineers present then, enjoyed. It was a once-in-a-lifetime opportunity for the department's engineers and one that occurred in two phases. Initially, Montana's Interstates were two-lane facilities, except in the vicinity of the Butte, Great Falls, and Billings metropolitan areas where highway traffic counts warranted four-lane highways. Between 1958, when the Highway Department let the first Interstate projects to contract and 1966 when the Federal-Aid Highway Act mandated that all Interstates be four lanes, the highway department had built 491 miles of Interstates. Then they had to go back and expand the two lane segments into four lane segments!

When Montana's portion of the Interstate System was completed in 1988, the state had 1,188 miles of four-lane Interstate highways. The longest was Interstate 90 at 542.6 miles, with I-15 and I-94 following at 395.2 miles and 247.8 miles, respectively. There were also two connector Interstates, I-115 at Butte and I-315 at Great Falls. The big projects over the Continental Divide and through the canyons north of Helena were completed by 1966. Between 1968 and 1988, the bulk of the superhighway construction was on Interstate 90. The last section of the Interstate System completed in Montana was a little over seven miles of I-15 in Beaverhead County nine miles south of Dillon in southwestern Montana—a few miles north of where the state's first Interstate highway segment was constructed in the late 1950s. When completed, Montana's portion of the Interstate System cost $1.22 billion with the average cost per mile at $1.03 million. At nearly 95 percent, Montana has the highest proportion of rural Interstates in the United States.

The Multi-modal Years

Since the completion of the Interstates in 1988, the MDT has diversified its activities over a wide range of transportation-related subjects that are critical to the state. Montana has owed much of its program to U.S. Senator Max Baucus, a native of the state, who was instrumental in the development and passage of significant federal highway legislation from the mid-1980s until his retirement in 2014. That legislation has had a profound impact to the MDT with funding growth for Montana and MDT transitioned into an asset management approach to managing the state's highway system. The MDT has been proactive in dealing with tribal, wildlife, wetland, and cultural resource issues as well. Statewide improvements have matured since this time as well to include wider shoulders for bicyclists, roundabouts at busy intersections, passing lanes, wildlife considerations, and more context sensitive design.

In 1991, in response to Congress's enactment of the Intermodal Surface Transportation Efficiency Act (ISTEA), the state legislature reorganized the old Montana Department of Highways into the MDT, absorbing the Aeronautics Board, the Montana Department of Commerce's aviation, rail, and transit programs along with the Department of Justice's Highway Traffic Safety Office. ISTEA had a significant impact on the state because it transformed the federal program into a more multi-modal approach and established the authority for the National Highway System, which eliminated the old federal-aid primary, secondary, and urban systems and the traditional methods of funding them. Funding allocations for these systems were continued by the Montana Legislature through state law enacted in 1993

Program Growth, Innovation, and Streamlining

Congressional passage of the Transportation Equity Act for the 21st Century (TEA-21) in 1998 and Safe, Accountable, Flexible, Efficient Transportation Equity Act—A Legacy for Users (SAFETEA-LU) in 2005 also had an enormous impact on the MDT as increased funding enabled the department to expand its highway construction and public transit programs. During this period, MDT shifted its approach to best manage their funds based on needs and asset management principles. This ensures the right treatment at the right time through a more robust pavement preservation program and an optimal project mix of reconstruction, rehabilitation, and resurfacing. This, along with innovative contracting techniques— such as design build projects—have significantly streamlined the MDT's programs.

In 2000, innovative financing thru a mechanism called Utilizing Grant Anticipation Revenue Vehicle (GAR-VEE) bonds accelerated project delivery and sealed a deal for reconstruction of 40 miles of US 93 after decades of spirited discussion amongst MDT, the Federal Highway Administration, and the Confederated Salish and Kootenai Tribes. The context-sensitive design yielded a combination of two and four lane roadway, passing lanes, and controlled access that serve to ease the flow of traffic and improve safety on a busy and formerly dangerous highway, while preserving those aspects of the environment important to the Salish and Kootenai people such as wildlife connectivity and cultural features. This was a unique situation given the roadway and project specific sensitivities, timing, and the parties involved reaching a consensus for improving this significant highway across tribal lands.

The Road Ahead

The future holds uncertainties for transportation funding at both the state and federal level but Senator Baucus said it best upon the passage of MAP-21 out of the Finance Committee in February 2012, "Montana was a highway state, and we've seen firsthand that smart investments in our transportation system yield big returns for jobs and business. Every investment in a bridge is an investment in a good paying construction job, and every investment in a road is an investment in a Montana business that ships goods and services across the state and across the country." Montana is, indeed, a highway state. Its dedication to building better roads to better serve the traveling public has been a hallmark of the MDT's efforts for over a century.

NEBRASKA

Nebraska Department of Roads

Randall D. Peters, P.E.
Director–State Engineer

YEAR FORMED **1895**

FTE **Approx. 2,292**

KEY FACTS

TOTAL STATE ROAD MILES
(OWNED BY STATE HIGHWAY
AGENCY) **9,949**

STATE-OWNED BRIDGES **3,903**

TRANSIT TRIPS PER YEAR
5.96 million

One of the earliest major road-building projects in Nebraska Territory came in 1862, five years before statehood, when the Otoe County Commissioners decided to construct a road for steam wagon travel from Nebraska City west 180 miles to Fort Kearny. The steam wagon concept was abandoned after the first attempt because the steam-powered tractor, pulling 10 freight wagons, broke an axle about eight miles west of Nebraska City. Being wartime, replacement parts were not available for the tractor and it was abandoned along the road, becoming a familiar landmark for travelers. However, the "Steam Wagon Road" continued to serve as an important route from the Missouri River to the West for many years.

Soon many other road-building projects were completed and through the years Nebraska developed an extensive state, county, and municipal road system of approximately 100,000 miles. The 1879 Legislature spurred this development when it declared all section lines to be public roads and authorized the counties to open them to a width of four rods (66 feet).

From about 1880 to 1910, Nebraska's counties and townships built individual systems of roads leading from farm communities to trade centers. Little attention was given to roads between major cities, as the railroads served these needs. Bridge construction during this period was financed either by private companies, which built and operated toll bridges over major stream crossing, or by the counties and townships. Not until 1905 did the legislature pass the first law involving the state in road and bridge problems. This law required the State Board of Irrigation, when requested by the county, to furnish plans for bridges costing more than $200.

More active state participation began in 1911, when legislation was enacted requiring the state to act jointly with the counties in letting contracts for certain bridges, with the state paying half of the construction costs. This law also provided that such bridges should be constructed with a load capacity of not less than 20 tons. This foresight resulted in great savings to the state when heavy truck traffic began, since many of these bridges did not have to be replaced.

The state began participating in road construction in 1914 as a result of a 1913 law which provided that the state and counties should act in partnership on the construction of certain roads, with the cost being split on a 50–50 basis.

Gasoline Tax Finances Progress

The forerunner of the present Nebraska state highway system was laid out in 1917 with the creation of a state-aid road fund, financed by property taxes, to match funds available from the 1916 Federal-Aid Road Act. During the next two years, a state road system of about 4,500 miles was designated, with the state required to pay the counties for the maintenance of these roads. In 1926, the state assumed the responsibility for the maintenance of all roads on the state-federal system. This was financed by Nebraska's first gasoline tax, two cents per gallon in 1925.

Over the years, the agency responsible for state road building has operated under various names. The State Board of Irrigation, created in 1895, handled early bridge problems. In 1911, its name was changed to the State Board of Irrigation, Highway, and Drainage. Then in 1919, the board became the Department of Public Works. In 1933 it became the Department of Roads and Irrigation and in 1957, its name was changed to the Department of Roads.

Administration of the state highway department from 1895 to 1919 was under a board consisting of the governor, attorney general, commissioner of public lands and buildings, and the state engineer. Since 1919, the state engineer, appointed by the governor and confirmed by the legislature, has been the head of the department.

The State Highway Commission was created in 1953, consisting of eight lay-members appointed by the governor with the approval of the legislature. The commission acts in an advisory capacity to the state engineer in the establishment of broad policies for carrying out the duties and the responsibilities of the department. Also, to keep the public informed of the policies and activities of the department, the commission holds highway hearings throughout the state.

Notable Events

To note memorable events over the past 25 years, several major milestones were celebrated. The first took place in 1995, with a year-long tribute paid to the department as it celebrated its 100-year anniversary, including a proclamation from the governor, a special commemorative silver coin, and festive functions held across the state.

A second event occurred in 2005, as the department commemorated the 50th anniversary of the building of Interstate 80 in Nebraska by joining other states retracing the original convoy route taken by Dwight D. Eisenhower as a young Army officer in 1919. Commemorative souvenir license plates and pins were distributed, and a booklet was published outlining significant dates and people connected with the building of the Interstate across Nebraska.

In 2013, in conjunction with the centennial year of the Lincoln Highway, the nation's first transcontinental highway, the 500th state historical marker was placed in Nebraska at Elkhorn on an original brick section of the highway that was paved in 1920 and is one of the best-preserved stretches.

The original 4,500-mile state system of loosely connected rural roads, maintained by the counties, has grown to a well-integrated system of almost 10,000 miles, constructed and maintained by the department. Total annual highway expenditures have increased from about $250,000 in 1917, when the state-aid road fund was established, to over $198 million in 1989. While revenue for the state highway program came from property taxes in 1917, today it is derived almost entirely from road use taxes and lees. With the exception of a $20 million bond issue in 1969, Nebraska's state highway program has always operated on a conservative "pay-as-we-go" basis.

As a result of the department's 1988 Highway Needs Study, the 1989 Legislature provided a substantial increase in road-building revenue, which enabled the department to accelerate its future program. This legislation is one of the most important events in Nebraska highway history.

Vision 2032

In 2012, Vision 2032, a 20-year long-range statewide transportation plan was released, providing a process to build upon the past and help prepare for the challenges of the future. The plan provided an overarching policy guide that established the goals, objectives, and strategies to address the transportation challenges and opportunities facing Nebraska over the next 20 years. The Vision 2032 goals were centered on four themes: 1) Safety, 2) Mobility, 3) Environmental Stewardship, and 4) Coordination & Cooperation. Vision 2032 was designed to be stakeholder-driven, system-oriented, focused, and responsive to federal as well as state policy directives.

After completion of Vision 2032, the department's leadership team reviewed the agency's strategic plans, goals and performance measures, resulting in a streamlined mission statement: "We provide the best possible statewide transportation system for the movement of people and goods," as well as eight strategic goals: safety; fiscal responsibility; environmental stewardship; project delivery; asset management; mobility; communication;

coordination, collaboration and cooperation, and workforce development.

In July 2013, the department entered a new era with the Build Nebraska Act, which will benefit Nebraskans from east to west through its provisions for funding long-awaited and planned improvements. The Act was passed by the Nebraska Legislature in 2011 and dedicates a quarter-cent from the state portion of the 5.5 cent sales tax to road improvements for 20 years. It provides a new source of revenue to address highway capital improvement needs. Under the two-year lead period, from the time of the bill's enactment to its effective date, the department diligently prepared projects for the first 10 years of the program, from 2014 to 2023. Several projects, including beltway, bypass, and expressway projects, will be completed, thanks to these additional funds.

Thanks to the diligence and dedication of employees, transportation partners and stakeholders, the groundwork has been laid for safety, mobility, environmental priorities, and economic vitality to continue its forward movement in Nebraska.

Recollections of a Director–State Engineer

The following includes excerpts from The Nebraskan, *a book authored by George E. Johnson, published by Anna Publishing, 1981. George E. Johnson (1885–1967) was Director-State Engineer of the Nebraska Department of Roads from 1915–1923. He also served on the very first AASHTO Advisory Board.*

"One of the first things I did after being appointed was to work with other state

engineers to get a law passed in the United States Congress — the first Federal Aid Road Bill making allotments of money to the states, for the construction of inter-connecting highways between the states. This law was passed with the condition that a state given money by the federal government would raise a matching sum. The bill provided that each state must set up a highway department that would be capable of handling the engineering and construction work required in the program.

"The first state law implementing this Federal Aid Road Bill was passed in Nebraska in 1917, and accepted the aid authorized by the federal government. It also authorized the State Highway Department to cooperate with the counties and the federal government in laying out the highway system. This assignment required a great deal of traveling by both Roy Cochran and me. Many conferences were held with different county groups throughout the state. We began setting up appointments with the county boards to explain how the program would work and to enlist their support.

"Now anyone who has had any experience with county boards in Nebraska knows that this was a Herculean task. These county boards were made up of many rugged individualists who often did not agree among themselves and who frequently had different axes to grind. However, the work went well; we secured many favorable resolutions from the county boards, and Roy Cochran and I soon worked out the location of the state highway system. Then, we got many resolutions from county boards recommending that the money allocated to their counties be spent locally on the roads selected as the state highway system.

"This problem of locating the state highway system turned out to be not only an engineering problem but a real problem in diplomacy. Before the work was completed, the United States had entered into the First World War. Roy Cochran secured a captain's commission and went to France. The work which had been started on the state highway system before the war slowed down. However, during the war period, much of the ground work was laid through field engineering activities in preparing plans and specifications to get ready for a large program when the war ended.

"Soon after the war was over, President Wilson called the heads of the state highway departments for a meeting in Washington. He told us that he was concerned about the depressing conditions, especially unemployment. We were quick to react. We told the president that while the original program had provided only seventy-five million dollars for all of the states to be spread over a five-year period, we had developed

our field and office work to the point at which we could award contracts immediately for an additional two-hundred million dollars. We pointed out that this would go a long way toward relieving the depression and unemployment.

"At that time, I was a member of the Executive Committee of the Association of State Highway Officials and the State Highway Advisory Board which served as a liaison committee between the Federal Highway Department and the State Highway Departments. Each committee member represented a group of states. I represented Iowa, Kansas, Nebraska and Missouri. This committee was appointed by the Secretary of Agriculture as the Federal Highway Department at that time was under the jurisdiction of the Agriculture Department. I was first appointed by Secretary David H. Huston and then reappointed by Secretary Edwin T. Meredith. Still later, I was reappointed by Secretary Henry E. Wallace, father of Henry A. Wallace who became vice-president.

"I mention these facts to show that the stimulus for the expansion of the State

Highway Department was an effort by the federal government to beef up the economy after the First World War. Each year the heads of the state highway departments combined to urge Congress to spend additional monies under this good roads program. These efforts were successful, additions were made every year, and by 1923, when I resigned as State Engineer, the State Highway System was essentially completed. Moreover, this system was completed largely on locations originally selected by Roy Cochran and me with the cooperation of the county commissions. More than three-thousand miles of highway had been completed. The staff of the State Highway Department, which had only a handful of people in 1915, had been expanded to more than six-hundred. Work had been provided for thousands. The original objective of President Wilson to stimulate the economy during the depression and unemployment following World War I had been accomplished. By 1923, the total highway system in Nebraska, which consisted of roads other than those getting federal support, consisted of about 6,500 miles."

NEVADA

Nevada Department of Transportation

Rudy Malfabon, P.E.
Director

YEAR FORMED **1917**

FTE **Approx. 1,785**

KEY FACTS
TOTAL STATE ROAD MILES (OWNED BY STATE HIGHWAY AGENCY) **5,293**

STATE-OWNED BRIDGES **1,041**

TRANSIT TRIPS PER YEAR **64.82 million**

In Nevada, pioneer trails of the mid-nineteenth century westward expansion paved the path on which the modern roadways of today were built. In 1917, the Nevada Legislature created a Department of Highways. As transportation needs grew, so too did the highway department. Initially a small department subsisting on monies from the general fund, racetrack revenues, truck rentals to contractors and other meager revenue generators, the Department of Highways grew to the largest unit of state government in the early 1920s. It was only the start to the meteoric growth of a transportation system criss-crossing the state's 109,826 square miles of desert and mountain expanse.

As reported by the U.S. Census Bureau in 2011, Nevada was the fastest-growing state for five straight decades. In fact, the state experienced a staggering 650 percent population increase between 1950 and 1990 and a 35 percent increase just from 2000 to 2010. As the population sky-rocketed, so too did miles traveled on Nevada roads- rocketing up from 5.75 billion annual vehicle miles of travel in 1978 to 22.8 billion in 2012. Likewise, the department's responsibility for urban roadways increased. In 1976, there were 5,214 miles of state-maintained road designated as rural. By 2013,

that rural mileage had dwindled to 4,726, while urban mileage increased.

But how to accommodate the transportation needs that come with such rapid growth? The first step was a move to a truly multi-modal transportation system. The state's Department of Highways became the Nevada Department of Transportation in 1979. In the same year, the Nevada Legislature enabled the department to prepare a state rail plan. Both milestones were indicative of a move toward a truly diverse agency which now supports all modes of transportation, from more than 13,000 lane miles of state road to airport inspections, rail planning, and oversight of federal funding providing more than one million rides annually on buses and other transit vehicles across the state.

And, as Nevada's population skyrocketed, the Nevada Department of Transportation's work program ramped up accordingly, from capital expenditures of $41 million in 1967 (as a sample year) to the state's largest-ever capital work program of $723 million in fiscal year 2012. As just one example, a highway super project program launched in the late 1990s formed the basis for many freeway improvements now encircling Las Vegas and Reno. Interstate 15

was widened from Las Vegas south to the California state line. A lifeline of Nevada's economy that supports more than 75 percent of southern Nevada's heavy truck traffic, the interstate also carries an influx and exodus of tourists between California and "Sin City" every weekend. Near the Hoover Dam, the Mike O'Callaghan–Pat Tillman bypass bridge now safely and more directly routes cars across the Colorado River, replacing a previous narrow two-lane road and helping enhance security at the neighboring dam. The super project program also set in motion important transportation enhancements of today. In the northern Las Vegas Valley, US 95 continues to be enhanced and widened as development plunges northward. And in northern Nevada, the state capital was connected to the interstate system with the 2012 opening of the I-580 freeway extension. Meanwhile, bypasses around Carson City and Boulder City progress forward.

While the last quarter century has infused the state with innovative road projects, it has also seen construction management innovations such as the use of design-build and construction manager at risk contracting methods. In such projects, design and construction are developed more collaboratively,

leading to construction efficiencies and reducing both project length and cost and minimizing risk. Launched in 2008, the department's first de-sign-build project, the I-15 North Design-Build, completed nearly a year ahead of schedule and improved traffic mobility and safety for the approx-imately 250,000 vehicles that travel the stretch of interstate daily. Another recent milestone came with completion of other award-winning design-build projects on the vital I-15 thoroughfare that runs alongside the Las Vegas Strip and across southern Nevada. Mean-while, the department is embarking on Project Neon, a multi-year mega project to provide ever-increased connectivity, mobility, and safety to accommodate expansion along Las Vegas' primary interstate corridor.

Faced with construction costs that have roughly quadrupled since 1977, the department has also made transporta-tion financing progressions. The state has issued nearly a billion dollars in transportation bonds since 2000 for the construction of five "super projects." By providing an influx of otherwise-un-available funding, bonding can help provide the money necessary to build the vital projects needed today. Not only are important projects completed

more quickly than other funding could provide, but it also helps the depart-ment reduce both potential construc-tion inflation costs and tax increases. Just in 2013 alone, the department completed a $131 million Highway Revenue Refunding Bond sale that will net the state savings of $12.6 million on existing debt service payments.

And, from the horse-drawn-road projects of the past century to the in-novative and technologically-advanced construction of today, the Nevada Department of Transportation has fully integrated technology into administra-tion of state road projects. Today, elec-tronic bidding, contract e-signatures, and electronic construction documen-tation provide the most efficient con-tracting and administration of many department construction contracts. The department's electronic bidding alone will help save an estimated $60,000 in paper, printing, and mailing costs every year, not to mention greatly advancing staff and contractor efficiency. A formal contractor working group and other collaborative efforts between NDOT and the contracting community have paved the way to more efficient proj-ects. In fact, major NDOT construction projects closed out in 2013 cumulative-ly came in $200,000 under budget.

In Nevada's harsh high-desert environment, it is not just building quality roads that matters. Maintaining and operating those roads across the rugged desert and mountain landscape is also crucial. NDOT's skilled maintenance crews are utilizing ever-more sophisticated techniques for increasingly urban and highly-traveled roadways. Gone are the days when a chip seal would suffice as a new pavement surface running through the heart of the capital city and past the state capitol itself. More sophisticated maintenance efforts, with enhanced traffic control to account for increased urban traffic, are the name of the game.

The department also looks to the newest technology as an ally in maintaining Nevada roads, such as roadside weather reporting stations and professional meteorological reports to forecast the path of impending storms along Nevada's freeways and interstates for the most targeted response. In fact, Nevada was one of the lead states testing in-vehicle sensors in some snow plows and haul trucks to remotely track and respond to weather conditions. An equipment preservation program launched in 2008 works to effectively, and cost efficiently, keep NDOT maintenance vehicles safely on the road. Consisting of four components, including equipment refurbishment and rebuilding as well as proactive preventative maintenance and performance-based specifications to purchase longer-lasting, quality equipment, the program saved Nevada taxpayers over $20 million in a sample two-year span while providing a top state fleet of vehicles ready to preserve and make safe Nevada roads.

With new construction and maintenance innovations, the department has not lost sight of those it serves: Nevada citizens and transportation stakeholders. While building and maintaining the state's transportation network, the department keeps Nevada citizens and travelers front and center. Nevada motorists can utilize a bevy of Nevada Department of Transportation on-line TV cameras, as well as travel time and road weather reporting systems, to get a view of the road ahead before traveling. The traveler information is an important way for drivers to make decisions based on road conditions. Is there an incident blocking the roadway, or perhaps extreme weather conditions? Knowing that before driving allows motorists to plan appropriately, which makes for less congested and safer roadways.

And, NDOT knows that there is nothing more important than traffic safety. In 1979, there were 302 traffic deaths on Nevada roads. As an ever-rising number of miles were traveled on Nevada roads, traffic deaths spiked to 431 in 2006. That same year, NDOT and stakeholders statewide came together to develop the Strategic Highway Safety Plan, with life-saving strategies targeting the state's most prevalent traffic safety issues, from unbelted, impaired, and distracted driving to pedestrian and intersection safety. The state's Zero Fatalities traffic safety campaign, launched in 2011, has also reached 95 percent of Nevadans with life-saving safe driving messages through TV, radio, and more. In 2013, thanks in part to the state's unified traffic safety efforts, traffic deaths were lowered to 268.

Throughout all major NDOT activities, the department benefits greatly from the oversight and direction of the state transportation board. Comprised of the governor, lieutenant governor, state controller, and four public members, the board guides the direction to the best and most efficient transportation projects and initiatives for all stakeholders statewide. In 2011, the board began monthly instead of quarterly meetings. Also established at the same time was board review of project contracts of over $5 million and service agreements of more than $300,000.

It takes dedication and expertise to efficiently and cost-effectively construct, maintain and operate a transportation system across a state as vast as Nevada. NDOT employee workloads and numbers continue to be balanced by improved technology, streamlined processes and hard-working staff. With increased Nevada population and transportation needs, the department workforce has risen from 1,469 employees in 1990 to the 1,700+ employees who now plan, build, operate, maintain, and administer an integrated, statewide transportation system that will keep Nevada moving through the next century and beyond.

Today, 13,000-plus lane miles of state road connect Nevada, from the tourism mecca of Las Vegas to the gold and silver-laden valleys of Goldfield and Tonopah, and from the blue depths of Lake Tahoe to the snow-capped Ruby Mountains. Where pioneers once tread, the pioneering spirit remains alive in advancing Nevada transportation for all who rely upon it.

NEW HAMPSHIRE

New Hampshire Department of Transportation

Christopher D. Clement, Sr.
Commissioner

YEAR FORMED **1905**

FTE **Approx. 1,558**

KEY FACTS

TOTAL STATE ROAD MILES
(OWNED BY STATE HIGHWAY
AGENCY) **3,925**

STATE-OWNED BRIDGES **1,298**

TRANSIT TRIPS PER YEAR
1.3 million

From its earliest colonial days, the evolution of transportation in New Hampshire has had a major impact on the economy, population, and daily life in the Granite State. European settlers traveled by canoe or footpaths established by Native Americans. Many of those footpaths became the first primitive roads that were the foundation of immigration, settlements, and commerce.

By the mid-1800s, horse-drawn carriages were the personal mode of choice, even as railroads began connecting citizens and towns and shortening distances to markets and vacation destinations.

The advent of the automobile in the early 1900s drove the need for a better road system. In 1905, the New Hampshire Legislature created the State Highway Department and authorized the construction and maintenance of highways with state funds. By 1919, state road mileage had increased to 989 miles. Four years later, a road toll tax of one cent per gallon was established. And so began an extended era of building an extensive modern highway system to serve New Hampshire citizens and visitors.

Following World War II, the New Hampshire Legislature authorized the construction of an Eastern Turnpike from Seabrook to Portsmouth. The growth of the state's Turnpike System was in response to the need to expand the highway system in the southern part of New Hampshire to meet increased demand.

The New Hampshire Turnpike System currently consists of 90 miles of limited access highway, 36 miles of which are part of the Interstate System. Since beginning operations in 1950, the Turnpike System has contributed to the development of New Hampshire. It has also been a major factor in the growth of the tourism industry in the state.

In 1955, the first automatic toll machines in the world were installed on the Everett Turnpike in Merrimack. Five decades later, the Turnpike System introduced electronic tolling, followed in 2011 and 2013 by the first high-speed "Open Road Tolling" facilities in the New England region in Hampton (Blue Star Turnpike) and Hooksett (Everett Turnpike).

Road construction and widening increased in the 1950s, and accelerated dramatically in the 1960s when the completion of I-93, I-95, and

I-89 opened up access to central and northern New Hampshire. Travel times across the state were dramatically reduced as motorists and goods moved about more freely. People had the flexibility to live further away from work locations, both from outside and within New Hampshire, and began commuting longer distances.

In 1986, the Department of Public Works and Highways was reorganized as the New Hampshire Department of Transportation, a reflection of the growing and broadening role required of the state agency. Its mission—"Planning, developing, and maintaining a state transportation network which will provide for safe and convenient movement of people and goods throughout the state by means of a system of highways and railroads, air service, mass transit, and other practicable modes of transportation in order to support state growth and economic development and promote the general welfare of the citizens of the state."

Many of New Hampshire's historic bridges, whether made of wood, steel, stone, or concrete, collectively, represent two centuries of changing technology, engineering and style.

Some 80 bridges in the region are listed on the National Register of Historic Places, including more than 60 functioning covered bridges.

The Memorial Bridge replacement project on New Hampshire's seacoast is just the latest example of how the NHDOT has utilized innovative design, technology, and construction to improve the state's infrastructure. In addition to its economic importance to the region—connecting Portsmouth, New Hampshire and Kittery, Maine, and restoring the missing link on U.S. Route 1 between Ft. Kent, Maine, and Key West, Florida—the new $84 million lift bridge is a historical and emotional bond to the past. The motto for the project was fitting—"Connecting Generations and Building Communities."

The new Memorial Bridge's engineering innovations also make it a vision for the future of transportation. It is the first truss bridge of its kind in the world, designed and built without gusset plates. The three spans were designed with an uninterrupted and consistent profile, thus expediting fabrication and construction. It took just 18 months to demolish its predecessor and build the new bridge.

Long known for its excellence in winter maintenance, the New Hampshire Department of Transportation has been a model state for many years in effectively clearing snow and ice from roads during winter storms. In 1941, New Hampshire was the first state in the United States to use salt as an anti-icing tool for routine winter maintenance.

For much of the past 25 years, New Hampshire has been one of the fastest growing states in the nation. While it remains a relatively rural state, many of its residents commute long distances to their workplaces. This has produced the ongoing need to increase highway capacity when possible, while upgrading and improving safety along many two-lane corridors. There is also renewed emphasis on maintaining and preserving the highway system so that it continues to meet the ever-increasing demands of 21st century commuting, commercial, and recreational use.

Another major challenge is meeting the transportation needs with more mobility options, primarily bus transit. Passenger rail service remains limited in New Hampshire, even as studies are ongoing as to the feasibility of extending current passenger service north from Massachusetts.

One of the largest highway projects in New Hampshire history is the ongoing rebuilding and widening of 18 miles of Interstate 93 from the Massachusetts State Line north to Manchester, New Hampshire's largest city. This $800 million project will transform a four-lane Interstate highway that was constructed 50 years ago into an eight-lane highway with much-needed additional traffic capacity and safety improvements.

Today, the New Hampshire Department of Transportation and its dedicated employees remain committed to providing a safe and reliable transportation system for Granite State residents and visitors. Despite the great challenges being faced to maintain, preserve, and improve the system, the NHDOT's mission is clear—"Transportation excellence enhancing the quality of life in New Hampshire."

NEW JERSEY

New Jersey Department of Transportation

Joseph Bertoni
Acting Commissioner

YEAR FORMED **1966**

FTE **Approx. 3,443**

KEY FACTS
TOTAL STATE ROAD MILES (OWNED BY STATE HIGHWAY AGENCY) **2,323**

STATE-OWNED BRIDGES **2,371**

TRANSIT TRIPS PER YEAR
401 million

NJDOT—Building the Future of Transportation

The contrast between New Jersey's multi-modal transportation network of today and our means to get from point A to point B in prior centuries is so vivid that it is easy to overlook some features that have endured or have gained renewed appreciation.

New Jersey's 17th-century European settlers relied upon the same footpaths created by Native American inhabitants, eventually converting many of them to dirt roads for stagecoaches and later to paved highways. Fast-forward to the present, where the New Jersey Department of Transportation (NJDOT) and nearly 100 municipalities have embraced Complete Streets policies to once again make some of these routes safe for those traveling on foot.

In 1906, the state legislature established the Division of Motor Vehicles to help bring some order to the 13,000 unlicensed motorists who drove wherever they pleased at any speed they wished. Today, there are six million licensed drivers in New Jersey, and it is the primary mission of NJDOT to keep them safe.

The department promotes safety through a variety of programs that rely on data to drive and prioritize investment decisions. These range from major road and bridge projects funded in the annual capital program, to smaller initiatives that target high-crash locations for safety measures such as guide rail, lighting, or rumble strips.

New Jersey is the most densely populated state in the nation, with 8.5 million residents sharing 8,729 square miles. That is 974 residents per square mile sharing 38,100 miles of highways, county roads and local streets as they travel to work, school, shops, restaurants, and other destinations every day. In this environment, technology and communication play critical roles in maintaining mobility.

Building Toward Safety

Consistently high-investment levels in roads and bridges have become a hallmark of Governor Chris Christie's administration. NJDOT is responsible for 13,300 lane-miles of highways and 2,574 bridges. The department has more than $6.5 billion in projects in concept development, preliminary engineering, or active construction, including more than 100 projects currently in construction.

Its $1.9 billion proposed FY 15 capital program targets those roads and

bridges most in need of repair and funds preventive maintenance programs to extend the useful life of these assets.

Reports on the condition ratings of roads and bridges help the media tell the story of aging infrastructure to the public. NJ-DOT views these news accounts as opportunities to help residents understand why we select some projects for immediate attention, and how we promote construction methods, such as pre-cast bridge components that save time and money, which allows the department to advance more projects sooner than otherwise would be possible.

- In 2008, just 47 percent of NJDOT highways were rated in acceptable condition. That figure now stands at 58 percent, with the goal to drive that number to 80 percent by 2021.
- A total of 330 bridges owned or maintained by NJDOT were rated structurally deficient in 2010. By the beginning of 2014, that number had been reduced to 293, with the goal to reduce that figure to 165 by 2021.

Among the notable projects currently underway is the $1 billion-plus Pulaski Skyway Rehabilitation Project, which is the largest single project in the history of NJDOT. It is the first complete overhaul of the 3.5-mile-long structure that links

Newark and Jersey City since it opened to traffic in 1932. It has been designated as structurally deficient since 1983.

The project entered a critical phase in April 2014, when the two northbound Skyway lanes were closed to traffic for a period of two years. The closure followed intensive collaboration with local officials and successful efforts to identify alternate routes and travel modes for the 40,000 motorists who drive the northbound lanes each day.

Another major project affects the Jersey Shore. The department is accelerating a $265 million reconstruction of Route 35, a highway that was severely damaged during Superstorm Sandy in October, 2012. The department is balancing the desire to complete the job as quickly as possible with the need to maximize travel capacity during the busy summer tourist season.

Despite right-of-way constraints, the Department was able to design the project to incorporate designated bike lanes along 10 miles of the 12.5-mile-long project, with sharrows and roadside signs in the remaining portion.

A $900 million Direct Connection project involving I-295 outside of

Philadelphia, Pennsylvania will improve safety and the operational performance of the busiest interchange in the southern part of the state.

Safety is a product of planning, and NJDOT is currently updating its strategic safety plan to better coordinate a wide range of initiatives with sister agencies, state metropolitan planning organizations and local stakeholders. Our goal is to create a unified safety asset management plan that uses data to drive investments in the same way we prioritize road and bridge projects.

The department's Safety Service Patrol quickly responds to incidents along heavily traveled commuter corridors throughout the state during peak travel times. The patrols move disabled vehicles from travel lanes or fix a problem to get disabled vehicles on the move as quickly as possible.

This program helps reduce the number of secondary crashes that are caused when motorists unexpectedly encounter congestion caused by the initial incident. The average time for NJDOT to clear an incident is now less than 50 minutes. Twenty years ago, it took more than two hours.

Building Capacity
Through Information

It is financially and geographically impossible for NJDOT to build or expand its way out of traffic congestion. There is neither the money nor space to do so. That's where technology and communication come in.

The department has deployed numerous Transportation Systems Management & Operations strategies to maximize the capacity of its roadway network. These strategies include Intelligent Transportation Systems (ITS), Work Zone Management, Special Events Management, and Emergency Management.

ITS includes surveillance and early detection CCTVs and real-time communication with motorists through Dynamic Message Signs (DMS) and its *www.511nj.org* website.

Traffic responsive and adaptive signal systems give the department powerful tools to manage traffic. The department has 300 traffic responsive signals that operators can adjust from a remote control room based on video of traffic volumes fed from the signals to the control room.

Adaptive signals take this process one step further and automatically adjust signal times without any input from an operator. These signals process video images at the signal control box at the intersection and give more green time where it is needed most. They revert to a baseline cycle when congestion is cleared.

This technology is in place near the Meadowlands Sports Complex where the Jets and Giants play NFL football games, and is being used at locations affected by the Pulaski Skyway and Direct Connection construction projects.

NJDOT has 175 DMS installed along its highways. The department gathers data from Bluetooth readers, E-ZPass tag readers, and third parties to compute trip times and display this information on DMS. This informs motorists of congestion ahead and provides them with an opportunity to consider adjustments to their route.

Social media is an increasingly important way to communicate with motorists. The department has launched its own YouTube channel (NJDept-Transportation) and created a Twitter account (@skywayrehab) in connection with the Pulaski Skyway project.

NEW MEXICO

New Mexico Department of Transportation

Tom Church
Cabinet Secretary

YEAR FORMED **1912**

FTE **Approx. 2,448**

KEY FACTS
TOTAL STATE ROAD MILES
(OWNED BY STATE HIGHWAY
AGENCY) **11,965**

STATE-OWNED BRIDGES **2,967**

TRANSIT TRIPS PER YEAR
15 million

New Mexico is one of the youngest states in the United States, admitted to statehood 102 years ago. New Mexico is famous for many things, including our green chile, spectacular sunsets, the Roswell incident, the Los Alamos National Lab (the birthplace of the atom bomb), and the world famous Balloon Fiesta. But we are also known for our vast highway infrastructure.

It all began in 1912, the year of our statehood. That July, James French was appointed New Mexico's first State Engineer by then-Governor William C. McDonald. During his tenure, French was responsible for creating the first state road map, in addition to developing and creating the first road and bridge system in New Mexico.

French found the roads throughout New Mexico to be "deplorable" and "impossible to travel from county to county with any degree of comfort." No systematic road building had been accomplished due to lack of centralized organization. He took the lead in developing and creating the implementation policy necessary to direct all highway operations.

Today the New Mexico Department of Transportation (NMDOT) is one of the largest business enterprises in

New Mexico with a budget of over $830 million and a workforce of 2,487 employees.

Like any business, we are accountable to our customers, who are the people we serve and the users of the transportation system.

New Mexico serves as a bridge connecting major trade corridors with Arizona, Texas, Colorado, and Mexico. The NMDOT supports the economy through our activities to maintain our roadways and preserving our infrastructure, pavements and bridges. We are focused on rehabilitating and preserving existing infrastructure to maintain our assets in good condition.

Over the years, New Mexico has seen great accomplishments in its transportation infrastructure. Today New Mexico's transportation system is the foundation for improving our economy and leveraging our resources. It connects every part of the United States allowing goods and services to be distributed all across the country in a safe and effective manner, be it by rail, mass transit, train, or aviation. The most historic highway in New Mexico follows an important historic north-to-south transportation corridor paralleling the

Rio Grande, Called El Camino Real de Tierra Adentro, "The Royal Road to the Interior Lands," linking Mexico City to Santa Fe, New Mexico. In honor of this historic trade route, the first major highway in New Mexico was officially named El Camino Real Highway in 1905. It later evolved into the present day realigned Interstate 25, where it is still the major north-to-south arterial in New Mexico.

Route 66 runs through New Mexico, a major thoroughfare for those heading west which was superseded by the completion of the Interstate System through the state.

The first New Mexico urban project was on US 66 in Tucumcari. First planned and designed in New Mexico between 1925 and 1927, US 66 went through several alignment changes through 1985, when Interstate 40 was built.

The completion of the Rio Grande Gorge Bridge near Taos in 1965 was a major undertaking. The 600-foot-tall bridge is the second highest in the U.S. highway system and is part of U.S. Route 64, a major east–west road. The bridge underwent a $2.4 million "facelift" from 2011–2012 that included repair and restoration work including structural steelwork, a new concrete deck surface, new sidewalks, ramps, curbs, and gutters.

Another major undertaking began in 2000 with the two-year reconstruction of the Big-I. The interchange is where Interstates 25 and 40 meet in Albuquerque, which is also New Mexico's largest city. The NMDOT rebuilt the interchange to make it safer and more efficient, providing far better access. The project involved 111 lane-miles of construction and 45 new and 10 rehabilitated bridges. The Big I contains a total of 55 bridges within the project, of which eight precast concrete segmental bridges are curved "flyover" ramp bridges facilitating traffic north-to-south and east-to-west.

We are grateful to AASHTO for its help with strengthening our transportation system by providing training, technology, and other resources.

As we look forward, transportation funding is among the most important trends and emerging issues that will influence, shape, and strengthen the next century of achievement using ever-evolving technology and its role in transportation.

NEW YORK

New York State Department of Transportation

Joan McDonald
Commissioner

YEAR FORMED **1907**

FTE **Approx. 8,700**

KEY FACTS
TOTAL STATE ROAD MILES
(OWNED BY STATE HIGHWAY
AGENCY) **15,024**

STATE-OWNED BRIDGES **7,460**

TRANSIT TRIPS PER YEAR
3.78 billion

New York State has been a leader in transportation innovation for generations, from the opening of the Erie Canal in 1825 to operating the nation's largest transit system today. The state's history is riddled with transportation superlatives, long enjoying the "first" and "biggest" designations spawned by drive and invention.

Building upon the state's rich past, creative, efficient, and cost-effective transportation improvements continue. Governor Andrew Cuomo knows the value of investing in transportation and has used it to help to create jobs, support the state's growing economy, enhance safety and mobility, and protect the environment.

New York City is at the heart of that efficiency. Its 8.3 million residents make it the nation's largest city, but more than half of its households do not own cars. They rely on transit.

That means one out of every three mass transit users in the Untied States lives in New York City or its suburbs. Approximately two-thirds of the nation's rail riders travel on one of the New York City metro area's lines. Subways, buses, and railroads operated by New York's Metropolitan Transportation

Authority (MTA) provide 2.62 billion trips each year. In the suburbs, that includes the two largest commuter railroads in the United States—the Long Island Rail Road and Metro-North Railroad. All told, the MTA operates the most fuel efficient transit system in the country.

Being at the forefront of transportation is nothing new for New York.

- The first traffic regulations in America were enacted in 1652 in New York City (then called New Amsterdam), directing that wagons and sleighs not be driven at a gallop.
- The world's first commercially operated steam ferry began service between New Jersey and lower Manhattan in 1811.
- The opening of the Erie Canal in 1825 changed New York State and the nation, spurring development west of the original colonies and making New York the financial capital of the world. Decades later, the canal served as a critical supply line that helped the North win the Civil War and stimulated economic growth across the country. Today, the canal remains a significant commercial and tourism route.
- The New York metropolitan area has the busiest airport system in

the United States, including John F. Kennedy International Airport and La Guardia Airport in Queens.

The New York State Department of Transportation (NYSDOT) has overseen much of the state's transportation history, tracing its roots back to our nation's founding. Today's NYSDOT had its beginnings in the Office of the Surveyor-General, which was established following the Revolutionary War. It was the State Engineer who was charged in 1817 with digging the Erie Canal. By 1846, a combined Office of State Engineer and Surveyor was established. It was renamed the Department of Public Works in 1878.

The "Good Roads" movement began in New York and quickly spread throughout the nation. New York's privately owned dirt turnpikes eventually became 81,000 miles of paved public highways, due in large part of the Highway Act of 1909, which established the Department of Highways. That agency helped build the first parkways and expressways in the nation, including—with the Governor Thomas E. Dewey Thruway (Thruway)—the beginnings of the Interstate System before there was a federal program to fund it.

With the advent of Interstate highway construction, growing transit service needs in urban areas, and expanding ports and air travel, the NYSDOT was established in 1967. Voter approval of a bond issue provided the new agency with $1.25 billion for highway and bridge improvements, $1 billion for public transportation capital projects and $250 million for airport improvements.

The state's primary emphasis after World War II was constructing new highways and bridges, but national financial difficulties in the 1970s undercut the state's ability to finance its aging infrastructure. In response, under former Governor Mario M. Cuomo, voters approved a $1.25 billion bond act in 1983, allowing New York to take advantage of an expected additional $1.92 billion in federal funding from the federal gas tax to repair or replace 1,500 state and local bridges and improve 2,100 miles of highways. In 1988, voters approved another bond act for $3 billion to continue the process of repairing and rebuilding highway infrastructure. Voters in 2005 also approved a $2.9 billion bond act for transportation projects statewide.

In recent years, under the leadership of Governor Andrew M. Cuomo, New

York State has been repairing, replacing and hardening its transportation infrastructure. The state's highway bridges are some of the oldest, most heavily used in the nation and they are brutalized by Northeastern weather. Governor Cuomo has made transportation investment one of the cornerstones of his economic development policy.

Governor Cuomo's landmark NY Works program, introduced in 2012, invested more than $1 billion to accelerate more than 2,000 miles of paving and the rehabilitation or replacement of 120 bridges. Many of those projects took advantage of legislation the Governor signed in 2011, allowing projects to be designed and built under a single contract in order to save time and money.

That work has been completed in keeping with DOT's strategy of using resources wisely. It calls for preserving highways and bridges by keeping them in good condition through maintenance and rehabilitation, rather than building new ones.

The Governor also has launched initiatives that place a new focus on resiliency planning for all transportation modes.

In the face of an increasing number of extreme weather events, Governor

Cuomo in 2013 introduced the New York Rising Community Reconstruction Program. The federally funded program empowers communities that suffered significant storm damage to create and implement locally oriented strategies to rebuild and better prepare for future extreme weather.

Early this year, Governor Cuomo and Vice President Joe Biden launched "Reimagining New York for a New Reality," a $17 billion strategy that will transform New York's infrastructure, transportation networks, energy supply, coastal protection, weather warning system and emergency management to better protect New Yorkers from future extreme weather. This includes replacing and repairing more than 100 bridges at risk due to flooding

At the same time, the state has undertaken one of the largest infrastructure construction projects in the country. The New York State Thruway Authority began construction last year on the New NY Bridge to replace the Tappan Zee Bridge spanning the Hudson River north of New York City. The $3.9 billion project, which will help ensure regional mobility and economic health in the Hudson Valley and beyond, got un-

derway following more than a decade of delay. The bridge is scheduled for completion in 2018. It is being designed and constructed to last 100 years without major structural maintenance. It will feature eight traffic lanes, four breakdown/emergency lanes, state-of-the-art traffic monitoring systems, and a dedicated commuter bus lane.

Meanwhile, the NYSDOT early this year released for public comment an environmental impact statement about proposed improvements to intercity passenger rail service along the 463-mile Empire Corridor, which connects New York City to Albany and Niagara Falls. The study lays the groundwork for faster, more convenient service along the state's primary rail line.

In New York City and across the state, transportation agencies are harnessing technology to make traveling smarter, safer and more efficient, while connecting more and more directly with their users.

In the 1990s, it was the MetroCard, for example, that made it quicker and easier to pay fares on New York City's subways and buses. At the same time, the E ZPass electronic toll-collection system on the Thruway—at 559-miles the longest toll

superhighway in the United States—did the same for highways. The technology has spread across the East Coast, making tolling more efficient and reducing traffic congestion. The New York State Thruway Authority upgraded EZ Pass at several critical locations in 2007, enabling tolls to be collected from vehicles traveling at full highway speeds.

Similarly, advances in traffic monitoring and real-time traffic data collection has enabled New York's 511 intelligent transportation system to publicize highway conditions, manage traffic, and better direct travelers to avoid congestion. 511 also has trip planning and ride-share features to assist travelers and motorists.

From Long Island to Niagara Falls, the Southern Tier to the Canadian border, transportation is critical to New York State's economic health, and the mobility and well-being of its residents and visitors. The NYSDOT and its sister agencies are well positioned to address the challenges of the 21st century. By working smartly, embracing technology, and effectively managing their resources, New York's transportation agencies are supporting the state's growth while preserving its infrastructure and modernizing it for future generations.

NORTH CAROLINA

North Carolina Department of Transportation

Anthony J. Tata
Secretary

YEAR FORMED **1915**

FTE **12,500**

KEY FACTS
TOTAL STATE ROAD MILES
(OWNED BY STATE HIGHWAY
AGENCY) **79,274**

STATE-OWNED BRIDGES **16,976**

TRANSIT TRIPS PER YEAR
65 million

North Carolinians have long understood the intrinsic link between a strong economy and a well-connected, well-maintained transportation system. As towns grew up around seaports and along the railroad, citizens recognized the need for better trade and travel connections in the state's expanding economy.

The "Good Roads" movement in North Carolina began long before the creation of the State Highway Commission. In 1879, the North Carolina General Assembly passed the Mecklenburg Road Law, which was the first step toward creating a road system. While the law was intended to apply to the state as a whole, as worded, it only applied to Mecklenburg County. It allowed the county to build roads with financing from a property tax, and with four days of labor required of all males between the ages of 18 and 45.

As the 21st century dawned, interest in better roads spread from the mountains to the coast, and by 1895, most of the state's progressive counties had established tax-based road building plans. Emerging leaders in the state were able to look beyond local boundaries and see how a stronger road system could lead to greater opportunities. Charles B. Aycock, who later became known as the "Education Governor," was one such person. He said that good roads were needed if the state was to have good schools.

Countless individuals labored for better roads in these early years, but three stood out above the rest: Dr. J.A. Holmes, Col. Joseph Hyde Pratt, and Harriett Berry. Each was associated with the North Carolina Economic and Geological Survey, which was described as the "cutting-edge" of the roads

RECENT HIGHLIGHTS

– The landmark Strategic Transportation Investments legislation was signed into law in 2013, establishing the Strategic Mobility Formula, a data-driven approach that makes better use of existing funds to complete improvements that support economic growth and quality of life in North Carolina.

– Through the State-Funded Bridge Improvement Program we are investing more state funding in our bridges to help improve their condition. Through this program, the largest of its kind in state history, NCDOT is investing $810 million over four years to not only replace, but also strategically preserve or rehabilitate, existing bridges to help extend their lifespan and stretch existing resources further.

– We have also invested in our rail infrastructure to help improve mobility, connectivity and economic development across the state. In FY 2012–13, we began construction on projects as part of the Piedmont Improvement Program, investing $500 million in American Recovery and Reinvestment Act funds to improve the rail corridor between Raleigh and Charlotte. This initiative will greatly benefit both passenger and freight rail.

movement of the state. Each also headed the North Carolina Goods Roads Association during the two critical decades in which that association led the struggle for roads across the state. Berry quickly became an uncompromising force in the campaign for better roads. She pushed for the establishment of the State Highway Commission and, in 1915, helped draft legislation designed to establish and maintain a statewide highway system. The public supported Berry and began demanding a "unified state highway system." In response, the General Assembly passed the Highway Act of 1921, which authorized the state to take over some 5,500 miles of county roads; established a one-cent-per-gallon motor fuel tax to pay for the state's new responsibilities in highway construction and maintenance; and authorized and issued $50 million in state highway bonds for the construction of a state system of "hard surface and other dependable roads connecting the various county seats and other principal towns of every county." The decision to accept debt as a means of getting better roads was a pivotal one in the state's transportation history.

Road building continued full steam until the Great Depression. It was at this critical time, under the leadership of

Governor O. Max Garner, that the state assumed responsibility for all roads. Recognizing the damage done to the highway system from neglect during the Great Depression years, the General Assembly of 1935 made an emergency allocation of $3 million for bridge repair. Later in that session, more comprehensive action was taken to restore the financial stability of the road program.

By 1948, 64,000 miles of roads were linked across the state. One important area of this highway system, however, had been neglected—secondary roads. In the state that was leading the nation in school bus operations and ranked second in small, family farms, there was little cause for pride in the conditions of its school bus routes and farm-to-market roads. To address this growing concern, in 1949 a $200 million road bond was authorized and issued for secondary road improvements. This was one of several road bonds that enabled residents to build for the future and construct a highway system that earned North Carolina the title of the "Good Roads State."

During the years of the 1950s through the 1960s, the state's highway system developed into a complex network of highways reaching every corner of the state and affecting every citizen. State

and local leaders saw that the state's growth potential demanded an economy-oriented system that was responsive to rapidly changing needs in all areas of transportation. To meet this demand, the General Assembly, in 1971, placed the Highway Commission in the newly established Department of Transportation and Highway Safety (Highway Safety, which was the law enforcement arm of the agency, was moved out in 1979).

Specialized internal divisions were formally created in the mid-1970s for rail, ferries, public transportation, and bicycling, which was expanded in 1992 to include pedestrian activities. NCDOT's Division of Bicycle and Pedestrian Transportation is the oldest comprehensive state program of its kind in the nation. Additionally, the aviation function was transferred from the Department of Conservation and Development, and incorporated into the Department of Transportation, and major new funding amounts to support the state's airports were approved by the General Assembly.

Several milestones over the past 25 years led to greater investment in not only our highway system, but also in expanding other modes. The milestones helped develop the robust transportation network we have today.

1977—Voters approved a $300 million road bond issue to build a highway network to more efficiently link all regions of the state.

1989—The General Assembly created the Highway Trust Fund to provide dedicated funds for highway construction and improvements.

1993—The Governor's Highway Safety Program was established, and launched the "Click It or Ticket" and "Booze It and Lose It" campaigns, which became national models for such initiatives.

1994—Gov. Jim Hunt unveiled Transportation 2001, a plan to speed up highway construction, complete key transportation corridors, eliminate the highway maintenance backlog and develop a master plan for public transportation.

1996—A $950 million highway bond was approved to accelerate construction of urban loops and intrastates, and to pave secondary roads.

1997—The Transit 2001 Commission unveiled a plan to improve public transportation statewide.

2002—The General Assembly established the N.C. Turnpike Authority to develop, implement, and oversee toll road construction and maintenance in the state.

2003—Gov. Mike Easley signed into law North Carolina Moving Ahead!, a $700 million transportation initiative to address critical transportation needs—highway maintenance, modernization, and public transportation.

2007—The North Carolina Board of Transportation approved the state's first round of projects to be financed through Grant Anticipation Revenue Vehicles, commonly referred to as GARVEE bonds. The department's GARVEE program has helped fund critical transportation projects years earlier than through traditional financing and enabled the department to realize a net inflation-related savings of $540 million through 2013.

2011—Opened the first section of the Triangle Expressway, the state's first modern toll road.

2013—Governor Pat McCrory unveiled the Strategic Mobility Formula (SMF), which was passed by the General Assembly as part of the landmark Strategic Transportation Investments law. SMF modernized the way transportation projects are funded in North Carolina by using a data-driven approach.

Just as the state's leaders did in the 19th century, our leaders today understand that our transportation system plays an integral role in our state's economic growth and having a broad range of options is essential to meeting the travel and logistics demands of an ever-evolving society.

The state's 21st century transportation system consists of nearly 80,000 miles of modern roadways, the nation's second largest state-maintained highway system; as well as the nation's second largest state-operated ferry system that serves as a critical extension of our highway system along the coast. Transit systems provide transportation options to residents in all 100 counties, and a comprehensive system of bicycle routes

and greenways provides recreational opportunities, as well as commuting options in communities across the state. Both freight and passenger rail service continue to expand to meet the growing demands of customers. Additionally, the state that was the birthplace of modern aviation is now home to nearly 400 airports, heliports, and other landing areas, and continues to be on the leading-edge of this industry. A number of large, aviation-based companies have located to North Carolina because of our well-connected transportation system and talented skill base of employees. In addition to the divisions, the department also oversees North Carolina's Division of Motor Vehicles, Turnpike Authority, State Ports Authority and Global TransPark.

We want to ensure that all aspects of our transportation system are aligned and used to their full potential to create jobs, meet logistics needs and position North Carolina for future economic growth. We also want to maximize our existing financial resources and invest them in a way that will offer the greatest benefit to the state, while balancing the diverse needs of our communities. To that end, NCDOT developed and worked with the N.C. General Assembly to pass the landmark Strategic Transportation Investments law, establishing the Strategic Mobility Formula, a data-driven approach that makes better use of existing funds to complete improvements that support economic growth and quality of life in North Carolina.

With the Strategic Mobility Formula laying the groundwork for our future, we are now developing a vision for the next 25 years, which will allow us to fully implement our strategic direction for North Carolina and ensure we are leveraging our infrastructure to support job creation and economic development for decades to come. As our primary sources for funding our transportation system—the highway use tax, DMV fees and the gas tax—are becoming less reliable, we must look at other funding options to meet our needs over the long term. While we face significant challenges ahead, with the right investments, we can meet those needs head on, and add to North Carolina's story a reputation not only as the "Good Roads State" but as the "Good Transportation State."

NORTH DAKOTA

North Dakota Department of Transportation

Grant Levi, P.E.
Director

YEAR FORMED **1917**

FTE **Approx. 1,054**

KEY FACTS
TOTAL STATE ROAD MILES
(OWNED BY STATE HIGHWAY
AGENCY) **7,384**

STATE-OWNED BRIDGES **1,131**

TRANSIT TRIPS PER YEAR
2 million

The North Dakota Department of Transportation (NDDOT) has been part of a quiet revolution since it was established in 1917. Dirt roads have become highways, small cars and primitive trucks have become much larger, faster, and more sophisticated, and traffic counts have exploded.

North Dakota has the second smallest department of transportation, in terms of employees, in the nation and maintains more lane-miles of roads per maintenance employee than any other state—second only to Hawaii. During the 1960s and 1970s, the NDDOT took its can-do approach to another level by becoming the first state to complete its Interstate System.

Since then, the department has evolved with eight districts maintaining and working on over 17,000 lane miles of state roadways and 1,706 state bridges across North Dakota. Each of these districts' personnel is responsible for highway construction, engineering and administration, roadway and bridge maintenance, roadside maintenance, rest area/visitor center maintenance, materials testing, equipment and vehicle maintenance, traffic engineering, and highway sign maintenance.

Grant Levi, P.E., was appointed NDDOT Director in May 2013 by Governor Jack Dalrymple. As director, he leads the department, which has a $2.8 billion biennial budget and provides quality services for motor vehicles, driver's licenses, operation, construction, and maintenance of the state's highways. Levi is responsible for NDDOT's day-to-day operations, along with the executive staff that include: Deputy Director for Business Support Darcy Rosendahl, Deputy Director for Engineering Ron Henke, and Deputy Director for Driver and Vehicle Services Mark Nelson, along with over 1,000 employees across the state. NDDOT employees use state-of-the-art technology to maintain roads, survey and build roads as well as plan the state's transportation network.

The department hit a record number of more than one million vehicle registrations in 2011 and the trend continues to grow. Along with the increased number of vehicles, the number of licensed drivers is also growing at a rapid pace with over half a million licensed drivers taking to North Dakota's roads.

This growth is due to a number of factors including a growth in agriculture, manufacturing, and energy. Since the

1950s, North Dakota has seen a 405 percent increase in agriculture, and in the 21st century the state has seen a steady upward climb in the manufacturing industry and huge unprecedented growth in the energy industry, which all affect the state's transportation infrastructure. In fact, just 10 years ago North Dakota produced about 30,000 barrels of oil per day and in 2013 that number climbed to 860,000 barrels per day and it is predicted that this number will climb to over one million per day by the end of 2014, second only to Texas.

These and other factors have caused unprecedented traffic growth. From 2010–2012, North Dakota saw a 22 percent increase in traffic statewide and a 53 percent increase in traffic in the oil counties located in western North Dakota on all state highways.

The department is working hard to enhance roadways and services to meet the demands of this economic growth and, for the first time in history, North Dakota is one of America's most productive oil states, creating many challenges along the way.

Bringing an oil well into production requires about 2,300 inbound and outbound truckloads. Also an additional 32,000 to 40,000 wells will be drilled in the state's oil producing region over the next 15 to 20 years and oil-related traffic is expected to be a long-term trend that will have lasting impacts on traffic and infrastructure for many years to come.

But with these changes, comes new opportunity to enhance already successful systems at the NDDOT. It is why the department is always seeking ways to improve its technology, equipment and services.

The NDDOT is working hard to meet extra demands on the transportation infrastructure due to a number of unforeseen issues such as extreme winters creating record snowfall and spring flooding.

During the winter months, the NDDOT utilizes a fleet of 350 snowplows and various other snow-fighting tools to keep our state highways clear of snow and ice. The cabs of today's snowplows incorporate 21st century technologies and are nearly as high tech as the cockpit of a commercial airliner.

The latest tool in the department's arsenal is the TowPlow, a trailer-mounted plow pulled and operated with the ability to work in multiple lanes. The Tow-Plow is equipped with steering axles that will swing the trailer from behind the truck to the right and into an adjacent lane. This allows crews to clear wide roadways, such as interstates, ramps and wide shoulders more efficiently than is possible with a traditional plow.

One tool used by the department to help maintain the state's roadways is the use of a Pathways van. The van which travels at normal highway speeds is equipped with numerous cameras, computers, lasers, and a GPS to measure and catalog data and roadway images. These high-speed, high-resolution cameras gather views of the roadway while a linescan camera mounted in the back of the van collects digital images of the pavement surface. Engineers then use the data collected to evaluate and prioritize what work needs to be done on the state's roadways making them safer for the traveling public.

Another way the department has met the challenge of statewide growth is through an aggressive construction program which addresses infrastructure improvements to enhance safety and traffic movement. The NDDOT and the state legislature have invested millions of dollars to preserve and improve the transportation infrastructure.

In recent years, the department completed major road projects such as widening roadways, adding passing and turning lanes, enhancing road surface conditions and load carrying capacity, and by adding truck reliever routes in and around oil patch communities to alleviate traffic congestion and to make the roadways safer for motorists.

Overall, the challenges that North Dakota is facing are really no different than many of the challenges faced by the department's pioneers. Today's NDDOT no longer deals only with highway construction and maintenance, but is concerned with everything from rail and transit to state scenic byways. By embracing technology, the NDDOT has the opportunity to communicate with the public about road conditions and other transportation concerns that may impact them. Providing these services will continue to be a team effort and the employees of the North Dakota Department of Transportation are always willing to take on the challenges of providing a transportation system that safely moves people and goods.

NDDOT
North Dakota
Department of Transportation

OHIO

Ohio Department of Transportation

Jerry Wray
Director

YEAR FORMED **1905**

FTE **Less than 5,000**

KEY FACTS
TOTAL STATE ROAD MILES
(OWNED BY STATE HIGHWAY
AGENCY) **19,256**

STATE-OWNED BRIDGES **10,345**

TRANSIT TRIPS PER YEAR
117.1 million

RECENT HIGHLIGHTS
– Ohio's Jobs and Transportation Plan—
  $3 billion transportation plan

– The George V. Voinovich Bridge
  in Cleveland

– The Nelsonville Bypass in
  Southeastern Ohio

Transportation Shapes Ohio

Much of the character of Ohio is defined by transportation. Historically, the state's location has made it an important link between eastern America and parts further west and it has been largely shaped and distinguished through the communities born along its pathways of trails, rails, rivers, lakes, and canals. Throughout the 20th century and into the next, transportation is the figurative lifeblood of the economy and the defining element for a better quality of life for Ohioans and citizens throughout the country.

The state's legislature recognized the importance of transportation by calling for the creation of the Ohio Department of Highways (ODOH). With a purpose of research and education on the physical makeup of highways and their repair, the department began serving the public in 1905. Its duties expanded over the next decade, from creating a designated state system of highways to building and expanding that system.

In support of the United States' entry into World War I, ODOH began its practice of snow removal during the winter months of 1917–1918. What began as a means to ensure safe access for government troops and transports

became a much appreciated public service which continues to this day. After the war, a focus on improving highways for better year-round use in all weather conditions led to the upgrade of several thousand miles of roadways during the Roaring Twenties. As always, better roadways provide economic advantages, and Ohio's improving highway system was key in aiding farmers and industry with their quest to get goods to market and allowing travelers to make their way in the early era of the automobile.

In the early 1930s, the federal Work Progress Administration (later renamed the Works Projects Administration) began administering federally aided road projects nationwide. In Ohio, that meant employing more than 11,000 Ohioans in need of jobs during the Great Depression. During World War II, ODOH again continued its role of supporting a worthy transportation system able to serve the needs of the nation's war efforts. And out of that conflict, Eisenhower envisioned America's answer to the Autobahn network in Germany—the Interstate System. Transportation in Ohio and America changed forever through the Federal Aid Highway Act of 1956, which realized his vision and put the wheels in motion for the largest public

Courtesy of Ohio DOT, photo by William Rieter

works project in the country's history. Ohio would ultimately complete more than 1,500 miles of Interstates, and the state's location, as always, make these routes a significant crossroads in America's transportation network.

Though highway development remains essential, the transportation infrastructure in Ohio includes multiple modes beyond just roadways. The Department of Highways became the Ohio Department of Transportation (ODOT) in 1972 to reflect a stake in a broader base of transportation-related programs and services. ODOT now supports public transit, rail, waterways, aviation, pedestrian, and bicycle transportation programs while continuing to oversee the ever-important need for highway maintenance and improvement.

Transportation Today

Now more than ever, a robust transportation system in Ohio is a major engine for the state's economy and is essential for keeping and creating jobs. ODOT's transportation budget currently averages $2.8 billion annually. With the department's "results over resources" formula for maximizing its return on investment by focusing on what matters most to the state's transportation system, Ohio is well positioned to handle

current system challenges and plan for future system needs.

Ohio's transportation system is truly sizable in scope, and ODOT's role in overseeing a network of great importance to the region and the nation is reflected by these statistics:

- The department maintains the fourth largest segment of Interstate System in the country, with 6,700 lane miles.
- Statewide, Ohio has the nation's second largest total number of bridges, with 43,412.
- Ohio is third in the nation for total active rail miles.
- There are 716 miles of navigable waterways along the state's border. Ohio maritime ports and river terminals handle more than 103 million tons of cargo valued at $11 billion per year. Ohio is eighth in the nation for total water tonnage moved—more than the Panama Canal. Overall, Ohio's 26 ports have an economic impact of $6.5 billion annually.
- Ohio has 163 public-use airports, with six commercial airports averaging 11 million passengers each year. Overall, Ohio's general and commercial airports generate $10.5 billion in economic activity.

- The state is home to more than 3,000 miles of designated bike paths, and an estimated 4 million bicycle owners.

Modern Highlights
The Ohio Jobs and Transportation Plan

Governor John R. Kasich's Jobs and Transportation Plan, announced in 2013, commits nearly $3 billion in state, local, federal, and Ohio Turnpike funds to advance major new transportation projects across the state over a six-year period. These funds will go to construct 41 projects which improve motorist safety, reduce congestion, add capacity, and bolster the economy. The $3 billion in funding is comprised of $1.5 billion in bonds backed by toll revenues provided by the Ohio Turnpike and Infrastructure Commission, with an additional $1.5 billion raised through matching federal and local funds. This plan erases delays and accelerates most construction projects by more than 10 years.

Greater Department Savings

ODOT has identified ways to save more than $600 million through various means, including reducing its workforce by more than 700 through attrition and without lay-offs, purchasing energy more efficiently, and reducing underused vehicles. ODOT has also worked to implement a web-based payroll system, improving equipment management, and upgrading computer systems for information and resource management. These savings have been and will continue to be channeled into the budget for transportation projects that are helping Ohio's economy. The department as a whole is committed to new innovation and new approaches that continue a trend of reducing costs while improving service to the traveling public.

Division of Innovative Delivery

The ODOT joined many other states in embracing Public–Private Partnerships (P3) for delivery of public projects and services. This approach can provide numerous benefits in the finance, design, construction, maintenance, and operation of transportation projects.

To facilitate this approach, the department formed the Division of Innovative Delivery to develop and implement policy and programs. The division evaluates potential projects and assists in the development of procurement options for a project. Through the use of P3s, ODOT is more able to facilitate timely delivery of large scale projects consistent with state, regional, and local transportation plans.

The division is also seeking to identify and generate alternative funding sources from the state assets, such as the Ohio Turnpike and a sponsorship program for state-owned assets like rest areas, bridges and sections of highway.

The Columbus Crossroads Project (Phase 1)

This is the largest construction project in Central Ohio for ODOT. The work includes 22 new bridges, additional travel lanes on I-670, 31 retaining walls and the start of two new city streets that parallel the interstate. This project will improve safety, reduce congestion, and add capacity. Through aesthetic enhancements, wider sidewalks, bike lanes, decorative lighting, and landscaping, neighborhoods will once again feel connected to downtown Columbus.

The first phase of the I-70/I-71 construction, costing $200 million, is expected to be completed in 2014. On one of the bridges over the interstate, there will be a 240-foot cultural wall, subtly lit at night and only visible from the city street. This public display of art, designed by two Ohio artists, is a first for the state and reflects the cultural heritage of the region, past, and present.

The Cleveland Opportunity Corridor

Cleveland Opportunity Corridor is a $334 million transportation and economic development project aimed at connecting Interstate 490 to the University Circle. The Opportunity Corridor encompasses nearly 1,000 acres on Cleveland's southeast side. The area between I-490 and University Circle has become known as the "Forgotten Triangle" due to the lack of economic activity. Apart from the transportation benefits it could bring to the Cleveland area, this effort opens the potential for new economic development, new jobs, and a new identity for the community. Phase

1 of the project is anticipated to begin construction in the fall of 2014.

The Nelsonville Bypass

Completed at the end of 2013, this $200 million project was the final major piece of work transforming U.S. Route 33 from Franklin County southeast to the Ohio River into a modern, safer, four-lane roadway. This improved corridor serves as an Appalachian Gateway, offering greater connection and better mobility for the southeast region of the state.

The Cleveland Innerbelt (Phase 1 and 2)

The Cleveland Innerbelt Modernization Plan is focused on improving safety, reducing congestion and traffic delays, and modernizing travel along I-71, I-77, and I-90 through downtown Cleveland. This ongoing investment rehabilitates and reconstructs about five miles of urban interstate roadways, including the construction of two new bridges to carry I-90 traffic. This project addresses operational, design, safety, and access shortcomings for this heavily-travelled corridor.

The first of the new structures, officially dedicated as the "George V. Voinovich Bridge," was opened in November 2013. Employing as many as 500 people in its construction, this first bridge has become the largest project in ODOT history. It has earned national attention as one of the top 10 bridges in the nation. A second structure begins construction in 2014.

Ohio—

Building on a Strong Foundation and Continuing Its Legacy as an Important Piece in the Transportation Network of Our Nation

In the 21st century, transportation is conducted on a scale and scope that the earliest residents of Ohio could never have envisioned. Wild animal trails, worn-down Native-American foot paths, crude dirt and stone roads have given way to highly-engineered and well-constructed superhighways; horse-drawn wagons and carriages have been replaced by gas–powered vehicles of all kinds; steam-driven riverboats and trains have made way for their diesel or electric counterparts. And adding to all of it is the wonder of air travel.

Though there may be obstacles to continued growth, there is also a determination to beat those obstacles. The state's transportation program is a coordinated, statewide effort focused on what matters most to Ohioans. Major projects which add greater capacity to the current highway system will be critical to the state and the nation's transportation future.

For all of its enormous scale, transportation's role in Ohio and in the lives of its residents still remains the same. It is the means by which the state finds economic prosperity and improved quality of life for its citizens.

ODOT continues to live by its mission: To provide easy conveyance of people and goods from place to place; to take care of what we have, make our system work better, improve safety, and enhance capacity.

OKLAHOMA

Oklahoma Department of Transportation

J. Michael "Mike" Patterson
Director

YEAR FORMED **1911**

FTE **2,342**

KEY FACTS

TOTAL STATE ROAD MILES
(OWNED BY STATE HIGHWAY
AGENCY) **12,267**

STATE-OWNED
HIGHWAY BRIDGES **6,799**

The Beginnings of State Transportation

When Oklahoma was granted statehood in 1907, most roads were either extensions of frontier and military trails or rough section line roads. In 1911, the Oklahoma Department of Highways was legislated into existence by HB 318. The bill provided for a single highway commissioner, appointed by the governor and approved by the state senate. Sidney Suggs, an Ardmore newspaper publisher, was named Oklahoma's first commissioner and given an office in the state Capitol building and a two-person staff. The budget for salary and expenses was set at $9,000 per year funded by a $1 automobile license fee. However, the budget was wildly optimistic, since evasion of the license fee was widespread.

Suggs created a general highway plan for the state, with six primary corridors laid out for development. The first two followed the present-day I-35 and I-40 routes across the state. The others can be found along major corridors still in use today. Other early work by the commissioner included inspecting the condition of existing roads, then under the jurisdiction of counties and municipalities, as well as compiling lists of road-building materials and their locations. In 1913, the first biennial report from the

highway commissioner listed 499 miles of "improved" roads, surfaced by graded earth, sand, and clay or gravel.

Construction of Oklahoma's Transportation Network

The Federal Aid Road Act of 1916 helped finance the construction and maintenance of Oklahoma's roads and, in 1923, a one-cent gas tax was levied on Oklahoma motorists to raise state funds for highways. Construction continued at a moderate pace in the 1930s and the highway department's current system of eight field divisions was established. The State Highway Commission grew from one to three members, appointed by the governor.

During World War II, highway work slowed considerably as construction materials were restricted to the war effort. In 1947, the Oklahoma Turnpike Authority (OTA) was established and in 1947, it opened a modern tolled highway from Oklahoma City to Tulsa. The OTA now operates 10 turnpikes statewide that stretch more than 600 miles, financed only with toll revenue. The State Highway Commission also grew to its current size of eight members.

The 1950s and 1960s saw rapid development of the state's highway network

as construction of the Interstate System made Oklahoma an important national crossroads. In 1976, the Oklahoma Department of Highways was reorganized and became the Oklahoma Department of Transportation (OKDOT). The new name reflected the mission of the agency's involvement in all modes of transportation—auto, transit, rail, air, and waterways.

In the late 1970s and early 1980s, the state legislature empowered OKDOT to actively assist in preserving many rail lines from being abandoned and dismantled after several railroad companies went bankrupt. At its peak, OKDOT owned more than 880 miles of railroad, which were leased to private freight operators. The department takes great pride in successfully selling and returning 650 miles of state-owned railroad back to private hands in recent years. The agency continues to invest in rail improvements through its annually-updated State-Owned Rail Construction and Maintenance Work Plan.

Passenger rail service returned to Oklahoma in 1999 with the launch of Amtrak's *Heartland Flyer*. Now sponsored in partnership with Texas, the train's daily round-trip between Oklahoma City and Fort Worth continues to

increase in popularity and consistently receives some of Amtrak's highest customer satisfaction ratings. Since 1999, more than one million passengers have ridden the *Heartland Flyer*.

More than a century after highway construction began, Oklahoma ranks 17th in the nation for number of centerline highway miles at 12,265 miles, placing the state just behind states like California and New York. The state's central location and major highway corridors like I-40, I-44, I-35, US-75, and US-69 are important to the nation's trade and commerce network and crucial to Oklahoma's agriculture and energy industries.

Funding Reforms

Despite Oklahoma's large highway system, the state has a long history of underfunding transportation. Prior to 2005, state highway funding was based almost entirely on a share of motor fuel taxes, which had remained stagnant at about $200 million annually for decades. The result was that in 2005, state funding for OKDOT was actually less than it was in 1985. Due to the unpredictability of state funding, highway construction was almost completely funded with federal dollars and long-term planning was extremely difficult. However, the poor

condition of Oklahoma's bridges in the 2000s would bring about a renewed focus on state funding for transportation.

On May 26, 2002, an errant barge struck the I-40 bridge over the Arkansas River near Webbers Falls, bringing a section of the bridge down into the river and killing 14 travelers. The loss of the bridge on a major coast-to-coast corridor caused a massive travel interruption, as Interstate traffic was detoured on narrow rural highways while the interstate bridge was repaired. Work was performed around the clock and the I-40 bridge reopened just 65 days after the accident. The detours brought public attention to the deplorable condition of bridges on state highways. This became a catalyst for improved transportation funding in the following years.

In 2005, the governor and state legislature created the Rebuilding Access and Driver Safety (ROADS) fund, which provides a state allocation of income tax revenue to OKDOT, in addition to fuel tax revenue. Incremental increases to the ROADS fund in recent years will yield about $775 million in annual state funding by 2018.

In 2002, OKDOT implemented its Eight-year Construction Work Plan, which focuses on addressing the state's greatest transportation needs in an accountable and fiscally responsible manner. Each year, transportation commissioners work with the department to identify the state's most critical projects and create a balanced statewide transportation plan that evaluates anticipated state and federal funding and divides that funding between the eight field divisions. The first eight-year plan in 2003 contained less than $2 billion infrastructure improvements and only 220 bridge projects. The 2014 eight-year plan includes $6 billion and 924 bridge projects—more than four times as many as a decade ago.

Recent Accomplishments

Thanks to the eight-year plan, funding from the American Reinvestment and Recovery Act of 2009 allowed OKDOT to accelerate several major projects and build about one year's worth of road work, including improvements to more than 350 miles of highways and nearly 100 highway bridges. Oklahoma led nearly every state in putting transportation stimulus money to work quickly and the percentage of stimulus funds used on highway-related projects.

About 6,800 state-owned highway bridges are maintained by OKDOT. After years of topping national lists for bad bridges, additional funding provided by state leaders has allowed OKDOT to replace or rehabilitate hundreds of bridges, reducing the number of structurally deficient highway bridges from an all-time high of 1,168 in 2004 to 482 at the end of 2013. Governor Mary Fallin's Bridge Improvement and Turnpike Modernization plan and increases to the ROADS fund approved by the legislature will allow OKDOT to

repair or replace all remaining structurally deficient bridges by the end of 2019. Nearly 16,000 city and county bridges are maintained separately by local governments. The County Improvements for Roads and Bridges Program, created in 2006, provides millions of dollars in dedicated state funding administered by OKDOT for critical county projects.

Along with the continued bridge effort, OKDOT's future transportation goals include improving pavement conditions and safety on major highway corridors. More than 300 miles of Interstate pavement have been significantly rehabilitated or reconstructed since 2003 and OKDOT's current eight-year plan includes major improvements to 552 miles of high-volume highways and interstates. Also included are shoulders and other improvements to 567 miles of two-lane roads.

In 2011, OKDOT observed its Centennial with a year-long statewide celebration that involved employees, retirees, current and former state lawmakers, business leaders, construction and engineering industry partners and the public. Through an extensive public outreach campaign that included educational exhibits, special events, open houses, a coffee table book, and a documentary, among others, OKDOT's centennial provided an exceptional opportunity to thank the public for its support and show how investment in transportation is linked to the state's success, in the past, present and future. It was also the first time the agency had officially documented its 100-year history.

In January 2012, OKDOT reached the culmination of one of the largest

projects in state history, the more than 20-year, $680-million effort to plan, reroute and rebuild the I-40 Crosstown in downtown Oklahoma City. Relocation of the Crosstown eliminated the state's longest structurally deficient bridge and allowed OKDOT to recycle more than 2,000 bridge beams for counties to use on local bridge projects. The new, state-of-the-art Crosstown features 10 lanes for more than double the traffic capacity of the original and is built on a new alignment at ground level in the state's capital city. Later that year, OKDOT completed a $78 million project to construct the state's first double decker multi-modal bridge on I-244 near downtown Tulsa that features highway lanes on top, two dedicated future rail lines and bicycle/pedestrian bridge below. This bridge was made possible by a combination of federal funds and a nearly $50 million competitive Transportation Investment Generating Economic Recovery grant from the U.S. Department of Transportation.

Since 2012, OKDOT has opened two new weigh and inspection stations at key border crossings, and begun construction on a third. Construction of nine new state-of-the-art facilities is part of an interagency initiative to improve the enforcement of trucking regulations and safety standards, which will help protect the traveling public and the state's infrastructure system.

In an effort to cut costs and promote domestic energy, OKDOT is also leading the nation in a multi-state initiative let by Governor Fallin to use compressed natural gas powered vehicles in state government fleets. In 2012, OKDOT was the first state agency to make a large purchase of these vehicles, and now has more than 180 CNG cars and trucks in its fleet. With potential fuel and maintenance cost savings of $20,000 per vehicle, OKDOT leaders have set a goal to replace most of the agency's 1,085 vehicle fleet with CNG cars and trucks in the coming years.

Oklahoma is also a national leader in making highway travel safer as the first state in the nation to use the four-strand cable barrier system on highway medians. Following a successful 2007 pilot program, 635 miles of cable barrier have been installed, or are under construction, and 26 additional miles are planned for installation. During this time period, the number of crossover fatalities on Oklahoma highways and Interstates decreased from 39 in 2007 to six in 2012.

In 2013, longtime transportation executive Gary Ridley retired from the agency after 44 years of service, including 12 years as director. A well-respected engineer who began his career as a field maintenance worker, Ridley has worked with state lawmakers to dramatically improve transportation funding and has been called several times to testify before Congress on critical transportation issues. Ridley remains on the Cabinet as Secretary of Transportation, a position he was first appointed to in 2009. Commissioners selected Mike Patterson as Executive Director. Patterson has more than 30 years of experience with OKDOT, most recently as Deputy Director and Chief Financial Officer.

Today, OKDOT is nearing completion of the final phases of some of the largest highway construction projects in state history. These include major metro area interstate projects like the nearly $400 million reconstruction and widening of I-44 in Tulsa, $100 million reconstruction and widening of I-40 between El Reno and Oklahoma City and $35 million I-35 interchange reconstruction and highway widening in Norman.

In the past century, transportation in Oklahoma has grown from dirt trails to a modern system of highways, Interstates and streets that link all corners of the state and connect the people and businesses of the Heartland to the nation. Thanks to increased funding, support from lawmakers, the public and committed leadership, OKDOT has the resources and a plan to move Oklahoma into the future by addressing the state's remaining structurally deficient bridges, reconstructing major interstate corridors and interchanges and improving the safety and quality of highways statewide.

West end of the I-40 Crosstown corridor.

OREGON

Oregon Department of Transportation

Matthew Garrett
Director

YEAR FORMED **1913**

FTE **4,544**

KEY FACTS
TOTAL STATE ROAD MILES
(OWNED BY STATE HIGHWAY
AGENCY) **7,667**

STATE-OWNED BRIDGES **2,706**

TOTAL TRANSIT MILES
123.7 million

MOTOR CARRIER INSPECTIONS
PER YEAR **45,825**

ORIGINAL MOTTO
Getting Oregon Out of the Mud

Oregon Department of Transportation: Innovation as a Way of Life

Since the beginning—more than 100 years ago—Oregon has been a leader in transportation innovation: from building functional yet beautiful bridges to creating an award-winning bicycle and pedestrian program, from implementing the first road funding method to installing the nation's first solar highway. And it all started with the state's inaugural effort: "Getting Oregon Out of the Mud."

Throughout 2013, Oregon celebrated the 100th anniversary of the Oregon Department of Transportation (ODOT), which began life as the State Highway Department. Over the past century, transportation in Oregon has been characterized by impressive eras of progress; innovators, their creations, and the Oregonians who supported them; and noteworthy achievements, which have all combined to help shape Oregon's highly valued way of life.

We invite you to learn more about the history of transportation in Oregon. There are many accomplishments from the past century, and many more on the horizon, that we can be proud of supporting.

The Early Days

In 1913, the Oregon State Legislature created the Oregon Highway Commission to oversee the new State Highway Department, and the first commissioners were Governor Oswald West, Secretary of State Ben Olcott, and Treasurer Thomas Kay. That same year, Governor West proclaimed ocean beaches from the Columbia River to California as public highways. That's a legacy that lives on today, with all of Oregon's beaches considered public property. In its first year, the department began construction of the Pacific Highway (now Interstate 5) in southern Oregon's Jackson County.

One of Oregon's most well-known firsts occurred in 1919, when the state enacted the nation's first gasoline tax of one cent per gallon. In 1923, to wrap up its first decade of existence, the department completed construction of the Pacific Highway, making Oregon the first state west of Mississippi to have a paved highway the entire length of the state.

Combining Beauty, Efficiency, and Practicality

Bridge Designer and Engineer Conde B. McCullough headed ODOT's bridge program for 18 years, from 1919 to

1937. He made ODOT a leader in highway bridge design in the first half of the 20th century and became one of the leading bridge engineers in the United States. The pinnacle of McCullough's career was completion of five major bridges along the Oregon Coast Highway (now US 101) in 1936—the Yaquina Bay Bridge at Newport, the Alsea Bay Bridge at Waldport, the Siuslaw River Bridge at Florence, the Umpqua River Bridge at Reedsport, and the Coos Bay Bridge at Marshfield/North Bend.

McCullough was an impassioned promoter of state-sponsored bridge building that incorporated engineering efficiency with economic practicality and aesthetic appeal. Many of McCullough's bridges are rich in architectural detail; the finest among them are embellished with Classical, Gothic, and Art Deco/Moderne elements.

McCullough died from a stroke in 1946, just weeks short of his 59th birthday. Because of his work in Oregon, McCullough is recognized as a bridge engineer of national and international importance. In 1947, the State Highway Commission renamed the Coos Bay Bridge the Conde B. McCullough Memorial Bridge.

Increasing Safety and Efficiency

In the late 1920s, increased travel demand brought on a series of road improvements that would allow Oregonians to travel the state more safely and efficiently, such as the first electric traffic signal lights installations in 1927 and electromagnets mounted under trucks in 1928 to pick up nails and other dangerous materials. By 1929, year-round travel was available to all of Oregon between the principal centers of population. Oregon adopted a uniform system of warning and directional signs to help make driving safe and predictable.

Robert Hugh Baldock was "Mr. Highway" for Oregon at a critical time when the state was completing its large collection of primary and secondary roads and beginning construction on what would become its contribution to the nation's interstate highway system. Baldock was an engineer with ODOT from 1915 to 1956.

Baldock is credited as a big promoter of innovation in building highways. Under Baldock's leadership, ODOT adopted geometric highway design in 1936 and it became a national standard in 1946. Geometric highway design established the controlling design criteria that are used in building roads. Today, these

include: design speed, lane width, shoulder width, bridge width, structural capacity, horizontal alignment, vertical alignment, grade, stopping sight distance, cross slope, super elevation, vertical clearance, and horizontal clearance.

Baldock saw the state highway department through a period of great road building in the decade before U.S. involvement in World War II. When he retired in 1956, the agency that he helped shape was well equipped to complete Oregon's portion of the Interstate System.

Seen as a national leader among highway engineers, Baldock served as president of American Association of State Highway Officials, the predecessor of AASHTO, in 1948. In 1950, AASHO presented Baldock with the George S. Bartlett Award, described as the highest award a highway engineer can receive.

Expanding the Transportation System and Making Use of Technology

After World War II, the Oregon Highway Commission focused on planning construction projects designed to improve highways to meet postwar transportation needs. In the early 1950s Congress authorized millions for planning and constructing the Interstate System.

The first contract awarded in Oregon under the Federal Aid Highway Act of 1956 was for I-5's Fords Bridge Unit of the Myrtle Creek-Canyonville section in Douglas County. Undoubtedly, building this interconnected road system drastically changed how Americans lived and continues to have impacts today, due to both its existence and its age.

In 1957, ODOT became the first state agency in Oregon to use a computer system. It was an IBM 650. Oregon experienced another "first" when Interstate 5 was completed was in 1966, making it the first complete freeway within state boundaries in the United States. Also that year, Oregon installed its first computerized traffic signals.

The year 1968 was the last for the State Highway Department. The name changed to the Oregon Department of Transportation in 1969. The Driver and Motor Vehicle Services Division (DMV), State Highway Department, the Parks Division, State Board of Aeronautics, State Ports Commission and the newly created Mass Transit Division became part of ODOT.

In 1971, the monumental "Bicycle Bill" passed in Oregon, setting aside one percent of Highway Funds annually for footpaths and bike paths. Ten years later, Mount St. Helens erupted, sending ash all over the western United States and creating extra work for ODOT crews. The Oregon Legislature made driving under influence of intoxicants a criminal act in 1982.

In 1988, the Arch Cape Tunnel on U.S. 101 near Manzanita was closed for four months for reconstruction. Crews also repaired Elk Creek Tunnel on Ore-

gon 38 between Drain and Reedsport, salvaging over 58,000 board feet of Port Orford cedar for use in the Mosier Twin Tunnel restoration project on the Historic Columbia River Highway. That same year, the partial collapse of Sunset Tunnel on US 26 east of Portland killed ODOT bridge inspector Dennis Edwards. It was a sad day for everyone.

In 1995, inmate crews began work to beautify Oregon highways. ODOT also began using Light Emitting Diodes (LED) elements to replace incandescent red bulbs in traffic signals. ODOT's first female director joined the agency in 1996. Grace Crunican, who now serves as director of Bay Area Rapid Transit in San Francisco, led the agency for five years. Also in 1996, the historic Columbia River Highway and Volcanic Legacy Byway were named All American Roads by the federal government. Oregon Coast Highway (US 101), McKenzie and Santiam Loop, Cascade Lakes Byway, and Outback Byway were named scenic highways.

In 1997, ODOT introduced the "COMET" prevention and intervention truck patrols in Portland (now known as incident response). The first Oregon Highway Plan was adopted in 1999, and Region 5 sign crews installed eight electronic reader boards on Interstate 84 between Pendleton and Powder River.

Legislature Makes Significant Investment in Bridges

The Oregon Transportation Investment Act (OTIA), a series of funding packages passed in 2001–2003, provided the largest investment in transportation in Oregon in 50 years. OTIA raised $3 billion for highway and bridge construction work and used revenue from truck

and automobile title and registration fees to finance the sale of construction bonds. It proactively updated critical links in Oregon's highway network to increase safety, improve mobility, and facilitate the free movement of goods on which the state's economy depends.

ODOT used innovative methods and processes to deliver the OTIA III State Bridge Delivery Program, such as grouping—or bundling—nearby projects so local firms across the state could compete for contracts. ODOT's philosophy for the bridge program was based on stewardship: Take care of what you have so current and future generations can prosper. The improved network of bridges spurred job growth during design and construction and helped preserve the highway infrastructure fundamental to Oregon's economy. A new way of doing business, with outsourced program management, led to other new approaches, both in processes and in tools. Environmental programmatic permitting put us directly in touch with our counterparts at the natural resource agencies, which benefited both human and threatened species. Highways met high tech, as nine geographic information systems helped us manage and make use of data on hundreds of bridges.

Taking a Multi-modal Approach

In 2011, ODOT created a new Active Transportation Section combining several related programs that, by merging funding and strategic management, maximize the value of transportation investments locally, regionally, and statewide. It is designed to help communities make smarter transportation project decisions and includes our Bicycle/Pedestrian, Transportation Enhancement,

Certification for Local Agencies, and our Sustainability programs, along with Program and Funding services and our Economic and Financial Analysis Unit.

As part of the newly formed Active Transportation Section, the Sustainability Program is working with partners to promote multi-modal and sustainable transportation solutions. ODOT was the first state agency in Oregon to have a comprehensive Sustainability Program and the first to develop a Sustainability Plan.

In 2012, ODOT released its Climate Change Adaptation Strategy Report, which assesses the potential impacts of climate change on the transportation system and begins to outline a process to address these impacts within ODOT's business practices. ODOT is a leader in addressing climate change through both mitigation and adaptation activities. Volume III of the ODOT Sustainability Plan is under way; the Sustainability Council and program staff, in consultation with others at ODOT, provide a framework for the sustainable management of the transportation system, including project development and delivery.

Leading the Way

The first-in-the-nation solar highway was completed in 2008, and a second installation—and the largest in the United States—was completed in 2011 and began adding clean power to the grid in January 2012. ODOT's successful program has received national and international awards and attention and has set the stage for more renewable energy projects.

ODOT plays an integral role in building a network of charging stations for electric vehicles to encourage and accelerate private investment in and consumer acceptance of the electric vehicle industry. In the past few years dozens of charging stations opened on Interstate 5, from Eugene to Ashland, as part of the West Coast Electric Highway and other destination routes across the state. Recently, the program placed the first EV fast-charging station at a ski resort; this installation completed one of Oregon's scenic "electric" byways.

ODOT will be the first state in the nation to implement a "per-mile" fee that will replace the current fuel tax motorists pay at the pump. The 2013 Oregon Legislatures passed Senate Bill 810, which authorizes the ODOT to set up a mileage collection system for 5,000 volunteer motorists beginning July 1, 2015. ODOT may assess a charge of 1.5 cents per mile for up to 5,000 volunteer cars and light commercial vehicles and issue a gas tax refund to those participants. This is the start of an alternate method of generating fuel tax from specific vehicles to pay for Oregon highways.

Finding a way to generate sustainable revenues that will maintain and operate the transportation system is a topic of great interest to nearly every state. Many agencies, businesses, elected officials, and transportation stakeholders believe a "per mile fee" or a "road usage charge" could help address the projected diminishing revenues, due in part to the fuel efficient vehicles gaining in popularity in Oregon and even around the world. Oregon, as in many other endeavors, continues to lead the nation in researching ways to ensure motorists driving fuel efficient vehicles support the roads they travel.

An Innovative History— A Promising Future

The transportation system continues to experience profound changes, and Oregon continues to respond in award-winning ways. As we reflect on our first 100 years and look forward to the next 100, we will continue to seek ways to further our mission of providing a safe, efficient transportation system that supports economic opportunity and livable communities for Oregonians.

PENNSYLVANIA

Pennsylvania Department of Transportation

Barry Schoch, P.E.
Secretary

YEAR FORMED **1970**

FTE **Approx. 12,833**

KEY FACTS

TOTAL STATE ROAD MILES (OWNED BY STATE HIGHWAY AGENCY) **39,792**

STATE-OWNED BRIDGES **15,202**

TRANSIT TRIPS PER YEAR **445.4 million**

Pennsylvania is taking bold steps to invest in all transportation modes thanks to the leadership of Governor Tom Corbett and bipartisan support in the Pennsylvania General Assembly.

In November 2013, Governor Corbett signed Act 89, a far-reaching, multi-modal transportation plan that will invest roughly $2.3 billion to $2.4 billion more a year by 2018. These investments will better position the state Department of Transportation (Penn-DOT) to tackle a backlog of needs on the nearly 40,000 miles of department-maintained roads and 25,000 state-owned bridges. Overall, travelers amass 272.7 million miles of travel each day on Pennsylvania's nearly 120,000 miles of state and locally-maintained roads.

Act 89 also:
- Created a new Multi-modal Fund to provide dedicated funding for transit, aviation, rail, ports, bicyclists and pedestrians. Pennsylvania has more railroads that any other state (67), 132 public-use airports, 301 private-use airports, and 293 private-use heliports. PennDOT supports passenger and freight rail and 16 intercity bus routes, and manages nine long-distance bicycle routes.
- Will stabilize 36 fixed-route and 26 community/shared ride transit systems that provide nearly 450 million rides a year and allow people with no other mobility options access they need to reach the store, educational opportunities and medical services.
- Increases state support for local governments, responsible for about 77,000 miles of roads and nearly 6,400 bridges.

A Multi-modal Agency

Created in 1970 in a merger of the Highways Department with transportation functions scattered in other agencies, PennDOT for the past 30 years has earned a reputation for innovation.

One area where customers felt tangible benefits was Driver and Vehicle Services, which oversees the issuance of more than 8.8 million driver's licenses and the registration of more than 11.5 million motor vehicles. Customers have the option to do transactions online, by mail or in person at 71 driver license centers, 26 stand-alone photo centers or through 255 online, privately owned messenger sites. A customer counter area is also available at an easily accessed location in Harrisburg, the state capital. State-of-the-art mail sorting operations are used to help another state agency with their billing functions.

Innovations Abound

While reducing its complement 44 percent over the past 40 years, PennDOT has managed costs within its $6 billion to $7 billion annual budget while enhancing its value to the people of Pennsylvania. The latest chapter, PennDOT's Next Generation program, recently achieved a milestone by increasing the department's efficiency twofold in two years. PennDOT has identified another $50 million resulting in a total of $100 million in recurring savings by embracing innovative practices, sharing resources, and implementing proven technologies.

PennDOT has been working internally as well as with various external stakeholders to find the best ways to improve as not only a business partner, but also an employer.

For instance, PennDOT has been coordinating with the Turnpike Commission, a separate agency, on many initiatives to share facilities and resources. By sharing design specifications, the Turnpike Commission has already saved $14 million.

PennDOT's highway and bridge team identified strategies to eliminate nearly 60 redundant reviews. After full implementation in 2014, the department will save more than $8 million over the next 10 years.

Through coordination with private industry, PennDOT will save $5.8 million over the next 10 years through implementation of Virtual Reference Station (VRS) technology for surveying.

PennDOT is also innovating the way it collects information. The department developed three mobile applications that are saving approximately $400,000 each year. Two apps are assisting in data collection to inventory locally owned infrastructure and assist in field inspections. PennDOT's Driver License Skills Exam app also enhances customer service by saving our customers 20 to 30 minutes in the process.

Launched in 2013, PennDOT's Local Bridge Bundling Pilot program targets deteriorated county-owned structurally deficient bridges, with a focus on rapid delivery and cost savings in both engineering and construction. It is estimated that nearly $4 million was saved through economy of scale in design and construction, and the projects were accelerated by two to five years in delivery time.

P3's Fast Approaching

In 2014, PennDOT received Statement of Qualifications submittals from teams interested in its Rapid Bridge Replacement Public–Private Partnership (P3) plan. The plan is to maximize efficiencies and leverage the economies of scale that come through bundling the design, construction, and ongoing maintenance of between 550 and 650 bridges. PennDOT retains ownership, but will be relying on the private sector to design, build, and maintain these bridges at a savings to the public.

Passenger Rail Enhanced

PennDOT, working with the federal government and Amtrak, has invested more than $155 million in upgrading the 104-mile long Philadelphia to Harrisburg Keystone passenger rail Corridor. The work, done between 2002 and 2013, included station upgrades and track, catenary, signal, and communications upgrades to allow speeds of up to 110 mph. An additional $25.5 million in station upgrades and $40 million in additional track, signal, and communications upgrades are underway. Other projects either underway or planned include $32 million for a new station at Middletown, $21 million for eliminating three grade crossings and $8.5 million for additional track and signal improvements. Total ridership has grown as the travel times have improved on the corridor. Ridership rose to 1.5 million in Fiscal Year 2012–2013 compared to 961,450 in Fiscal Year 2001–2002.

Building Support for Better Transportation

PennDOT has worked diligently over the decades to win the support of elected officials and their constituents. With Act 89, PennDOT looks forward to new successes supporting residents' mobile lifestyle and enhancing Pennsylvania's economy.

PUERTO RICO

Departamento de Transportación y Obras Públicas

Miguel Torres-Diaz, P.E.
Secretary

YEAR FORMED **1952**

KEY FACTS
TOTAL STATE ROAD MILES
(OWNED BY STATE HIGHWAY
AGENCY) **4,582**

STATE-OWNED BRIDGES **1,572**

Overview

The Puerto Rico transportation system is a multi-modal network of highways, transit, and ferry services, and bicycle and pedestrian facilities that serve the island's residents, businesses, tourists, government, defense, ports, and seaports. Puerto Rico is a densely populated island with a total area of 3,425 square miles and 3.7 million residents. Nearly 94 percent of the island's population lives in urban areas which places extra demands on some components of the transportation system.

The Department of Transportation and Public Works (DTPW), established in 1952, oversees the island's transportation system to meet mobility needs and promote economic development. Within the agency, the Puerto Rico Highways and Transportation Authority (PRHTA) is responsible for construction, operation, and maintenance of the island's toll-road network, major highways, and mass transportation facilities. The Public Works Directorate repairs and maintains all other roads throughout Puerto Rico.

The two transportation-department operated public transportation systems are:

- The 10.7-mile Tren Urbano rapid rail which provides passenger service

in the San Juan Metropolitan Area. It opened in 2004 with 16 stations and has an average daily ridership of about 25,000.

- The Metropolitan Bus Authority which provides daily bus transportation to residents of San Juan and the surrounding communities. It has a fleet of nearly 300 buses with an estimated annual ridership of 25,000 to 30,000.

The Metropolitan Planning Organization of Puerto Rico (MPO) is the organization created in compliance with federal regulation to manage the transportation planning process in metropolitan regions. Unlike the 50 states, Puerto Rico has a single, islandwide MPO which coordinates all transportation planning activities, working closely with DTPW as the MPO's operational arm. That structure has led to a strong connection between the department of transportation and the MPO supporting parallel planning activities and transportation system oversight, policies, and priorities.

Building and Maintaining a Highway System

During most of the 1960s, the department focused largely on road construction. At the beginning of the

decade, there were 3,379 miles of roads in Puerto Rico, more than 70 percent of which were unpaved. Today, Puerto Rico has an extensive highway system made of up of 16,691 miles of roads including 282 miles of Interstate roads and 2,222 bridges. More than 80 percent of the total highway mileage in Puerto Rico serves the urban areas where the population is concentrated.

Like Hawaii and Alaska, Puerto Rico's Interstates do not connect to the rest of the Interstate System. The three Interstates in Puerto Rico are signed as Puerto Rico routes (PRI-1, PRI-2, and PRI-3) and were not required to meet conventional Interstate standards.

Despite recent government investments in public transportation, mobility in Puerto Rico remains very automobile-dependent, which has led to significant congestion and wear and tear on the highways, particularly in urban areas.

In 2011, Puerto Rico entered into a public–private partnership to upgrade two of its busiest toll roads. The 40-year lease of the PR-22 and PR-5 toll roads will generate $1.456 billion in private infrastructure funds to immediately upgrade the busy highways and

strengthen the island's economy. The 52-mile PR-22 toll road, also known as the Jose de Diego Expressway, is the busiest toll road in Puerto Rico with average daily traffic of more than 85,000 vehicles. It has 15 interchanges and 7 toll plazas including the Buchanan Toll Plaza through which more than 26 million vehicles pass annually. Improvements that were part of the lease agreement focus on paving, signage, lighting, vehicle flow, safety, and service and toll areas.

The partnership is administered by the Puerto Rico Public–Private Partnerships Authority and the Highway and Transportation Authority. The DTPW long-range plan calls for exploring additional opportunities for public-private partnerships to jointly fund and accelerate implementation of infrastructure improvements.

Focusing on Safety

In March 2014, DTPW initiated development of a comprehensive strategic road safety plan for the first time in the history of Puerto Rico. The participatory and collaborative process brings together multiple government and non-government organizations and focuses on improving safety for drivers, cyclists, and pedestrians.

As part of the process, Puerto Rico held its first Road Safety Summit in May 2014 to engage key stakeholders and government in developing strategies for reducing fatalities and injuries on the country's roads.

DTPW and the Puerto Rico Commission for Safety also launched an educational campaign to improve safety of cyclists. With cycling on the rise in Puerto Rico, the educational campaign focuses on both drivers and cyclists to increase awareness of the rights and duties of cyclists and drivers on public roads. Longer range plans include improving the infrastructure for safe bicycle and pedestrian traffic.

Research and Development

The Puerto Rico Transportation Technology Transfer Center was created in 1986 to support research and development in transportation-related activities in Puerto Rico and the U.S. Virgin Islands. The center is housed in the Department of Civil Engineering and Surveying at the University of Puerto Rico, Mayagüez campus. Its mission is to foster a safe, efficient, and environmentally sound surface transportation system by improving skills and increasing knowledge among the transportation workforce and decisions makers through training, service, and technical assistance.

The center is one of 58 throughout the United States under the Local Technical Assistance Program (LTAP).

Long Range Transportation Plan
In 2013, the DTPW published a blueprint to provide a framework for transportation planning through 2040. The long range transportation plan identifies policies and strategies to meet the needs and expectations of residents, promote economic development, create

more livable communities, and advance environmental sustainability. The plan's goals, objectives, and action strategies are built around four themes for transportation system management and development:

- **Effectiveness**—Improving how well the transportation system provides mobility and accessibility.

- **Efficiency**—Improving the transportation system so that it works better for users at a lower cost, provides better safety and security, and

optimizes the condition and use of assets.

- **Economy**—Managing the transportation system so that it productively contributes to the island economy for both business and societal interests with a more sustainable funding strategy.

- **Environment**—Supporting actions to minimize greenhouse gas and other adverse environmental effects and to advance smarter land uses with more livable communities.

RHODE ISLAND

Rhode Island Department of Transportation

Michael P. Lewis, P.E.
Director

YEAR FORMED **1902**

FTE **Approx. 772**

KEY FACTS
TOTAL STATE ROAD MILES
(OWNED BY STATE HIGHWAY
AGENCY) **1,107**

STATE-OWNED BRIDGES **593**

TRANSIT TRIPS PER YEAR
20 million

Rhode Island is widely regarded as having one of the nation's most distinct and rich environments. Iconic images dotting the state's landscape such as sunset over Newport Bridge or winding roads along the more than 400 miles of coastline continue to be powerful drivers for tourism and sources of great pride for residents. The intersection of Rhode Island's natural and man-built environments has always made it a rather special point on our national map.

One of the most crucial components of a healthy economy and quality of place is a sound transportation system. Throughout the country, centers of transportation have long been catalysts for economic growth and innovation. And in Rhode Island, given its geographic location, this infrastructure has emerged as one of the state's most important assets.

Rhode Island is the second most densely populated state in the nation and a critical link in the movement of people and goods throughout the Northeast corridor. Interstate 95, as it passes through the capital city, is one of the most heavily trafficked stretches of interstate in the East today—with more than 220,000 vehicle crossings per day.

The state's highway program dates back to the late 1800s—when the Rhode Island Legislature first appointed a committee to study roadway conditions with an eye toward building for the future. With the advent of the Interstate Age in the 1960s, the state built three highway systems, totaling 71 miles of roadway. And by 1990, nearly $2 billion had been invested in Rhode Island's highway program.

With the Interstate boom long passed, Rhode Island turned its attention over the past 25 years to widening the lens through which it understood transportation. A laser focus on building large-scale highway systems was replaced by a broader definition of mobility. This new era would be marked by not only a desire to connect Rhode Island to the rest of the world but also to connect Rhode Islanders more meaningfully to each other and to opportunity.

Throughout the 1980s, this fundamental shift in how Rhode Island thought about and invested in mobility was well underway; nowhere was this shift more evident than in the state's capital city of Providence. Over the course of more than a decade, highway interchanges were rebuilt in the city; railroad tracks

relocated; and rivers rechanneled to make way for development.

The federal government funded much of the work, contributing more than $160 million to the building of a new Amtrak station, the relocation of rail lines, and the rebuilding of interchanges. This money also funded the movement of rivers and the construction of Water place Park and the riverwalk—a feature that in the years ahead would propel Providence into the national spotlight.

The City of Providence contributed an additional $6 million for historical and landscaping work in the area.

The Rhode Island Department of Transportation (RIDOT) provided $10 million toward the building of additional rail tracks and the expansion of the Providence Station; the latter allowed Rhode Island to, for the first time, offer commuter rail service to Boston through its partnership with the Massachusetts Bay Transportation Authority (MBTA)

Today, the Providence Station is ranked one of the top three busiest stations in the Authority's network, with more than 2,000 daily passengers.

Following these public investments, more than $600 million in private funding fueled the next wave of development in the city throughout the 1990s—including the construction of the Providence Place Mall, the Rhode Island Convention Center, and several hotels. The Providence Renaissance was in full swing.

With the city's transformation came a wave of new energy and creativity to start the new millennium. Providence's new downtown became a mecca for small business and arts and entertainment—with popular attractions such as WaterFire drawing scores of tourists and suburbanites into the city.

At the same time, the Rhode Island Public Transit Authority (RIPTA), which operates the state's bus system, was undergoing its own transformation. With a new "Ride the Wave" brand to mark this new era, RIPTA invested heavily in adding new lines and upgrading its fleet. New buses and paratransit vans came online as well as RIPTA's first clean fuel vehicles.

A new water ferry service was also launched that linked popular tourist destinations, Providence and

Newport, and new programs such as Rack n' Ride, which equipped all buses with bike racks, were added in response to the state's new multi-modal strategy.

As the 2000s rolled in, RIPTA also opened a new Intermodal Transportation Center in downtown Providence and built its first new maintenance facility in over 100 years.

RIPTA, in partnership with RIDOT and many others, is currently working on plans that will open a new chapter in intermodalism in the capital city. This new approach will provide convenient connections between rail and bus and create multiple transit centers, linking popular downtown areas.

Throughout the years, the transportation landscape has indeed changed. And as the streets have grown more congested, so have the highways.

Decades after the great Interstate era of the 1950s and 1960s, the maze of highway routes through Providence stood as a reminder of a day gone by and years of inattention due to inadequate maintenance funding.

Built in the 1950s for an average of 75,000 vehicles a day, I-195 was crumbling under the pressure of more than 160,000 vehicles a day by the 1980s.

Tight curves as well as left-hand and closely-spaced exits added to the traffic woes along this corridor, spilling over onto I-95 and other routes.

Several designs were considered before the state landed on a final new design for I-195 in 1999 (construction value of $610 million). The new alignment would not only address safety and congestion-related issues but also open up nearly 20 acres of land along the Providence waterfront.

Dubbed the "Iway," construction on the realigned I-195 began in 2003 and involved 14 new bridges, including the signature Iway Bridge.

In the summer of 2006, thousands of people lined the shores of Narragansett Bay to watch the bridge as it was floated up the river from the southern reaches of the state to its new home in the capital city. It was lowered into place the following day to similar fanfare. And seemingly overnight, it became the crown jewel of the Providence skyline.

In 2011, the I-195 Redevelopment District Commission was established to lead development efforts for the freed-up land. And to date, RIDOT continues work under two separate contracts to reconnect city streets and communities once cut off by the old highway.

Further south, Rhode Island's second largest city, Warwick, was also a hotbed for transit-oriented development. Formed in 1992, The Rhode Island

Airport Corporation (RIAC) took over authority of five general aviation airports as well as the state's flagship airport, T.F. Green, from RIDOT.

Over the past 25 years, major upgrades have been made to T.F. Green, including the opening of the Bruce Sundlun Terminal in 1996 with 15 jet gates, followed by a four-gate expansion in 1998. A Federal Inspection Services Facility was added shortly after, allowing the airport to process international flights. With these improvements in place, its central location and ease of access to I-95, T. F. Green achieved double-digit growth as the millennium began.

In 2005, it served more than 5 million travelers. And by the close of the decade, RIAC had hit its stride in building the foundation on which the state's first transit-oriented development district would be built.

By 2010, the InterLink Transportation Hub was opened to the public. With funding from RIDOT, RIAC, and the Federal Highway Administration, the $267 million project involved the construction of a commuter rail station, parking garage, rental-car hub, and a 1,200-foot skywalk connecting the facility to T. F. Green Airport.

A collaborative effort, involving public and private partners, is now underway to market and guide mixed-use development in the area. The CityCentre Warwick district consists of 95 acres surrounding T. F. Green, the InterLink, and Interstates 95 and 295.

In addition to creating a true multi-modal center in Rhode Island, the InterLink also allowed MBTA commut-

er rail service to extend to points south of Providence for the first time in the state's history.

Two years later, service to Wickford Junction, 12 miles south of Warwick, was added. Opened in April of 2012, Wickford Junction helped solidify the state's vision of building a modern, statewide intermodal system. The $44 million facility includes an indoor waiting area, parking garage, platform, covered bicycle storage, and charging stations for electric vehicles.

RIDOT continues to explore opportunities to further expand rail service in Rhode Island and to potentially introduce the state's first in-state rail shuttle service in the near future.

Intermodalism is increasingly the new way of life in Rhode Island. Investments in rail, transit, air, bike paths, and highways are helping to transform the state and position it to better compete in a global economy. What's more, these investments are connecting Rhode Islanders to job centers, social spaces, and recreational areas within the state—as well in neighboring states. They are also helping to support the environment and public health.

In recent years, the rails-to-trails movement in Rhode Island has inspired the construction of more than 60 miles of paved bike and pedestrian paths—with more than 25 miles of path still under design.

Some of the state's longer bike paths, such the Blackstone River Bikeway and the East Bay Bike Path, are part of an ambitious effort by the Rhode Island-based East Coast Greenway

Alliance to create a contiguous bike path from Maine to Florida.

Rhode Island can ill afford to turn off the spigot on investments that support both its economic recovery and quality of life for its residents, yet an antiquated transportation financing model threatens to do just that.

The state's transportation system is heavily reliant on federal support—a funding source that is currently in jeopardy given an impending cash shortfall in the Highway Trust Fund (HTF).

The total highway program for Rhode Island averages $240 million annually, with $200 million each year from HTF apportionments. In order to be eligible for these funds, the state provides a match of $40 million annually—which is derived through license and registration fees, Rhode Island Capital Plan funds, and previously-issued bonds. There is no state-funded highway improvement program in Rhode Island.

The highway program encompasses the research, planning, design, and construction of infrastructure: not only federally eligible roads and bridges, but also rail, bicycle, and pedestrian facilities. The program also helps to support management functions, along with preventative maintenance activities that qualify for federal reimbursement.

Maintenance operations are largely funded through the state gas tax, but bond debt service must be paid prior to allocating gas tax funds to operations. This situation has severely crippled the state's ability to keep its transportation system in a state of good repair.

At current funding levels, Rhode Island faces a daunting number of challenges in maintaining and improving its transportation system. While the number of projects requiring attention statewide continues to grow, a gap exists between what can be accomplished at these levels and what is needed to address the system as a whole.

Whether Rhode Island residents, visitors, and members of the business community drive private vehicles, take public transportation, walk, bike, or jog, the state's roads and bridges are critical links.

More than 63 percent of the state's roadways are rated fair or worse, and nearly 20 percent of the bridges are in poor condition. The latter is trending toward 40 percent by 2024.

To reverse this trend, the state would need to invest an additional $80 million each year over the next 10 years.

A long list of major highway projects and smaller, community projects remain unfunded, as the state awaits the fate of the HTF and works to identify state-level funding mechanisms.

Within the past three years, Rhode Island has enacted invaluable reforms to address its transportation funding needs. These efforts, however, start with the assumption that federal funding will continue at its historic level.

On average, 40 construction projects are awarded each year (average total construction value of $151 million). These projects, which range from minor roadway repairs to major bridge rehabilitations, take place throughout the state and make use of innovative techniques

such as accelerated bridge construction wherever possible.

In 2013, 46 projects were completed, including the replacement of a vital stretch of I-95, the Pawtucket River Bridge. And currently, there are 50 active construction projects statewide, totaling $400 million in construction value.

Over the past 25 years, more than $5.2 billion has been invested in Rhode Island's highway program, representing 1,332 construction projects. This total includes projects funded through the regular program as well as through special funds made available over the years.

For example, the stimulus funding of 2009 provided the state with a timely shot in the arm, making possible 73 highway, transit, and rail projects that would have otherwise remained unfunded. In all, the stimulus funding provided $170 million, allowing the state to complete repairs or replacement of eight bridges, resurface 55 miles of roadway, and complete pavement preservation work on another 75 miles.

In recent years, federal TIGER grants have also helped the state advance critical, large-scale projects.

Rhode Island continues to face its share of economic challenges—with one of the highest unemployment rates in the nation and the sobering reality of fewer and fewer available federal dollars. But it also continues to forge ahead with the same visionary thinking that first conceived of a modern statewide transportation system back in the 1800s.

SOUTH CAROLINA

South Carolina Department of Transportation

Janet Oakley
Secretary

YEAR FORMED **1977**

FTE **Approx. 4,861**

KEY FACTS
TOTAL STATE ROAD MILES
(OWNED BY STATE HIGHWAY
AGENCY) **41,409**

STATE-OWNED BRIDGES **8,395**

TRANSIT TRIPS PER YEAR
9.2 million

South Carolina charted a new direction in transportation in 1993 when an umbrella agency which included highways, motor vehicle administration and law enforcement was split into three by legislative action. The South Carolina Department of Transportation (SCDOT) emerged with a streamlined mission—to build and maintain roads and bridges and develop and administer mass transit services.

At that time, South Carolina's state highway system was rated as one of the best in the nation for the money spent. Then as now, however, SCDOT relied almost entirely on motor fuel taxes for its revenue. At 16 cents per gallon, the state had one of the lowest gasoline tax rates in the nation, and it has not been increased since then. The state is dependent on federal highway funds for over 60 percent of its revenue.

With over 41,000 miles, South Carolina has the nation's fourth largest state-maintained highway system, with 8,416 bridges, 1,624 of which are considered either structurally deficient or functionally obsolete.

In 1993, the state was already looking forward over 10 years at $3.2 billion in critical bridge and highway needs.

Today the state is projecting a $29 billion shortfall in funding to address critical road and bridge needs over the next 20 years, unless additional revenue sources are secured.

Despite serious revenue deficiencies, SCDOT can boast major achievements over the past two decades. Most noteworthy is the Arthur Ravenel Bridge, an eight-lane, cable-stayed bridge with two diamond-shaped towers allowing clearance for modern ocean freighters to access the Port of Charleston. The $632 million project, on US 17 between Charleston and Mount Pleasant, opened in July 2005, a year ahead of schedule and under budget.

It is the largest transportation project in the history of South Carolina, replacing the historic Grace Bridge and the Pearman Bridge, which had become obsolete and unsafe for travelers.

It is the longest cable-stay bridge in the northern hemisphere, with a cutting edge design to withstand a massive earthquake or a hurricane of the century. It also provides safe passage for pedestrians and bicyclists.

In Spring 2008, a major $275 million project was completed in Lexington

County on SC 6 and SC 60, which included stabilization, widening the roadway over the Lake Murray dam to four lanes, and a new 1.5 mile, 8-foot-wide pedestrian walkway across the dam, which has been an instant hit with pedestrians who get an impressive look at Lake Murray.

The project, which stabilized the Saluda River Dam and constructed new northbound lanes and the pedestrian walkway, involved collaborative efforts between SCDOT, the State Infrastructure Bank, and SCANA Corporation. It took almost three years to complete what was the largest active dam construction project in the United States.

The American Recovery and Reinvestment Act signed into law in 2009 allocated $463 million for "shovel ready" highways and bridges in South Carolina and $41 million for mass transit programs. SCDOT used the funds for resurfacing, Interstate maintenance, bridge replacements, and safety and traffic projects, as well as enhancement (sidewalk) projects in all seven engineering districts.

Also completed early and under budget was a $61 million rehabilitation project along seven miles of I-385, the most

direct and heavily traveled route between Greenville and Columbia. Completed in July 2010, this was the largest American Recovery and Reinvestment Act-funded project in South Carolina. It involved widening I-385 to six lanes and reconstructing the mainline pavement to accommodate interstate traffic. SCDOT saved about $35 million by closing the northbound lanes and finishing the project in eight months, rather than doing a traditional phased construction project under traffic that could have stretched over three years.

Safety has always been a number one concern of SCDOT. The first cable median barriers were installed on South Carolina interstates in January 2001. There are 442 miles of interstate with cable barriers. Since then, there have been 25,334 hits on the cable barriers resulting in the reduction of fatal median crossover collisions.

In 2007, SCDOT was proud to receive two national awards for excellence and innovation in operations, planning, and roadway design aimed at reducing fatalities and injuries on the highways. The awards from the Roadway Safety Foundation and the Federal Highway Administration recognized SCDOT for its "Let 'Em Work, Let 'Em Live" Work Zone Safety Campaign, including public

education and worker training; and for its Crash Reduction by Improving Safety on Secondaries (CRISOS) Program begun in response to the state's death rate on rural secondary roads.

South Carolina is also working to enhance highway safety through the use of intelligent transportation systems. The new 511 Traveler Information System received more than 80,000 calls during its first four months of operation in 2011. The system is a free telephone and Internet resource to help motorists save fuel, navigate roadways, reduce commuting times, and minimize the impact of traffic incidents.

SCDOT's 511 information is collected and continually updated by traffic management centers throughout the state. Data comes from traffic cameras, reports from the SC Highway Patrol, local law enforcement, and SCDOT's State Highway Emergency Program (SHEP) crews. Established in 1996, SHEP now serves motorists traveling in the Charleston, Columbia, Florence, Grand Strand/Myrtle Beach, Rock Hill, and Greenville/Spartanburg urban areas. Prepared to handle a variety of situations, SCDOT SHEP responders make minor repairs to disabled vehicles; assist with traffic control and incident management.

SOUTH DAKOTA

South Dakota Department of Transportation

Darin Bergquist
Secretary

YEAR FORMED **1973**

FTE **Approx. 1,026**

KEY FACTS
STATE-OWNED HIGHWAY
MILES **7,810**

- 679 miles of Interstate highway
- Carries 67% of vehicle miles travelled and 81% of heavy truck traffic
- 68% of SD truck tonnage originates, terminates in other states

CITY, COUNTY, AND TOWNSHIP
ROADS **74,726 miles**

- Carries 33% of vehicle miles traveled and 19% of heavy truck traffic

STATE-MAINTAINED BRIDGES
1,798

- 533 are large box and pipe culverts

ANNUAL BUDGET **$643 million**

- $251 million—State Highway Fund; $386 million—Federal Funds; $5.3 million—Other Funds

Mission:
To efficiently provide a safe and effective public transportation system.

Vision:
Achieve excellence in providing transportation facilities that meet the needs of the public.

Getting out of the Mud

Years 1914–1939 have been referred to as "getting out of the mud" because South Dakota focused on establishing graveled, graded highways. With the formation of the Highway Commission in 1913, followed by the creation of the Highway Department in 1917, South Dakota's main goal was to develop a uniform system of roadways throughout the state.

A State Highway Trunk System was established to connect county seats and town with populations of 750 or more. As gravel roads began replacing dirt roads in 1921, "getting out of the mud" became a reality. Bridging the Missouri River was another objective for the department. The Bridge Act in 1923 provided for the construction of the first five bridges across the Missouri River, which was completed in 1927.

While the use of automobiles was increasing, the 1930s brought the

Depression and drought. The objective of many South Dakotans became "getting out of the dust." The department's focus during the second period, 1939-1964, became the construction of widened, paved, all-season highways. This was not an easy task, especially during World War II, when resources were directed toward the war effort. Construction projects that were not a part of the Strategic Network of Highways were left unfinished. After World War II, four huge earthen dams were constructed across the Missouri River, forcing the relocation of several sections of major highways. Bridges were relocated, making them some of the longest in the country, as well as noteworthy engineering accomplishments. The establishment of this improved, uniform highway network provided an essential link for the economy of South Dakota. In addition, tourism flourished as travelers had the convenience of modern highways.

The Interstate Highway Era

During the next period, 1964–1989, South Dakota became the fifth state to complete its portion of the Interstate System. The state's average completed cost of $737,000 per Interstate mile is one of the lowest in the nation. At a rate of approximately 50 miles per year, I-90 was finished in 1976 and I-29

was completed in 1983, giving South Dakota total of 679 miles of four-lane, divided Interstate highways. The most costly section of Interstate construction was the I-90 crossing of the Missouri River at Chamberlain. Spanning the nearly mile-wide river was achieved efficiently by the innovative design and construction of a causeway extending 3,000 feet into the river, reducing the structure length to just over 2,000 feet. Construction costs for the causeway were less than half of a comparable length of bridge structure. The crossing, completed at a cost of $6.9 million, made it the most expensive mile in the state's portion of the Interstate System, but one of the least expensive water crossings of this length in the nation.

Where engineering had presented both the challenge and the most visible results of prior highway efforts, economic forces in the 1960s presented a less visible but more dramatic challenge to the highway program. Oil shortages and inflation in the 1970s combined to create a severe squeeze between declining user revenues and increasing costs of construction and maintenance. These economic forces were dominant factors in bringing about the reorganization in 1973, which combined the state's Highway Department and the

Aeronautics Commission to create the Department of Transportation. In 1975, the department was made complete with the addition of the Division of Railroads. Both aeronautics and railroads brought special challenges to South Dakota's Department of Transportation (SDDOT).

The Division of Railroads was forced beyond conventional governmental functions by extensive railroad abandonments in the early 1980s. Recognizing the essential role of rail service to agricultural competitiveness in domestic and world markets, the state acquired 1,316 miles of track in South Dakota, North Dakota, Montana, and Minnesota at a cost of more than $54 million. Financing was obtained through a temporary one-cent sales tax and bonds. Lease and lease-purchase agreements were arranged to provide rail service and retire the bonds. Through state programs and various federal rail rehabilitation loans and grant programs, the state provided approximately $36 million to rehabilitate the lines.

The Aeronautics Commission faced similar problems under the Airline Deregulation Act of 1978. Deregulation fundamentally restructured air service with a cycle of service reductions and

fares increases, which in turn cased enplanements to decline. The state's regional airports have maintained reduced service through the Essential Air Service (EAS) program.

In 1983, the department again made organizational changes. Engineering offices and maintenance shops were consolidated into region and area offices that oversee both maintenance and construction activities. The central office was reorganized from a modal to a functional organization to avoid duplication and decrease administrative overhead.

Sustainability

After completion of South Dakota's segment of the Interstate System, sustaining an extensive multi-modal transportation system in a geographically large state with a small population base became increasingly important to the department. Federal highway funds account for 80 percent of its highway construction program. South Dakota's transportation officials, working in conjunction with other states and interested parties, successfully garnered funding increases from 1985 to 1997 that allowed the SDDOT to complete $1.96 billion in construction projects critical to South Dakota's transportation system.

From 1987 to 1997, South Dakota received $36.3 million in additional federal spending authority as a bonus for efficiently and effectively letting highway construction projects to contract. This extra money came from states that were unable to obligate their federal funds by the deadline.

The Transportation Efficiency Act for the 21st Century (TEA-21) increased South Dakota's allocation of federal funds and authorized funding to build four-lane expressways from Pierre to I-90, from Aberdeen to I-29, and from Huron to Mitchell, and the Heartland Expressway from Rapid City to the Nebraska border.

In 2009, President Barack Obama's American Recovery and Reinvestment Act (ARRA) gave South Dakota $183 million in additional highway funds. Because the SDDOT developed and awarded projects quickly and efficiently, the department received an extra $15 million. South Dakota was recognized as having one of the largest stimulus funded concrete paving projects in the country—a 22.1-mile concrete paving project on the westbound lanes of I-90 between White Lake and Mt. Vernon—which also won an America's Transportation Award in 2010.

From 2003 to 2009, the state invested $1.657 billion in new construction or rehabilitation projects on nearly 40 percent of the total state system. This included resurfacing 25 percent (2,100 miles) of asphalt pavements and 630 miles of concrete pavements, reconstructing 460 miles of highway, constructing 180 bridges and culverts, and repairing another 550 bridges and culverts. Three of four expressways were completed during this period, with the fourth being completed in 2013.

Although South Dakota has seen a modest increase in revenues since 1999 when the gas tax was raised to 22 cents, inflation has reduced buying, what $1 could buy in 1999 for highway construction cost $1.96 in 2012.

South Dakota boasts a statewide average pavement condition index of 4.20 (on a scale of 5) in 2013, up from 3.34 in 1999. A thorough inspection, maintenance, and rehabilitation schedule on the state's bridges has also earned the state an Average Sufficiency Index of 89.5, where zero is unusable and 100 is excellent.

Technology and Innovation

Since the 1960s, South Dakota has pioneered construction programming techniques and application of technology to de-politicize the highway project selection process. All of the state's highway segments are ranked according to need for reconstruction, resurfacing, or rehabilitation. Priorities are assigned to projects by comparing and evaluating data on each segment.

In the 1980s, the department developed and promoted the South Dakota Road Profiler, which measured the elevation of the surface of the road so engineers could evaluate smoothness and rutting at normal highway speeds. The Road Profiler made network- and project-level measurements economical enough to be used by all state DOTs.

Bridge Engineer Kenneth Wilson played a leading role in steel bridge design that resulted in a jointless abutment that saved state government countless funds in bridge maintenance and repairs.

Wilson is also credited for adopting epoxy-coated reinforcing steel in bridge decks. To date, not one of those bridge decks has needed repair due to steel corrosion.

The SDDOT has led a multi-state effort to develop the Maintenance Decision Support System (MDSS) to better manage equipment, personnel, and chemicals during winter maintenance activities. The MDSS uses advanced weather forecasting and pavement modeling to predict developing road conditions and recommend the most economical and effective maintenance treatments and timing.

Together with North Dakota, SDDOT established the first statewide phone-based traveler information service in 1998. In November 2002, the "#SAFE" service became South Dakota's 511 Traveler Information System. Four years later, the department launched its 511 Traveler Information System website, *www.safetravelusa.com/sd*. The website provides up-to-date information on road conditions and travel advisories for all state-owned highways. The website's map and roadside camera views are widely used. Mobile South Dakota 511 "apps" supply the same information to smartphone users.

Connecting South Dakota and the Nation
Transit

Mass transit has seen increased demand and increased funding throughout the nation. Although South Dakota does not have an extensive intra-state public transportation system, public transportation options have become increasingly important for a state with an aging and widely dispersed population. More than

70 organizations provide some form of transit services covering approximately 70 percent of the geographic area within South Dakota. In 2012, 1.77 million specialized, rural public transit rides were provided.

Rail

South Dakota has long recognized the importance of rail transportation. The major intermodal transfer for grain in South Dakota is grain carried in trucks transferred to rail cars at elevators, shipped by trains to loading facilities on the West Coast for domestic or overseas markets.

In 2011, the department applied for and received a $16 million federal TIGER Grant to rehabilitate 61.6 miles of state-owned short line track between Mitchell and Chamberlain. The project cost $28 million total and was awarded an America's Transportation Award in 2012.

The rehabilitation of the MRC spurred construction of a new grain elevator near Kimball. The new elevator can handle 400 to 600 trucks dumping 100,000 bushels an hour each day. Producers will cut approximately 82 miles in each round trip and save an estimated $1.2 million in fuel costs per year. By raising the basis by 20 cents a bushel, nearly $3 million in additional producer profits may be realized and returned back into the local economy.

Air

Aviation plays a critical role in the lives of South Dakota citizens, businesses, farms, and ranches. The state has a rich aviation history that includes such names as Clyde Ice, Joe Foss, Duane Corning, and Nellie Willhite. South Dakota has 71 public use airports of which six offer commercial air service. Given South Dakota's geography, many businesses and communities depend upon general aviation aircraft of all types for mobility, access to medical treatment, economic opportunity, disaster relief, and a wide range of critical resources. General aviation helps meet the medical needs on the state's Indian reservations, aerial forest fire fighting in the Black Hills and across the state, and economic development in small communities. Agricultural aviation plays a vital role in the state's economy with the use of small businesses and pilots that use aircraft to aid farmers in producing a safe, affordable, and abundant supply of food for South Dakota and the nation.

It's the People

The success of the South Dakota Department of Transportation ultimately comes down to one thing, its people. From the time of the first state highway commission, whose members had no budget and paid many expenses out of their own pockets, to the engineers who designed and built the bridges across the Missouri faster and more economically than anyone thought possible, to the leaders of the department throughout its history that applied common sense and engineering savvy to problems, the department has always served the needs of the state, the region, and the nation.

TENNESSEE

Tennessee Department of Transportation

John Schroer
Commissioner

YEAR FORMED **1923**

FTE **Approx. 4,600**

KEY FACTS
TOTAL STATE ROAD MILES
(OWNED BY STATE HIGHWAY
AGENCY) **13,879**

STATE-OWNED BRIDGES **19,985**

TRANSIT TRIPS PER YEAR
29 million

In 1915, a year after AASHO was created, and as the national conversation centered on providing better roads, the need for a state agency to coordinate transportation in Tennessee was desperately needed.

Pre-1915

Leading up to the creation of the Tennessee Highway Department, road building activities were primarily directed by the governor or the legislature. With no central authority, building good roads was neither planned or well-managed. Road associations began to push specific highways. With emphasis on "getting out of the mud," and recognizing that planning was needed, it became apparent to the state that the job was too big for counties to handle alone. In 1915, the first state government authority to oversee transportation services was created. A forerunner to the Tennessee Department of Transportation (TDOT), the creation of the six-person State Highway Commission was approved. At that time the state system had less than 5,000 miles of roads.

1923: New Department, First Gas Tax

With federal funding beginning in 1916, the highway commission funneled money to counties. As the scope of the program grew, a voluntary commission had not provided much direction and in 1919, a three-person salaried commission was appointed. The basic structure of the highway department was formed, creating nine divisions that included four field divisions in Knoxville, Chattanooga, Nashville and Jackson.

Governor Austin Peay was considered to be the "Road Building Governor." In his 1922 election campaign, he made the highway department a major issue saying, "politics and roads do not mix" and promised to overhaul the department. Tennessee roads lagged behind border states and Tennessee was known as a detour state.

In his first year, Governor Peay reorganized state government and placed one commissioner in charge of the Department of Highways and Public Works. Governor Peay appointed J.G. Creveling as commissioner and instructed him to clean house. Creveling was unable to do this since there were not enough qualified people to take their positions.

Debates across the nation raged over issuing bonds versus the "pay-as-you-go" approach. In many cases, those impatient for roads relented to using bonds. In Tennessee, Governor Peay

stood steadfast in his belief that you only spend what you receive in revenue and, thus in his first message to the legislature, Governor Peay proposed a two-cent-per-gallon gas tax. It also resulted in shifting the tax burden from property owners to motorists, those who actually use the roads. The "pay-as-you-go" philosophy still continues in Tennessee.

1925: Interstate Highways Underway

By the mid-1920s, 12 widely known interstate highways existed in the South. One of the most traveled was the north–south Dixie Highway, which crossed the state in both Middle and East Tennessee.

Unlike a continuous route, the Dixie Highway meandered more than 4,000 miles in two parallel routes with connectors and side roads to special attractions. The Western Division ran from Lake Michigan down to Nashville, Chattanooga, Atlanta, and Tallahassee. The Eastern Division began at Lake Huron and traveled a route to Knoxville, Chattanooga, Atlanta and Jacksonville. In 1918, the Carolina Division traveled through East Tennessee.

The 500-mile long Memphis-to-Bristol Highway, although not originally an interstate route, tied in with other highways and functioned in much the same way. Soon after its creation in 1915, the Tennessee State Highway Department designated this corridor as State Route 1 and made it the top road priority. In 1926, the state designated about two-thirds of it as U.S. 70, the major east–west corridor in the region. In the late 1920s, the entire route became part of the Broadway of America Highway from California to New York. State Route 1 remained the main east–west route through the state until the completion of Interstate 40 in the late 1960s.

1930: The Great Depression and "Retrenchment"

The 1930s was a decade many would refer to as "retrenchment" of the highway department. Shortly after the untimely death of Governor Austin Peay, politics took root in the highway department with Governor Henry Horton trading roads for legislative votes on many issues. Shortly after reelection in 1930, the banking system collapsed nationwide. One particular Tennessee bank owned by a Horton protégé held millions of state deposits that resulted in a significant loss to the state. Impeachment never occurred, causing one historian to say, "Horton bought his way out with pardons, jobs, and roads."

In 1931, the "bloody July massacre" occurred in the highway department as a result of the discharge of all maintenance and construction forces due to a failure to fund it by the Tennessee General Assembly. A six-month stalemate battle over issuing bonds between the legislature and the governor found legislative members leaving Nashville without funding the department.

During the era traditionally known as the Great Depression years (1930 to 1946), highway expenditures were over two-thirds less than they had been in 1930 when $30 million had been spent. With economic disaster across the country, transportation departments were finding their revenues were being robbed by state officials and placed in the general funds of states, a tactic that was often repeated by both federal and state governments over the decades to come. This resulted in the federal government passing laws reducing federal funds for states using this tactic.

Tennessee is a prime example of the national trend in the federal increase of funds. Between 1922 and 1930, Tennessee received about $1.5 million each year. But, in 1933, the state received almost $11 million in federal dollars. This was primarily due to President

Franklin Roosevelt's "New Deal" which attempted to put people to work in federal programs such as highway construction projects. The New Deal also resulted in Tennessee's participation in projects referred to as landscaping, roadside development, and beautification. This concept initiated in 1934 resulted in several road-side parks, pull-offs, and overlooks for motorists to enjoy.

1945: The World War Almost Halts Construction

During the early 1940s, many states had come to rely on federal funds but they were diverted for construction on roads essential in supporting World War II efforts. Some state funds were used to help improve roads. During 1943–1944, the state spent only $3.8 million in a program called the Betterment Program to improve roads key to the transporting of troops and equipment for the war. A skeleton crew kept the highway department going as many men enlisted in the war. In 1944, Congress amended the Federal Aid Road Act of 1916 by establishing funding for primary, secondary, and then urban roads for the first time. The law also designated the National System of Interstate Highways, which was in anticipation of the war ending. It set up funding levels for roadwork over three years. However, funding an interstate system across the nation would not occur until over a decade later when a Tennessean would play a major role in the Interstate System as we know it today.

1956: The Interstate System and Tennessee

President Dwight Eisenhower is due much credit for pushing through

legislation which had a substantial impact on Tennessee's highway system and the nation's. His efforts were memorialized in 1991 when Congress named the nation's Interstate System, the Dwight D. Eisenhower National System of Interstate and Defense Highways. Like all key milestones in a nation's history, many were involved. Tennessee's Albert Gore, Sr. was the U.S. Senate sponsor, guiding the legislation to approval. Tennessee was allocated 1,047.6 miles. Initially, existing roads were to be used, but, the Tennessee Highway Department determined new locations for the state's portion of the Interstate System would be more practical. Tennessee's first Interstate project was a section of I-65 at the Alabama border in Ardmore, Tennessee. In 1987, Tennessee completed its original Interstate allocation with the completion of I-440 in Nashville.

1971: Landmark Supreme Court Ruling in Tennessee

In the 1960s and 1970s, the Tennessee Highway Department was primarily concerned in building its interstate system. At the height of this construction era, Tennessee had nearly 8,000 employees as compared to 4,663 positions allocated by the state legislature in 2014. In response to a nationwide movement for closer coordination among transportation modes, the name of the department was changed in 1972 to the Tennessee Department of Transportation (TDOT). As more and more interstates were being developed, constructed, and completed, new locations became issues as communities raised concerns about negative impacts. Interstate 40 later referred to as "America's Highway" would be forever impacted by a landmark case.

A 2,554-mile-long route, I-40 stretches across the United States from North Carolina to California through Tennessee. Tennessee has 455 miles, the longest section of any other state. In the original plan, Overton Park in Memphis was included. There was a time when parks and low-income neighborhoods were prime real estate for highway planners. In a landmark case, *Citizens to Preserve Overton Park v. Volpe*, the U.S. Supreme Court changed the course of I-40 and interstates nationwide that were intended to pass through locations like Overton Park. Credit is generally given to a group of women, dubbed by the media as "little old ladies in tennis shoes." They began the fight and were relentless in their campaign to stop I-40 from splitting their beloved Overton Park. For years the battle raged before finally landing in the U.S. Supreme Court in 1971 and the decision rested on laws approved five years earlier. In 1966, Congress said that Interstate highways could no longer pass through public park spaces unless there was no feasible and prudent alternative. The Supreme Court ruled in the Memphis case there was a feasible and prudent alternative for I-40, a planned beltway. In January 1981, the Overton Park section of I-40 was deleted from the master plan. Today, I-40 goes around the park and Tennessee and all states have a new approach to road building.

1986: Better Roads Program— Largest Program Ever

In the 1980s, Tennessee had a significant backlog of needed projects and motorists believed Tennessee's roads were falling apart. In his last year in office, Governor Lamar Alexander proposed a massive program projected to cost $3.5 billion over 15 years. TDOT's Better Roads Program was an ambitious highway improvement plan that included a three-cent increase in the gasoline tax. It was phased in over three years and was used to fund six Interstate-type parkways, 15 priority projects, and allowed TDOT to accelerate the existing highway program. Tennessee has a long history of funding its roads through a "pay-as-you-go" system. The gas tax has not changed since 1989. For 25 years, it has remained at 21.40 cents, one of the lowest in the nation.

One of the largest projects identified in the Better Roads Program was Interstate 840. This 78-mile route to the south around Nashville was an active TDOT project for 26 years, partly due to size of the massive project, but also due to law suits filed against the department over environmental issues in the late 1990s. When completed in 2012, the total project cost $757 million. Commercial and business development along the route has already proven SR 840s value by connecting several communities through southern Middle Tennessee. It also serves as a viable option for travelers seeking to avoid the Nashville urban area.

1989: Deaths on Hatchie River Bridge Produce National Inspection Changes

On April 1, 1989, three spans of the north bound lanes of US 51 over the Hatchie River collapsed and sent eight people to their deaths. This tragic incident and the investigation of the bridge failure resulted in the TDOT Bridge Inspection Program becoming one of the most respected in the nation.

With this failure and a 1987 collapse in New York, the FHWA strengthened its inspection manual to aiding with the new scour (erosion) and detection of scour on all bridges in the nation in 1991. Analysis and design manuals were developed for addressing scour at bridges. Scour design for new bridges is now a standard practice for all hydraulics engineers in the nation. Since that time, Tennessee has increased it expenditure on bridges to well over $100 million compared to $1 million before the 1989 failure.

In 2009, TDOT began a Better Bridges Program, the largest bridge program ever to address 200 structurally deficient bridges. In four years, TDOT replaced or repaired 200 state-owned bridges reducing the number of structurally deficient bridges on local and state systems to 5.9 percent. This brought Tennessee far below the national average of 11 percent.

Traveling from the east to the west coast, I-40 is a life line through the nation. As the talk of a possible earthquake along the New Madrid Fault Line increased in the 1990s, TDOT bridge engineers began to assess the risk of failure to the Hernando DeSoto Bridge (I-40) across the Mississippi River in Memphis. Thus, began a 15-year seismic retrofit project designed to protect this bridge and its approaches in the case of an earthquake of up to 7.7. The bridge is located about 100 miles from the same fault line that led to an 1811 earthquake. Assessments showed that a $4.5 billion economic impact to the United States would occur if the bridge were lost. The project is a collaborative effort between TDOT and our Arkansas state partners with well over $200 million dollars spent by completion in 2015.

1993: The Move to an Efficient Transportation System

In the mid-1990s, TDOT began looking at ways to be more efficient in moving motorists. Roads were no longer the complete answer to a good transportation system. A move across the nation inspired by environmental concerns about air quality prompted states to look at ways to move traffic more efficiently and reduce congestion. The first effort in Tennessee was installing high-occupancy vehicle lanes in Nashville in 1993, followed by one of the most popular programs with motorists. Operating in all four urban areas, the TDOT HELP program was launched in 1999 with the philosophy that removing incidents, debris or disabled vehicles quickly from the highways would reduce congestion and improve safety. As increased interest in intelligent transportation systems grew, TDOT began an ITS system that would provide monitoring of the urban highway systems and give motorists tools to help them make good driving decisions.

2003: Communities Become Involved

Eighty years later, in the 2002 election for governor, history repeated itself. TDOT became a hot-button campaign issue for candidate Phil Bredesen who campaigned that TDOT needed a culture change. After he won that election, there was a major philosophy shift to focus on communities helping TDOT find solutions to transportation issues. Environmental guidelines became a priority. Along with the Administrative Bureau and the Engineering Bureau, a third bureau was added, the Bureau of Environment and Planning. Public input was the number-one goal in project development and a new focus on deliberate and careful planning of highway projects. With a sluggish economy in 2009, President Barack Obama and Congress initiated a new program to get people back to work called the American Recovery and Reinvestment Act.

2009: The 21st Century Version of the 1931 National Industrial Recovery Act—ARRA

ARRA included a host of programs to help stimulate the economy. Transportation programs were one of the priorities. TDOT was well prepared to take immediate advantage of ARRA transportation projects, totaling $48 billion for all states. Tennessee completed over 300 highway projects with the $572 million received for highway infrastructure improvements, improved $21 million of transit related services and completed an airport expansion with $4 million.

2011: Efficiencies and Funding Issues Taking Priority

Even though economic ills were beginning to subside, by 2011 many states were looking at funding options for their transportation system. As part of an overall top-to-bottom state review by Governor Bill Haslam, newly appointed TDOT Commissioner John Schroer looked for ways to improve efficiencies by focusing on restructuring, expediting project delivery and improved processes. Those improvements have already saved TDOT millions of dollars and are expected to include more savings in the next decade. TDOT survived the recession financially, much better than most states because of its "no debt" status. However, it became clear that the flat tax system that began in the early 1900s may need to be revisited at least on the national level. While many elected officials recognize transportation is critical for a good economy,

and additional funding is necessary, a solution has not been solidified.

From the early 1900s, when a formal structure was organized to oversee transportation in Tennessee and a dedicated tax for transportation implemented, state leadership successfully set the state on a path propelling Tennessee's transportation system to one of the best in the nation. Even with conservative stewardship for the past 100 years, Tennessee has declining resources and must focus on preservation and efficiency more than ever in order to maintain an excellent system. As decisions are made at the state and national level on the direction our transportation system will take, the public stewards of Tennessee's transportation system will continue to be dedicated to meeting our obligations to taxpayers and motorists.

TEXAS

Texas Department of Transportation

Gen. Joesph Weber
Executive Director and
Chief Financial Officer

YEAR FORMED **1917**

FTE **11,635**

KEY FACTS

TOTAL STATE ROAD MILES
(OWNED BY STATE HIGHWAY
AGENCY) **80,231**

STATE-OWNED BRIDGES **33,513**

TRANSIT TRIPS PER YEAR
302 million

TOTAL RAIL ROUTE MILES **10,384**

RECENT HIGHLIGHTS
- Houston Grand Parkway
- Margaret Hunt Hill Bridge
- North Tarrant Express
- Dallas Horseshoe
- LBJ Express
- El Paso's Border Highway West
- Interstate designation for segments of I-69 from Texarkana to the Rio Grande Valley
- Bond, comprehensive development agreement, and design–build funding strategies

The Texas transportation system drives the state's strong economy, supporting businesses that create thousands of new jobs every year. Texas boasts $1.4 trillion in economic output, much of which is transported through highway, rail, aviation, and port systems. Thousands of transportation projects are underway across Texas representing improved quality of life for citizens in small towns, cities, and large metropolitan areas.

The Texas Department of Transportation (TxDOT) was established in 1917, a year after Congress passed the Federal Aid Road Act in 1916 to build a coordinated national system of roads. In 1923, the Texas Legislature established a tax of one cent per gallon on gasoline, three-fourths of which was allocated to the State Highway Fund. With that, the state was given administrative control over the highway system and road construction in Texas. The State Highway Building in Austin was completed in 1933 at a cost of $455,152. Three Texas Transportation Commissioners appointed by the governor and confirmed by the Texas Senate—oversaw the department and selected the executive director/chief engineer. Today's transportation commission includes five members.

The history of TxDOT and advances in the engineering profession symbolically merged with the selection of former TxDOT Executive Director Gibb Gilchrist as dean of engineering at Texas A&M in 1937. He later became president of the college and the first chancellor of the Texas A&M College System in 1948.

The post-World War II era was the beginning of a golden age for road building with an estimated 25 percent of all the highway work in the United States taking place in Texas. Federal legislation in 1956 created the Interstate Highway System and propelled robust economic development in Texas. Exceptional projects emerged from one border of the state to the other. The growth of Texas' largest cities parallels the development of the Interstate System and major transportation projects in Houston and Dallas–Fort Worth.

TxDOT expanded its focus to the beauty and quality of the transportation experience for motorists to stimulate travel to and within the state. The first issue of *Texas Highways Magazine* was published in 1974, and the magazine celebrates its 40th anniversary this year. The Adopt a Highway program originated in Tyler, Texas in 1985, providing

an opportunity for community and civic organizations to keep Texas roadways free of litter. Adopt-a-Highway is now a global initiative. The world-recognized "Don't mess with Texas®" anti-litter campaign began its more than 28-year run of encouraging motorists to keep trash off Texas highways in 1986.

TxDOT employees at the department's 12 travel information centers greeted approximately two million visitors in FY 2013. The Travel Information Centers generates an estimated $82.9 million in incremental visitor spending and supports 829 jobs, according to the Texas Office of the Governor, Economic Development and Tourism. TxDOT's more than 80 culturally unique safety rest areas provide respite for weary travelers.

Today, TxDOT oversees a vast multimodal transportation system. The department is responsible for maintaining 80,000 line miles of road and for supporting aviation, rail, public transportation, and maritime transportation.

During the past several years, with tools provided by the Texas Legislature such as Comprehensive Development Agreements, design-build strategies and the ability to issue bonds, TxDOT has continued to build. Impressive recent accomplishments include completion of segments of the planned 185-mile Houston outer loop called the Grand Parkway, State Highway 130 stretching from Waco to San Antonio, and the DFW Connector, LBJ Express and Margaret Hunt Hill Bridge in the Dallas–Fort Worth area. However, demands on the system are great.

Texas is the fastest growing state in the nation, according to many estimates, with more than 1,200 new residents moving to the state every day. The Texas population topped the 26 million mark in 2013, a 21-percent increase over the past 10 years. And that number is expected to continue to grow to 35 million by 2030.

TxDOT is streamlining processes wherever possible, creating value, and striving to achieve more each day with its allocated resources. Functioning more efficiently, the department directs savings to improving and maintaining our transportation system.

TxDOT has a long and proud history going back to the early days of the department in 1917. TxDOT builds and maintains a first-rate transportation system by consistently focusing on its goals to maintain a safe system; address congestion; connect Texas communities; and become a best-in-class state agency. The citizens of Texas deserve safe and reliable transportation solutions, and TxDOT's mission is to deliver.

UTAH

Utah Department of Transportation

Carlos Braceras
Executive Director

YEAR FORMED **1909**

FTE **Approx. 1,730**

KEY FACTS

TOTAL STATE ROAD MILES (OWNED BY STATE HIGHWAY AGENCY) **5,858**

STATE-OWNED BRIDGES **1,773**

TRANSIT TRIPS PER YEAR **42.9 million**

During the past 25 years, Utah has seen historic population growth, ranking in the top five in the country most years. This growth, while bringing economic benefits, has also brought challenges, particularly for transportation. The Utah Department of Transportation (UDOT) has steadfastly met those challenges through delivering innovative solutions while remaining focused on the implementation of its strategic direction.

UDOT's Strategic Direction

Providing safe, efficient transportation systems in a rapidly growing state requires more than just expertise in building roads. It requires a long-term vision, strategic planning and a unified Department working toward the same goals. In 2001 the UDOT established its Strategic Goals as the focus of all UDOT efforts. The goals drive every UDOT project and employee, and they have provided standards by which success is measured. The strategic goals are:

Preserve Infrastructure

Keeping Utah's bridges and pavement in good condition is the most effective way to extend the life of the transportation system at the lowest cost. UDOT maintains a multi-billion dollar system by applying well-timed preservation treatments and prioritizing critical needs.

Optimize Mobility

UDOT works to optimize traffic mobility through adding capacity, innovative design, managed lanes, signal coordination, and other measures. As a result of a steadily increasing population, Utah's average vehicle miles traveled continues to increase, but travel times and congestion remain stable or are improving.

Zero Fatalities

UDOT's goal to consistently improve safety on Utah's roads can be summed up in two words: Zero Fatalities. Safety requires effort in four main areas: engineering, education, enforcement, and emergency services. The number of fatalities has decreased by 41 percent since 2000, largely as a result of efforts such as properly planning, designing, and building safe roadways, executing public education programs, and providing snow and ice control.

Strengthen the Economy

This goal recognizes UDOT's role in creating and managing a transportation system that enables economic growth and empowers prosperity. Utah is one of the top ranked states in the country for job creation and economic

stability. Many new businesses and jobs that have been added to Utah's economy are focused in areas where infrastructure has been enhanced in the past 25 years.

Innovative Contracting for Shorter Schedules and Greater Value

UDOT leapt to the forefront of innovative contracting in 1997 with the planned reconstruction of I-15 in Salt Lake County. The estimated timeline to complete the project with a traditional design-bid-build method was 10 to 12 years, which would mean the project would not be done until five years after the 2002 Olympic Winter Games had come and gone. A more efficient timeline was an absolute necessity. UDOT chose to proceed with the design-build method, in which one contracting team is selected to both design and construct the project, with final design ongoing while construction is underway.

Design-build procurement for the Salt Lake I-15 reconstruction cut the timeline down to four years, and it became the first design-build project by a department of transportation, and it was also the largest project built using the design-build method up to that time. Design-build has since been employed by UDOT on many projects,

including the I-15 Corridor Expansion (I-15 CORE) in Utah County, which was constructed from 2010 to 2012. The design-builder made I-15 CORE the fastest billion-dollar public highway project completed in the United States by finishing in 35 months.

I-15 CORE was also UDOT's first use of fixed-price, best-design procurement, in which a set budget is established and design-build teams propose the scope they can complete for that budget. This method resulted in greater value, with a 60 percent greater project scope for the same budget.

UDOT has led the way in the use of Construction Manager/General Contractor (CMGC), with Mountain View Corridor as the premier example. By utilizing a collaborative process between UDOT and the contractor for scheduling, budgeting, risk allocation, and design solutions, construction costs were reduced by $110 million, and a year was shaved off the schedule.

Innovative Designs Optimize Mobility

When planning projects, UDOT designers and consultants identify the best solution for the specific needs of the community, constraints of geography,

and demands of traffic for the best value. Innovative designs include:

Diverging Diamond Interchange (DDI)

UDOT has constructed seven DDIs in Utah. This design has become a popular solution because it improves safety and mobility while reducing the length and cost of construction. Utah was the second state in the country to build a DDI.

Flex Lanes

UDOT opened its first Flex Lanes in October 2012. The Flex Lanes accommodate heavy directional traffic by alternating the direction of the lanes during peak hours of the day, significantly decreasing traffic delay with minimal construction costs. This project is unique in that it alternates the left-turn lane with directional traffic to improve traffic movement.

ThrU-Turn Intersection (TTI)

By eliminating all left turns at the intersection, the number and severity of crashes are greatly reduced. Motorists travel through the intersection, make a signalized U-turn and come back to the intersection, where they turn right. This helps improve intersection performance and significantly reduces wait times at traffic signals.

Express Lanes

I-15 Express Lanes are designated for carpoolers, paying Express Pass holders and low emission or clean fuel vehicles, but the lanes benefit all drivers by reducing the number of cars in the general purpose lanes and optimizing lane use. Utah has one of the longest continuous stretches of carpool lanes in the country with 62 miles currently in operation and an additional 10 miles to be constructed in the summer of 2014.

Continuous Flow Intersection (CFI)

CFIs separate the left-turn movement from the other movements at the intersection, reducing congestion and delays and improving safety. UDOT currently has 12 CFIs in operation.

Bridge Construction on the Move

UDOT is the national leader in bridge moves, having completed 123 bridges using accelerated bridge construction (ABC) methods. Included among these was the Sam White Bridge, which was the longest bridge moved by self-propelled modular transporters (SPMT) ever in the Western Hemisphere.

Asset Management

"Good roads cost less" is both a simple truth and a way of doing business every day at UDOT. Once a year, UDOT takes inventory of the entire state highway system to measure road conditions and catalog that information, including measuring the surface roughness, wheel-path rutting, surface cracking, and other surface defects.

The condition data is used to forecast decline of pavement conditions and prioritize preservation projects. This system allows the department to optimize funding and maximize the pavement life.

New to the process is the use of mobile LiDAR, which creates a complete three-dimensional picture of all UDOT assets from pavement to bridges to signs in a single pass. LiDAR creates a point cloud for a continuous accurate measurement of pavement and all surrounding roadway assets. Using LiDAR allows UDOT to maintain a single data environment for all assets, creating a more complete picture of assets and a more robust maintenance strategy.

Changing the Landscape of Transportation in Utah: A Timeline

1997

I-15 Design-Build Begins—After Salt Lake City won the bid for the 2002 Olympic Winter Games, UDOT took on the challenge of transforming I-15 in Salt Lake County into the model of an efficient, modern, urban freeway system. A traditional design-bid-build method would have made completion before the games virtually impossible, so UDOT became the first transportation department in the country to utilize a design-build procurement method for a major highway project.

2000

US 6 Improvements—UDOT focused on U.S. Highway 6 as an area for improvements and began a multi-year process to increase capacity and improve safety. UDOT widened sections, built passing lanes, installed rumble strips and concrete barriers, and added traffic signals and variable message signs, reducing serious and fatal crashes by 75 percent over the next 11 years.

2001

I-15 Reconstruction Completed—Sixteen miles of I-15 in Salt Lake County were reconstructed, including the addition of three lanes in both directions, replacement of 142 bridges, reconstruction of eight interchanges and three freeway-to-freeway connections. The project was completed in four and a half years at a cost of $1.32 billion with $32 million in savings at the end of the project.

2002

XIX Olympic Winter Games—With more than 75 events, 2,500 athletes, 11,500 media representatives, and 750,000 visitors, the XIX Olympic Winter Games was the largest event in Utah history. Despite fears of major traffic delays during the Games, interagency cooperation, effective public relations, and an increase in operational tools resulted in lower traffic rates during the Olympics than normal daily traffic.

"Who would've guessed they could hold an entire Olympic Games with, literally, no traffic? Either every native heeded Mitt Romney's warnings and fled town or the people at the Utah Department of Transportation...are the smartest people in the universe."

~ Devin Gordon, Newsweek

2006

Zero Fatalities Program Launched—Utah was one of the first states in the nation to establish a zero-based goal for traffic fatalities and create a program to aggressively pursue it. This objective is being accomplished through media and grassroots efforts and by partnering with Utah's Department of Public Safety, local health departments and state organizations to achieve the maximum results. Since program launch, annual statewide traffic fatalities have decreased by nearly 20 percent.

2007

First Continuous Flow Intersection (CFI)—Utah's first CFI in Salt Lake City allows 600 more cars to be served per peak hour. With fewer points of conflict, it has also increased safety. As the first intersection of its kind in Utah, UDOT carried out extensive public education on how to safely drive it.

First Bridge Move—Specialized heavy lift and transport equipment was used to remove a deteriorated four-million-pound bridge at 4500 South over I-215 and replace it with a new bridge during a single weekend. Traditional construction methods would have taken 9 to 12 months, with repeated closures of the freeway.

2008

Legacy Parkway Completed—Legacy Parkway was an environmentally sensitive project that included a multi-use trail and an equestrian trail running alongside the entire 14 miles of new roadway. UDOT delivered Legacy Parkway ahead of schedule and under budget despite an extraordinary set of managerial and environmental challenges. The first Monday Legacy Parkway was open, commute times were slashed from 45 to 20 minutes.

2009

Redwood Road Widening Completed—The S.R. 68 project widened Redwood Road from Bangerter Highway to Saratoga Springs. The project spanned two UDOT Regions, making cross-regional coordination essential to success.

Southern Parkway Segments 1 and 2 Completed—The Southern Parkway is a 26-mile long, four-lane, divided expressway beginning at the Atkinville Interchange on I-15 in St. George and connecting with S.R. 9. Segments 1 and 2 are 7.4 miles long and provide access to the new St. George airport.

2010

Innovate 80 Completed—Innovate 80 replaced 12 bridges in two months. The project was the largest and most ambitious of its kind in the world, prompting the National Geographic Channel to feature the project in a documentary series titled "World's Toughest Fixes: Interstate Bridges."

Utah's First Diverging Diamond Interchange—UDOT built the second diverging diamond interchange (DDI) in the country at American Fork Main Street on I-15. An interactive map, animation, movie theater ad, and DDI cards helped educate drivers how to safely navigate the interchange.

Electronic Tolling System for Express Lanes Begins—UDOT introduced the concept of allowing solo drivers to use underutilized carpool lane space by paying a fee that adjusts based on congestion. This system helps to optimize all freeway lanes and maximize throughput. By the end of 2013, approximately 13,000 Express Passes were in use.

2011

UDOT Traffic Mobile App Launched—The UDOT Traffic app is a free traveler information tool that pushes road construction, weather, crash, and special event information to the public. The app was downloaded nearly 16,500 times within just the first week, and it has now been downloaded 230,000 times.

First ThrU-Turn Intersection—The first ThrU-Turn intersection built in Utah allowed 30 percent more green time for the through movement traffic and ended significant delays at the 12300 South interchange in Draper.

2012

Access Utah County Projects Completed—Access Utah County used one team to handle all project management functions of five design-build projects: S.R. 77, Pioneer Crossing, Timpanogos Highway, Geneva Road, and environmental work for the Vineyard Connector. These projects, along with I-15 CORE, completely changed transportation in Utah County, significantly improving north–south and east–west travel and preparing the county for decades of population growth.

Utah County I-15 Corridor Expansion (I-15 CORE) Completed—I-15 CORE is the fastest billion-dollar public road construction project built in U.S. history. The project added two lanes in each direction for 24 miles, rebuilt or reconfigured 10 freeway interchanges, and replaced 63 aging bridges in 35 months.

Mountain View Corridor Phase 1 Completed—The Mountain View Corridor (MVC) team is using a phased and segmented approach to build a completely new 35-mile transportation system. The first phase of MVC in Salt Lake County was a new 15-mile roadway—the largest project delivered using CMGC in UDOT history.

VERMONT

Vermont Agency of Transportation

Brian R. Searles
Secretary

YEAR FORMED **1975**

FTE **Approx. 1300**

KEY FACTS
TOTAL STATE ROAD MILES
(OWNED BY STATE HIGHWAY
AGENCY) **2,631**

STATE-OWNED BRIDGES **1,084**

TRANSIT TRIPS PER YEAR
2.5 million

The Vermont Agency of Transportation (VTrans) is one of the few state transportation entities that is an all-modes agency and has been so since it was established in 1975, when the Departments of Aeronautics, Highways, Motor Vehicles, Rail, Bus, Waterways, and Motor Carrier Services were merged.

The Department of Highways had been in business since 1923 and some level of state assistance for local road improvements began with establishment of the Highway Commission in 1892. Formation of the Agency represented the culmination of the developing understanding that transportation modes are interconnected and interdependent. This understanding continues to inform our vision of a safe, reliable, and multi-modal transportation system that promotes Vermont's quality of life and economic wellbeing.

Today, VTrans is responsible for over 3,300 miles of highway, 305 miles of state-owned railroad, and 90 runway lane miles at its 10 airports. Much of Vermont's road network grew out of cow paths and trails over time and presents some of the most challenging topography and a dizzying array of micro-climates that keep engineers and maintenance crews on their toes. Roads

tread the space between steep mountain slopes and dynamic river valleys and Mother Nature is always, undeniably, in charge. Because Vermont is also one of the least populous states, VTrans is constantly under pressure to deliver state-sized services with the tax base of a medium-sized city.

Vermont is a state with a rich cultural history, which creates special challenges and opportunities for our unique system. Covered bridges by their very nature are often functionally obsolete and a thoughtful approach to preservation balanced with an acceptable level of service is an ongoing consideration. In the 1990s, the legislature developed plans to designate which were the representative structures that would be preserved as examples and which would be replaced with more modern structures. Because of our clear process and strict adherence to rules, VTrans was the first state transportation entity that is authorized to self-regulate on historic preservation.

One notable example of applying innovation in the interest of preservation is the Checkered House Bridge over the Winooski River on US 2 in Richmond. As the longest truss bridge in the state, it was on the list of structures to save. As

a crossing of a major river in the most densely populated county, its narrow width created safety issues. Through an innovative design/build project, the truss was widened in place and the traditional lines of the structure maintained above a deck that can accommodate current load standards.

Sometimes, the past just has to embrace the future, as in the case of the iconic Champlain Bridge between Vermont and New York State. In November 2009, it was determined that the crumbling piers could not be saved and rehabilitating the existing structure would not be prudent. The process of building a new bridge included an extensive public involvement process in design selection on an accelerated track because of the importance of reopening the artery. In November 2011, Vermont and New York celebrated the opening of a graceful new span across the lake that incorporates key historic architectural features, while becoming a modern bridge to accommodate all users, including bicyclists and pedestrians.

Also in the 1990s, VTrans found that proposed highway and bridge projects designed to national standards were meeting community resistance because of concerns that features such as wide

shoulders were out-of-scale to local conditions. As the number of stalled projects accumulated, the agency worked to develop a new and more flexible set of design standards that would allow the agency to apply lower-impact practices where appropriate. The standards were developed with input from a wide range of stakeholders, including other state agencies, local governments, and bicycle and pedestrian interests. In 1997, VTrans' Vermont State Design Standards were approved by the Legislature and formally adopted as agency rules.

There is no single event of the past 25 years that looms larger than Tropical Storm Irene. On August 28, 2011, Irene caused massive damage to Vermont's highways and railroads. One hundred forty-six state highway segments and 34 bridges were closed for a total of 531 miles of damaged state roadway and over 200 miles of state-owned rail were impassable. VTrans quickly mobilized to establish safe detours, re-establish contact with 13 cut-off communities, worked closely with utilities to restore services, and within 48 hours established three regional incident command centers to coordinate recovery efforts.

More than 700 VTrans workers were mobilized for recovery efforts with

support from the Maine and New Hampshire Departments of Transportation, National Guard units from Vermont and seven other states, and over 200 private contractors. By September 28, 2001, there were only six closed road segments totaling 13 miles and 6 closed bridges. Within three weeks of the storm, all rail lines were reopened. On December 29, 2011, the "Last Mile" of work was completed. In 2013, VTrans lent its disaster recovery experience to Colorado as that state responded to its own major storm event.

Several long-planned projects from the era of the interstates have been or are nearly completed. The second phase of the Vermont Route 279 around historic Bennington in southwestern Vermont opened in 2012 and in Fall 2014, the Morristown Alternate Truck Route will open in northern Vermont.

Many of our bridges are hitting the end of their lifecycle around the same time because of the dual bubbles of the massive rebuilding efforts in the wake of a devastating flood in 1927 and the construction of the Interstate System. Deployment of accelerated bridge techniques and design/build is helping us clear the bridge backlog faster, and taking the deep dive into the substructure at some of our oldest roads means more affordable and predictable maintenance going forward

Rail continues to enjoy tremendous grassroots support in Vermont as we work to expand our passenger and freight capabilities. In the years since the demise of Amtrak's overnight train between Washington, D.C. and Montreal, VTrans has re-launched Amtrak passenger service with the Vermonter and the Ethan Allen Express. Both have seen steady growth in ridership in recent years. An intercity rail grant yielded continuously welded rail for a smoother ride and higher speeds on the Vermonter line and plans are underway to restore service to Montreal. On the Western Corridor, grants are supporting bridge, track and crossing upgrades that put us within striking distance of extending service from mid-town Manhattan to downtown Burlington.

Rail freight remains a potent economic engine with over 5.9 million tons of cargo moving to and from Canada in 2012. Feed, salt, heating oil, paper, lumber, talc, limestone, granite, and marble are just a few of the commodities that ride the rails in Vermont each year.

The state owned airport system is becoming a collection of economic development hubs, where public–private partnerships are expanding passenger, charter and cargo services. Municipally owned Burlington International (BTV) remains the most active airport in the state with service from many major carriers, but commercial service is growing in Rutland and other airports are under consideration.

Public transit has evolved significantly in the past quarter century in Vermont. In the late 1980s, most riders used an array of private, intercity services and with few exceptions, rural public transit services were largely operated by community action organizations. Today, the state boasts 10 regional transit systems. Ridership is growing, with nearly 4.9 million riders in 2012. New commuter services between population centers including Montpelier, Burlington, Middlebury, and St. Albans have proven popular and after many years of decline, intercity service is also making a comeback.

Vermont will always be small, but VTrans and our partners see the value in big ideas and we will continue to deploy new technology and best practices to ensure sustainable growth to serve our economy and deliver on our mission to provide for the safe and efficient movement of people and goods.

VIRGINIA

Virginia Department of Transportation

Aubrey L. Layne, Jr.
Secretary

YEAR FORMED **1927**

FTE **Approx. 6,755**

KEY FACTS

TOTAL STATE ROAD MILES
(OWNED BY STATE HIGHWAY
AGENCY) **58,272**

STATE-OWNED BRIDGES **11,892**

TRANSIT TRIPS PER YEAR
74 million

The Virginia settlers who arrived at Jamestown Island aboard three small ships on May 13, 1607, had little need for a road system. Barely more than 100 in number, their first concerns were disease, hunger, shelter, and safety. Transportation came by the way of water—the great rivers that emptied into the Chesapeake Bay that would one day be known as the James, York, Rappahannock, and Potomac.

As the colonists hunted for food and cautiously began exploring, they discovered a network of paths made long before by Native American Indians and wild animals. The colonists began to use these trails, and many of the paths shaped the Virginia road pattern for years to come.

John Rolfe had begun experimenting with the cultivation of tobacco in 1612 and two years later exported a shipment to England. In less than 20 years, tobacco exports had reached 500,000 pounds annually and tobacco would remain the foundation for the Virginia economy throughout the colonial period. Inevitably, the success of the tobacco crop was to influence the colony's transportation needs as well.

After two decades, the colony's population was near 5,000 and growing.

The need for improving roads to better serve the social and economic life of the colony was among the matters facing members of the House of Burgesses as they met in Jamestown in September 1632. Before adjournment, they passed the first highway legislation in American history, an act providing, in the language of the day, that, "Highwayes shall be layd in such convenient places as are requisite accardinge as the Governor and Counsell or the commissioners for the monthlie corts shall appoynt, or accordinge as the parishioners of every parish shall agree."

Hundreds of years later, in Virginia, as well as across the nation, the public's delight with transportation—as well as the automobile in particular—grew by leaps and bounds. But in most places, the roads were not ready for this "horseless carriage."

Two governors gave strong support to the mushrooming movement for better roads. They were Andrew Jackson Montague, the state's chief executive from 1902 to 1906, and his successor, Claude A. Swanson, who served until 1910. Their recommendations to the General Assembly in 1906 helped set the state government's course in road development for the years ahead.

Meeting in Richmond, the legislature created the first State Highway Commission, giving final approval to the legislation on March 6, 1906. A state highway commissioner was appointed by the governor with General Assembly confirmation. Legislation required that the commissioner be a Virginia citizen, as well as a "civil engineer and a person well-versed in road-building."

By 1908, the need for better roads had reached the point that the legislature made its first appropriation for construction purposes under the new state program—$25,000 annually, beginning March 1, 1909. It was intended mainly for use in counties where convict labor was not available and was to be matched equally by the counties paying for road improvements.

By 1910, Virginians owned 2,705 motor vehicles, and the General Assembly decided the time had come to regulate their use. During its 1918 session in Richmond, the General Assembly approved establishment of the first state highway system, a network of 4,002 miles for which construction and maintenance would be the responsibility of the highway commissioner and his staff.

The so-called "Richmond–Washington Highway," the often muddy predecessor of U.S. Route 1 and Interstate 95, also was included in the system. A fully paved Route 1 was not completed until 1927. That same year, as part of a reorganization of state government, the Virginia Department of Highways was established. Five years later, the secondary road system was created under the Byrd Road Act, allowing counties to transfer responsibility for local roads to the state. All but four turned their roads over to the transportation agency at the time.

When the secondary system was established, it totaled 35,900 miles. It included 2,000 miles hard surfaced, 8,900 miles with soil or gravel surfaces, and more than 25,000 miles, or almost 70 percent, of largely unimproved dirt roads. Some counties had no hard-surfaced roads at all.

Within a decade, the amount of hard-surfaced roads had tripled, the mileage of soil or gravel roads had doubled, and the unimproved roads had been reduced by almost half. (By December 2012, the secondary system had gained 13,000 miles, but the makeup of those roads was very different. The system totaled 48,776 miles; 41,037 hard surfaced, 6,028 untreated all-weather surface, 1,590 untreated light surface, and 121 unsurfaced.)

With the arrival of the secondary system, the main roads for which the state had been responsible became known as the "primary" highway system.

The devastating effect of two world wars greatly impacted Virginia's road system. There was a labor shortage and the cost of building materials skyrocketed. At the same time, the highways had to remain operational for military traffic. By mid-1948, however, the state's road program had mostly recovered from the wartime slowdown.

In 1956, Congress authorized the development of a 40,000-mile Interstate System. Virginia's share was 1,070 miles. Eight years later, the state General Assembly authorized the development of a 1,700-mile arterial system of four-lane divided highways to connect areas not directly served by interstates.

In 1974, the department added rail and public transportation to its jurisdiction and with the change came a new name. The department went from being known as the Virginia Department of Highways to the Virginia Department of Highways and Transportation.

In 1985, the department was authorized to begin using a new allocation formula to distribute funds for highway construction and other road programs. The new formula increased the urban and secondary road allocations' share of the highway dollar.

In 1986, newly elected Governor Gerald L. Baliles presented a series of initiatives to improve transportation and prepare for the 21st Century. His initiatives and subsequent legislative action marked a period of sweeping changes that eliminated exclusive dependence on user fees and "pay-as-you-go" financing.

Special-session legislation expanded revenue sources for highway construction and public transportation, and ports and airports received new emphasis. The department was renamed the Virginia Department of Transportation and the Commonwealth Transportation Board (originally named "State Highway Commission" when established in 1906) was expanded from 12 to 15 members.

Major highway construction projects were completed during the 1990s, among them the last stretch of Virginia's interstate network, a section of I-295 around Richmond (June 1992). The completion of I-295 brought the number of miles of Interstate highway in the commonwealth to 1,105.

Completion of I-295 was preceded by a few weeks by the opening of the Monitor Merrimac Memorial Bridge-Tunnel (MMMBT). This massive project carries traffic over three and a half miles of the waters of Hampton Roads and under almost one mile of those waters through a tunnel of twin tubes. The tunnel required joining 15,300-foot sections of steel tubes, each wide enough to carry four lanes of traffic. When encased in concrete, each section weighed 28,000 tons and each had to be joined to others under the water with a tolerance of one inch. The MMMBT enabled I-664 to link Newport News and Suffolk and put the last piece in place in a 55-mile Interstate beltway in the region.

It became the second water crossing from the Peninsula to Southeast Virginia after the Hampton Roads Bridge-Tunnel, which opened its first two lanes in 1957 and its second two lanes in 1976. A choke point at the George P. Coleman Bridge across the York River between Yorktown and Gloucester Point was remedied with the conversion of the bridge from two lanes to four. It was a marvel of engineering that provided for construction of the new, larger spans in Norfolk and delivery by barge, to the reinforced piers. The new spans were set in place while closing the bridge to traffic for only nine days. The innovative project won several awards.

Meanwhile, renewing the aging interstates without disrupting travelers was a continuing challenge, one that was met with intense planning and innovative engineering. Chief among these projects was the intersection of I-395 and I-495 with I-95 in the Springfield Interchange in Northern Virginia. This facility carries almost 400,000 vehicles daily on traffic lifelines for the entire East Coast.

In the same period, VDOT implemented improvements on the I-81 corridor to include truck-climbing lanes. Meanwhile bridges on I-95 through Richmond, one of the earliest pieces of Interstate built in Virginia, were being rehabilitated. Despite the increase in construction activity, highway congestion continued to be a major concern for citizens, especially in Northern Virginia and Hampton Roads.

In 1993, ground was broken for the Dulles Toll Road Extension (known as the Dulles Greenway), a 14-mile stretch from State Route 28 at Dulles International Airport to Leesburg. It would be built and operated as a private enterprise—the first private toll road built in Virginia since the 1800s. It followed the General Assembly's 1988 Virginia Highway Corporation Act, which allowed a private corporation to build, own, and operate a toll road for profit.

In 1995, the General Assembly introduced a broader opportunity for privatization by passing the Public–Private Transportation Act (PPTA), a part of Governor Allen's legislative package. The act allowed private ventures to build new transportation facilities and expedited new cooperation between VDOT and the private sector.

The first PPTA project approved by the CTB was the Pocahontas Parkway (State Route 895), a toll road crossing the James River just south of Richmond connecting Chesterfield and Henrico counties. It provided much easier access to Richmond International Airport for many motorists in the metropolitan area.

While new projects were fewer in the early 2000s, some major road projects continued. The reconstruction of the Springfield interchange for I-95, I-395, and I-495 in Northern Virginia required building 50 bridges and widening I-95 to 24 lanes on one segment.

Another was replacing the aging Woodrow Wilson Bridge, which carries I-95 across the Potomac River. Widening Virginia's longest highway, U.S. Route 58, which stretches from the Atlantic Ocean to the southwest tip of the state, continued. The western loop around Richmond, State Route 288, was completed in 2004, and economic development followed closely. Environmental enhancements, including underpasses for animals to safely cross the road, accompanied the relocation of U.S. Route 17 in Chesapeake, which was completed in 2005.

Virginia's transportation infrastructure was aging, needing repairs, and sometimes reconstruction. Because funding for improvements and maintenance was stretched thin, innovative measures were taken to get more out of the network and the dollars appropriated for it.

VDOT has identified advancing public private partnerships as an important component in pursuing the agency's Business Plan. In 2011, the Office of Transportation Public–Private Partnerships (OTP3) was created to facilitate the commonwealth's PPTA program.

OTP3 continues to work with VDOT's private-sector partners to advance several ongoing and proposed projects. In fact, more than half of VDOT's Fiscal Year 2013 spending was with private-sector vendors.

Some Public–Private Partnership projects of note include the I-495 Capital Beltway Express Lanes and I-95 Express Lanes in Northern Virginia, the Midtown Tunnel/Downtown Tunnel/MLK Extension in Hampton Roads, the SR 58 widening the Coalfields Expressway project in Bristol.

No summary of Virginia's history on transportation would be complete without mention of the 2013 historic transportation funding bill, "Virginia's Road to the Future" (HB 2313), which provides more than $3.9 billion dollars in dedicated, sustainable new revenue for transportation statewide over the next six years. HB 2313 provides dedicated regional revenues in the amounts of $1.9 billion dollars in for Northern Virginia and $1.3 billion dollars for Hampton Roads.

Safety continues to be VDOT's number one priority. The department works with its research arm, the Virginia Center for Transportation Innovation and Research, to apply a broad array of research and academic resources to the complex problems and issues that characterize transportation in the 21st century.

Well-engineered highways, smooth pavements, strong bridges, and sophisticated traffic management systems are positioned on Virginia's 58,332 miles of state-maintained roadways in Virginia. That expanding transportation infrastructure has contributed to the commonwealth's economic development and continuing prosperity through the decades, as well as to the safety and convenience of its citizens. To preserve this perpetual condition, continual diligence, innovation and foresight will be required.

Virginia began the 20th century without a highway network, but rather with only a disjointed collection of rutted country roads. The Commonwealth of Virginia can recount epic steps in building transportation facilities to move millions of people and products every day and enhance quality of life.

Under the leadership of newly appointed Secretary of Transportation Aubrey L. Layne, Jr., and Commissioner Charles A. Kilpatrick, P.E., VDOT will continue to uphold the qualities instilled by former Commissioner Gregory A. Whirley in an effort to keep the agency moving forward: increase public accountability, focus on core business and launch necessary transportation improvements.

"Solutions to transportation problems go beyond engineering and construction and involve quality of life, economic opportunity, and environmental stewardship," said Kilpatrick. "We know who we work for—motorists, taxpayers, and citizens of Virginia. They entrust us to spend their money wisely and we will. We will listen to their concerns to understand their perspective and needs so we can provide the right solutions."

WASHINGTON

Washington State Department of Transportation

Lynn A. Peterson
Secretary

YEAR FORMED **1905**

FTE **Approx. 6,496**

KEY FACTS
TOTAL STATE ROAD MILES
(OWNED BY STATE HIGHWAY
AGENCY) **7,056**

STATE-OWNED BRIDGES **3,262**

FERRY PASSENGERS PER YEAR
22 million

TRANSIT TRIPS PER YEAR
235 million

RECENT HIGHLIGHTS
WSDOT is nearing the end of its largest construction program in agency history.
As of February 2014, 352 of 421 projects funded by 2003 and 2005 fuel tax increases are complete, with 81 percent finished on time and on budget.

Construction is underway on two new, 144-car, Olympic Class ferries, with a third approved for funding by the 2013 Legislature. The first vessel, M.V. Tokitae goes into service in spring 2014, and the second, M.V. Samish, is scheduled to go into service in early 2015. The vessels will replace the 1950s era Evergreen State Class ferries.

Washington: A State of Contrasts and Diversity

Washington state is a study of contrasts: from its major urban centers to rural communities to its varied geography, including coastal beaches, rugged mountain ranges, desert plains, farmlands, forests, and orchards. It is also widely diverse, both in terms of its cultural and ethnic makeup and in terms of its economic drivers—aerospace, information technology, timber, fishing, agriculture, viticulture, and manufacturing industries.

The state's diversity creates some of our biggest transportation challenges and greatest opportunities for innovation. During the past 25 years, the Washington State Department of Transportation (WSDOT) has risen to the challenge and is focused on providing transportation options for Washington's citizens, managing congestion in its urban areas, operating the nation's largest ferry system and keeping freight and goods moving to support our economy.

Transportation Investments Keep People and Goods Moving

Transportation is the backbone of Washington's economy—it gets people to jobs, and goods and freight to market. Like elsewhere in the United States, limited transportation revenue has placed greater emphasis on getting the most capacity from our existing system by creating an integrated, multi-modal system; using new technology; and making strategic corridor investments. The following are examples of how we are moving more people in fewer vehicles and providing transportation options:

- Washington's Commute Trip Reduction Act went into law 1991, encouraging commuters to consider transportation alternatives such as ridesharing or taking the bus to work, rather than driving alone. Currently more than 1,000 worksites and 530,000 commuters participate in the CTR program.
- In 1996, voters approved Sound Transit (ST), a regional commuter rail, light-rail and express bus system in the central Puget Sound region; WSDOT works in partnership with ST to coordinate and expand a

system of high-occupancy vehicle (HOV) lanes, freeway transit stations, and park and ride lots.

- WSDOT's Rideshare program began in 1996 to move more people in fewer vehicles, such as vanpools or carpools. Washington has the largest vanpool program in the nation, with more than 2,800 vanpools.

- With 22 vessels and 20 terminals, Washington State Ferries (WSF) is the largest ferry system in the nation. Its first passenger-only ferry started in 1998. Due to high-operating costs, however, the service ended in 2003. Three new 64-car ferries were added to the fleet in 2011, the same year WSF celebrated 60 years of service. Construction started on new 144-car ferries in 2012 and the first of three will begin operating in June 2014.

- Expanded use of new technology including, electronic tolling, traveler information signs, real-time traffic, variable speed limits, ramp meters, and mobile apps help WSDOT manage traffic and increase trip reliability for travelers. Three tolled highway facilities currently operate in Washington: SR 16 Tacoma Narrows Bridge in Pierce County, SR 520 bridge across Lake Washington, and the SR 167 HOT lanes in King County.

- Amtrak Cascades rail service between Eugene, Oregon, and Seattle started in 1999. Washington received $800 million in federal high-speed rail funds for improvements to provide additional rail-line capacity and upgrades to tracks, signals, and passenger stations. WSDOT reached the half-way point on a total of 20 high-speed rail projects in December 2013 and all projects will be completed by early 2017.

- Washington received the "Most Bicycle Friendly State" award in 2008, and has retained the title for six consecutive years, through 2013.

- Travel Washington, an intercity bus service, was established in 2007 to provide options for statewide travel, connecting towns and rural communities with major transportation hubs and urban centers. Four lines are currently operating in rural areas across the state.

- In Washington, electric vehicle drivers have access to DC fast charging stations along I-5, US 2 and parts of I-90. The first public charging stations opened in 2012. With the robust charging network, drivers can travel "border-to-border" along the 276 miles of I-5 between Washington's borders with Oregon

and Canada. Washington's segment of the West Coast Electric Highway connects drivers to similar fast charging networks in British Columbia and Oregon.

Helping Business and the Economy Prosper

Washington is one of the five most freight-dependent states in the nation with total imports and exports valued at $111.5 billion and gross business income totaling $450 billion. Forty-four percent of the state's jobs depend on freight. Below are some examples of the way we are keeping freight and goods rolling across and through our state:

- In 1994, the Washington Grain Train began operations with 29 grain cars and currently has 118 cars in the fleet. Since its beginning, the Washington Grain Train program has moved more than 1.2 million tons of grain from Washington to national and international markets.

- Interstate 90 is a major east–west freight corridor across the state for movement of local, regional, and international-bound goods and products. The I-90 Snoqualmie Pass East project is improving this essential corridor by adding lanes, and increasing reliability with minimized closures due to avalanche and rock slides. The first 3 miles of the 15-mile long project was completed in 2013.

- Commercial vehicle information systems and networks (CVISN) technology is installed at 12 weigh stations to electronically screen transponder-equipped trucks, allowing pre-cleared vehicles to bypass weigh stations. The industry savings in 2012 was approximately 101,000 hours of travel time and $12.4 million dollars in operating expenses.

- The first segment of US 395 North Spokane Corridor began in 2001. This project improves mobility by allowing motorists and freight to move north and south through metropolitan Spokane, from I-90 to US 395 at Wandermere. The northern half of this new 10.5-mile corridor was completed in 2012. The first two projects of southern half that will ultimately connect with I-90 began in 2013.

Building Infrastructure in a Challenging Landscape

There are 63 named mountain ranges in Washington and five active volcanoes, which includes Mount Rainier with the highest peak at 14,441 feet, and Mt. St. Helens which erupted in 1980.

Washington is also home to more than 160 named rivers and tributaries and is bounded by the Puget Sound and Pacific coast. Traversing those bodies of water are more than 7,800 bridges, of those nearly 3,800 are owned by the state. WSDOT builds and maintains many iconic structures, including four of the world's longest floating bridges (State Route 520 Albert D. Rosellini Bridge, Interstate 90 Lacey V. Murrow Bridge,

I-90 Homer M. Hadley Bridge, and SR 104 Hood Canal Bridge). Notable events involving bridges from the past 25 years include:

- I-90 Lacey V. Murrow eastbound bridge sank during construction in November 1990 when a storm flooded water into an open pontoon hatch, causing a chain-reaction. The completed bridge opened in 1993. Lessons from this engineering disaster were incorporated into floating bridge designs for future projects.

- In 2001, the Nisqually Quake rattled the Puget Sound area, registering 6.8 on the Richter scale and caused $1 billion in damages to roads and infrastructure, including the elevated SR 99 Alaskan Way Viaduct in Seattle. Debate over how to replace the structure was not resolved until 2008. In July 2013, the world's largest tunneling machine, "Bertha," arrived from Japan and began digging the Alaskan Way Viaduct Replacement tunnel. She broke down in December 2013, and is estimated to restart tunneling in late summer 2014.

- The new SR 16 Tacoma Narrows Bridge opened to traffic in 2007 and introduced electronic tolling to the state. Combined with the 1950s Narrows Bridge, the new bridge provides a safer, more reliable crossing for 40,000 daily travelers.

- In 2009, funding was approved to replace the 1960s, SR 520 Albert D. Rosellini floating bridge. Tolling to help pay for bridge began in December 2011. To date, pontoon construction is more than 50 percent completed.

- The 2013 collapse of the I-5 Skagit River Bridge made local, national and world news headlines. This terrible incident became the

model for how we "do hard things" in Washington really well. Working in partnership with local, state and federal entities, WSDOT reopened a temporary span in 27 days and a permanent replacement in 66 days.

Our Future: Stretching Our State's Transportation Dollars

The effects of inflation, fewer miles being driven and less gas being purchased continues to erode the ability of transportation fuel taxes to meet our increasing transportation needs. In response, WSDOT is implementing new strategies to get the best value from limited resources, and using performance management as the basis for investment decisions:

- **Practical Design**—WSDOT has adopted practical design to make significant improvements in project delivery and reduce project costs. Using a practical design approach allows roadway projects to be "right-sized" to achieve high priority transportation and community needs. Practical design focuses on investments that provide the greatest benefit to the transportation system as a whole. WSDOT projects a cost savings of up to 15 percent on selected projects during the initial implementation of this new practice.

- **Lean Practices**—WSDOT is implementing Lean strategies with the goal of achieving greater efficiency in government and to better meeting the needs of our customers. WSDOT has initiated 17 Lean projects since August 2012, with seven projects completed. Examples of improvements include streamlining sign production at a reduced cost, reducing wait time for collision reports, and eliminating duplicative or unnecessary steps in delivery of public records.

- **Environmental Streamlining**— Washington has some of the most stringent environmental requirements in the nation. WSDOT works in partnership with resource agencies to expedite project delivery while maintaining strong environmental standards. Since 1990, WSDOT has been recognized with 18 FHWA Environmental Excellence awards, including the latest in 2013 for its programmatic agreement to speed up federal agency review and approval of biological assessments. The agreement addresses 24 Endangered Species Act-protected species, including salmon, marine mammals, and rockfish.

- **Performance Measurement**— WSDOT was an early adopter and

is a recognized national leader in performance management and accountability. Since 2001, WSDOT has integrated performance management into its day-to-day work. Our quarterly "The Gray Notebook" performance report was described by "Governing Magazine" to "provide gold-standard data in a way that tells a story and is accessible to the average reader…" and points to the report as an example for other states to follow.

- **Sustainable Transportation**— WSDOT's fleet has been recognized with a Government Green Fleet Award for five consecutive years as being among the top 40 most sustainable and efficient government fleets in North America. The award recognized WSDOT for sustainably managing a mixed fleet that includes conventional, hybrid, and

alternative-fuel vehicles. WSDOT's fleet was one of the largest and most diverse to be recognized by these annual awards.

In addition, WSF is exploring an option to use liquefied natural gas (LNG) to fuel its six Issaquah class ferries. WSF burns nearly 18 million gallons of fuel each year and fuel is our fastest growing operating expense. The fuel budget in 2012 was nearly 30 percent of WSF's operating budget at a cost of $67.3 million, an increase of $51.7 million over a 12-year period. WSF anticipates achieving substantial savings on fuel over the remaining service life of the six Issaquah class vessels by converting to LNG. Converting to LNG would also mean a cleaner, more efficient future for our fleet by significantly decreasing emissions.

WEST VIRGINIA

West Virginia Department of Transportation

Paul A. Mattox, Jr., P.E.
Secretary of Transportation and Commissioner of Highways

YEAR FORMED **1913**

FTE **Approx. 6,300**

KEY FACTS
TOTAL STATE ROAD MILES (OWNED BY STATE HIGHWAY AGENCY) **34,623 miles**

STATE-OWNED BRIDGES **6,802**

TRANSIT TRIPS PER YEAR **5.3 million**

RECENT HIGHLIGHTS
– Completion of Corridor in WV
– Progress on Corridor H
– Fairmont Connector
– Mon-Fayette Expressway
– Coalfields Expressway
– US 35
– New River Parkway
– Pritchard Intermodal
– WV Route 10

Moving Mountains

West Virginia is defined by mountains. Its nickname is The Mountain State. Its official motto is "Mountaineers Are Always Free." And so it is no surprise that the West Virginia Department of Transportation (WVDOT) has become adept at working with the mountains, whether it requires moving them or connecting them. Before the 20th Century, West Virginia had a very distinguished presence in road building. The nation's first major highway, the National Road, extended into the booming town of Wheeling. That same highway was the impetus to build the Wheeling Suspension Bridge in 1849, which would be the first bridge to span more than 1,000 feet and would be the longest in the world at that time. The Wheeling Suspension Bridge is considered the father of American bridges that started the race to connect disparate points around the United States. In the state capital of Charleston, resident Mordecai Levi was tired of muddy roads making a mess of city streets; he built the first brick street in the nation, a method which would sweep the country, and provide a charm in many cities that can still be seen today.

West Virginia's governing agency over highway and bridge building shares with AASHTO the distinguished honor of celebrating its centenary. In 1914, public interest in road building from state and national clubs convinced the state legislature to create a centralized operation that would be called the State Road Bureau. This four member body provided financial aid to counties through the issue of bonds. These roads were mere improvements to the roadways that had been used throughout history, first as paths trod by bison, next as Native American hunting trails, and then as the roads used by settlers to the colonial West when they crossed those formidable mountains.

This agency would be transformed into the State Road Commission in 1917, with a charter stating the body was "to provide a complete system of laws governing the construction and maintenance of public roads and highways, the traffic thereon, to classify such roads and provide for a connecting system of highways." In 1921, the state legislature expanded the authority of the State Road Commission and developed methods of funding through licensing and a gas tax. Fifty years later the entity was renamed the Department of Highways, overseeing ten districts around the state. However, in 1989, the body would grow to become the all-encompassing agency

we know it as today, when the legislature created the West Virginia Department of Transportation, bringing the newly named Division of Highways (DOH) together with agencies overseeing aviation, river traffic, public transportation, and railroads.

In the 1940s and 1950s, states in the Eastern United States were eager to develop something that went by the name of "superhighway." The nascent term was used for evenly paved roads that allowed quick access between points on the map. Though such highways are taken for granted today, many states were working to be a part of the future and West Virginia was one of them. The West Virginia Turnpike was completed in 1954 and *The New York Times* reported that its construction required the removal of more earth than in the completion of the Panama Canal. Fortunately, with the Federal Aid Highway Act of 1956 signed into law by President Eisenhower, superhighways would become a joint effort between federal and state governments, and West Virginia's Interstates would connect all parts of the state and even incorporate the Turnpike into its plan. This enthusiasm for building major highways was taken one step further through creation of the Appalachian Corridor System,

authorized by the Appalachian Development Act of 1965 that had been fathered by the Mountain State's longtime U.S. Senator Jennings Randolph and supported by President Johnson. Federal dollars would aid Appalachian states in the creation of major road systems in isolated regions, especially in wilderness areas that would enable the growth of tourism devoted to skiing, hiking, and whitewater rafting. As with the National Road 120 years before, the construction of one of these corridors would require a landmark bridge. The New River Gorge Bridge would become one of the highest and longest arch bridges in the world and has become an icon for the state, taking its place on the official state quarter. Thanks to all of these efforts, trips around the state that had formerly required a whole day of travel, would now take just a few hours of driving. West Virginia's beautiful mountains could be enjoyed without the hairpin curves of the highways that had been their signature for decades.

Highways of Growth

West Virginia has no large metropolitan regions or major cities. The state's population of 1.8 million people is almost evenly distributed around its rugged landscape. When development and funding are considered, projects are

generally spread evenly around the state. Since the 1980s, Appalachian Corridor Highways have come to fuller completion. Named alphabetically, the corridor highways have undergone a long process of carving out earth and rock in steep places that had formerly resisted highway development.

- **Corridor G** (U.S. Highway 119) runs from Charleston, through the famous Billion Dollar Coalfields in Logan and right into Hatfield & McCoy country at Williamson. History buffs, hikers, and ATV riders are now using the highway to seek their diversions and feeding growth to a once declining region.
- **Corridor D** (U.S. Highway 50) connects I-79 at Bridgeport, in the center of the state, to Parkersburg along the Ohio River. With a new span crossing the Ohio, one can now travel from Central West Virginia to Cincinnati, Ohio, on a single highway, thus feeding the economic engines of that region.
- **Corridor H** (U.S. Highway 48) extends from I-79 at Weston in the north central part of the state, to the town of Elkins, and from there to the Virginia border, not far from Washington, D.C. This is the last of the corridors in West Virginia to still be a work in progress. Civil

War battlefields and the legacies of railroad and timber barons populate the history of this region, and great care had to be given to not disturb these historical sites. So far, 86 miles out of the planned 130 miles have been completed.

With the completion of **Corridors L and Q**, and the upgrade of **Corridor E** to become Interstate 68, the Appalachian Corridor System is on track to accomplish for West Virginia all that its creators had planned.

Various other highways have been on the fast track to expansion from two lanes to four. As is typical in West Virginia, they are in historically distinct regions to which great consideration must be given.

Interstate 64 connects the state's two largest metropolitan areas, Charleston and Huntington, creating what is called the MetroValley. With over 700,000 people in the region, it is a commercial and media focal point. Between the two cities is the collective community of Teays Valley, named for an ancient river that used to run through the area. Bearing the suburbs of the state's two largest cities, Teays Valley has become a crossroads in the Southwestern part of the state. With traffic running between the capital in Charleston and Marshall University in Huntington, the area has experienced huge growth that required the expansion of Interstate 64 to six lanes.

With increased traffic reaching record levels on U.S. Route 35 that stretches from Teays Valley to the historical town of Point Pleasant on the Ohio River, it became necessary to relieve the area of the congestion of commercial traffic. Due to a variety of concerns, it was better to build an entirely new four-lane highway than to expand the existing one. This
region, in Mason and Putnam counties, is one of the state's most agricultural, with family farm histories stretching back more than 200 years to the time when George Washington owned the land. Moreover, this region served as home for the prehistoric Adena people, who built mounds and villages here. It is typical for farmers to uncover ancient relics while tilling their fields, so it was no surprise to find that excavation of the new highway would uncover sites of antiquarian relevance. Working with Native historians and organizations, WVDOT was able to continue the process of road construction. With a small part of the road's central portion still to be done, the new highway connects the region to Chicago, Illinois, and Columbus, Ohio. The new US 35 has alleviated heavy traffic for farmers, while preserving the distinct heritage and history of the region.

As any student of geography knows, West Virginia has two panhandles. What may be less known is that both are a result of transportation.

West Virginia's Northern Panhandle was created when the state was still part of Virginia, which insisted that its investment in river traffic at Wheeling require that this land remain with the Old Dominion and not with Pennsylvania, as was planned with the creation of the Mason-Dixon Line. This slender piece of land is sometimes called Steel Valley for the production of metals and other heavy industry there. WV Route 2 is carved into the hillsides
that run along the river. Traffic increases have log-jammed this road, so it has been paramount that WV 2 be expanded to four lanes. In the narrow valley running along the great river with a steady population throughout, the highway expansion has been slow-moving, but in a topographical location as challenging as this, slow and steady wins the race.

The Eastern Panhandle of West Virginia was created by President Lincoln, who deemed the counties of Morgan, Berkeley, and Jefferson to be a part of the new Union state of West Virginia. These counties had significant railroad lines that were necessary to the Union's battle against the Confederacy. Today the Eastern Panhandle is part of the Washington, D.C. metro region and is served by a commuter line from the city courtesy of neighboring Maryland. The growth that has come with the region has been exponential as the suburbs push further west from the nation's capital. This necessitated the four-lane widening of WV Route 9, a project that met with much consternation, but today is a success story that has facilitated the region's quick growth.

In the northern part of the state, I-79, which originates in Charleston, connects Clarksburg, Fairmont, and Morgantown. With West Virginia University and the FBI fingerprinting facility anchoring the region's economy, this area is called the High-Tech Corridor. Widening Interstate 79 to six lanes and constructing the new Mon-Fayette Expressway has enabled the region to cultivate its development. Mon-Fayette has provided a new four-lane highway between this region and the city of Pittsburgh, helping Pennsylvania and West

Virginia to reverse the fortunes of this former coal producing region into one that produces high-tech initiatives and pharmaceuticals.

Bridging the Gap

Having become famous for its bridge building was not part of West Virginia's original plan. But having great rivers like the Ohio, Potomac, Kanawha, New, and Monongahela—just to name a few—requires a special prowess with bridge construction. Joining the Wheeling Suspension Bridge and the New River Gorge Bridge are a group of new crossings that earn their place in the family.

With the completion of Corridor D in Parkersburg, yet again, a new highway demanded a special bridge design. Corridor D would have to pass over a national historic landmark, Blennerhassett Island, a former plantation thought to be the location of Aaron Burr's alleged plans for revolution. The bridge had to be constructed so that it was high enough to allow navigation on the water, but low enough to not be seen from the historical aspects of the two-mile island. This daunting task was met with a unique network tied-arch structure, the Blennerhassett Island Bridge, which met all criteria and pioneered new construction techniques, winning international acclaim, including the Gustav Lindenthal Award.

In the Charleston metro region, Interstate 64 required a new and unique bridge to cross the Kanawha River that could facilitate the widening of the highway to six lanes. At a cost of $82 million, WVDOT built the longest cast-in-place concrete segmental box girder bridge in the United States. This distinctive structure looks deceptively narrow from below, but

carries three busy lanes of highway traffic into the city.

In the Eastern Panhandle, a bold new bridge crosses the Potomac River at Shepherdstown. Honoring one of the great innovators of steamboat engine design and one of the Mountain State's favorite sons, The James Rumsey Bridge offers a stylish crossing in a historical region.

Can the name of any river invoke as much history as the Shenandoah? Famous in song and stories, the Shenandoah River served as a barrier to the completion of WV Route 9, but the new bridge used a special "Y" design in the support structure, adding an aesthetic detail to a region already rich with beauty.

Off the Road

WVDOT's innovation extends beyond highway and bridge building and into concepts that can facilitate traffic flow with greater safety and efficiency. In March 2005, the DOH instituted a statewide Intelligent Transportation System (ITS) architecture to be in compliance with regional and national standards in preparation for the launch of a comprehensive statewide ITS initiative.

In November 2008, the centerpiece of WVDOT's ITS program was completed and operational. The Traffic Management Center is located in the Capitol Complex which provides a communication hub, or nerve center, for monitoring and controlling highly visible transportation resources. The system enables the management of traffic control, emergency response, and accident clearance functions, monitoring of transportation network conditions, and communication of traffic information.

In 2012, WVDOT launched one of its most popular and helpful communications initiatives with its 511 Network. Employing an application for smart phones, travelers in the state can use 511 to identify traffic conditions where they will be traveling, and even make alternative route plans if necessary. It was enacted for all Interstate and Appalachian Corridor highways, and improved direct communication to state drivers.

With a network of highways reaching all portions of West Virginia's spread out population, communication has been as key as the construction of better highways and great bridges. It is the goal of WVDOT to unite all travelers in the state in a smooth and simple process.

WISCONSIN

Wisconsin Department of Transportation

Mark Gottlieb, P.E.
Secretary

YEAR FORMED **1911**

FTE **Approx. 3,500**

KEY FACTS
TOTAL STATE ROAD MILES
(OWNED BY STATE HIGHWAY
AGENCY) **Approx. 11,764**

STATE-OWNED BRIDGES **5,165**

TRANSIT TRIPS PER YEAR
73.6 million

RECENT HIGHLIGHTS
– Mega projects underway

– DMV adds online services

– Traffic fatalities at historic lows

Overview

The year 2011 marked the 100-year anniversary of an official state transportation agency in Wisconsin. The 1911 Wisconsin Legislature created a State Highway Commission to oversee statewide roadway planning and construction activities. One of the commission's first actions was to organize a state highway department—a precursor to the current Wisconsin Department of Transportation (WisDOT).

Today, WisDOT oversees a comprehensive, multi-modal transportation system that includes approximately 12,000 miles of state, federal, and Interstate highways; 103,000 miles of local roads and streets; 13,700 state and local bridges; 81 public bus and shared-ride taxi systems; 131 public use airports; 29 commercial ports and harbors; 3,300 miles of railway track; and bicycle and pedestrian facilities.

WisDOT is unique compared to many other state departments of transportation. Not only does it have responsibilities related to all modes of travel, the department also includes the Division of Motor Vehicles and Division of State Patrol.

Wisconsin's multi-faceted transportation department has an overall mission to provide leadership in the development and operation of a safe and efficient transportation system. WisDOT's 3,500 employees perform their duties with the shared vision of being dedicated people creating transportation solutions through innovation and exceptional service.

Infrastructure Improvements

WisDOT joins together with many public and private partners to plan, design, build, maintain, operate, and support transportation in Wisconsin. The transportation infrastructure investments that are being made support economic development, job growth, and the great quality of life enjoyed in the Badger State. The transportation system provides mobility and reliability to get people to work, school, and recreation. It enables communities, both large and small, to grow and attract new business. The seamless, multi-modal connections move Wisconsin-made products to destinations around the world and bring millions of tourists to the state to enjoy year-round recreational and cultural attractions.

In the past 25 years, Wisconsin has made significant transportation infrastructure investments. Like many states, the need to address an aging network

of roads and bridges is a top priority. The state's first mega project, the $810 million reconstruction of the Marquette Interchange in Milwaukee, started in 2004 and was completed in 2008. Other notable road and bridge projects during this time include the expansion of U.S. Highways 51 and 53 and the opening of a new four-lane bridge over the Mississippi River at La Crosse. Travelers going east or west across the middle of the state once drove along a two-lane Wisconsin Highway 29 that had so many crashes it gained the unfortunate nickname of "Bloody 29." Today, a modern, four-lane WIS 29 provides safe, efficient travel between the Green Bay area and the far western part of the state.

In recent years, WisDOT's annual construction program has been exceeded one billion dollars with several large, multi-year improvement projects underway. In southeast Wisconsin, this includes reconstruction of the I-94 North/South Freeway and Zoo Interchange, along with a project to re-deck the Hoan Bridge. The US 41 Project in northeast Wisconsin and I-39/90 Project from Madison to the Illinois state line provide needed improvements in heavy traffic corridors. A joint project with the State of Minnesota to construct a new St. Croix River Crossing

in northwest Wisconsin got underway in 2013 after decades of planning and environment study.

These and other projects are moving forward with a commitment to using innovative techniques and management practices to ensure the projects are completed on time and on budget. The I-94 North/South Freeway Project used a self-propelled modular transport system to construct one of its bridge structures. The technique shortened the amount of time the bridge needed to be closed to a few weeks. More traditional construction methods would have required the bridge to be closed for several months.

Wisconsin dealt with two highly unusual and unpredictable bridge issues. The first occurred in December 2000 when several support girders on the Hoan Bridge in Milwaukee snapped, causing in a 217-foot span of the bridge to drop. In September 2013, a bridge pier on the Leo Frigo Bridge in Green Bay unexpectedly sank. Fortunately, neither event caused any injuries and both bridges were able to be quickly repaired and reopened to traffic.

Multi-modal Investments
Over the past few decades, WisDOT has also overseen thousands of airport

improvement projects and distributed funds for harbor, freight rail, transit and other transportation investments.

The state replaced the aging Merrimac Ferry in 2003 with a new ferry named, ColSac III. The state's only free ferry service, it shuttles traffic across the Wisconsin River as part of Wisconsin Highway 113.

In 2005, WisDOT opened the Milwaukee Airport Rail Station at Mitchell International Airport, one of the nation's few passenger rail-to-airport links. The station serves passengers traveling on the Amtrak Hiawatha. WisDOT also redesigned the downtown Milwaukee Intermodal Station to provide multi-modal connections. The facility's award-winning design has made it a city landmark and gateway to downtown. It is an important transportation link for the Milwaukee area allowing more than 1.3 million passengers per year to use the facility to make connections to Amtrak's Hiawatha and Empire Builder routes, as well as to Greyhound and other local and regional bus services, county transit, taxis, and personal vehicles.

The Intermodal Station also houses WisDOT's Statewide Traffic Operations

Center (STOC). The STOC is staffed 24 hours per day, 7 days per week. It is designed to improve the safety and efficiency of the system by reducing incidents and relieving traffic congestion. STOC staff communicates regularly with law enforcement, fire departments, and other emergency responders, as well as the news media. From the STOC, it is possible to use various traffic management tools, such as: closed circuit television, ramp meters, dynamic message signs, roadway sensors, and other tools. The STOC also operates the 511 Travel Information System. Travelers in Wisconsin can get up-to-the-minute travel information via phone, web, or social media.

WisDOT continues to plan for future transportation investments. Planning efforts over the past few decades have included individual modal plans and the adoption of two long-range multi-modal plans—Translinks 21 in 1995 and Connections 2030 in 2009.

Job Growth and Economic Development

Wisconsin's economic vitality and its ability to remain competitive depend on the efficient transport of people and goods to the nation and the world. WisDOT provides a number of benefits to Wisconsin communities and businesses in the area of economic development. Some of these services act directly as a catalyst for economic development, while others contribute to the prosperity of the state. One example is the Transportation Economic Assistance (TEA) Program. TEA grants provide a very direct job benefit by providing funds to cover up to 50 percent of project costs for road, rail, harbor, and airport projects that help attract employers to

Wisconsin, or encourage business and industry to remain and expand in the state. Started in 1987, the TEA Program marked its 25th anniversary in 2012. Since the program's start, WisDOT has invested more than $93 million in TEA grants—benefiting 363 businesses around the state. Those projects created or retained more than 80,000 direct and indirect jobs.

Safety

If there is a common thread reflected in everything the department does it is public safety. WisDOT works to improve traffic safety through a combination of engineering, enforcement, and education, along with coordination with many partners to improve emergency response.

Intersection safety is a key priority for the department and is an important initiative in Wisconsin's Strategic Highway Safety Plan. With proven results showing a significant decrease in severe (fatal and injury) crashes, many state highway projects include the installation of roundabouts— 40 new roundabouts alone are part of the US 41 Project. But roundabouts are but one piece of a broader department design safety initiative that also includes traffic signal improvements, upgrades in signing and pavement marking technologies, traffic signals that respond to varying traffic conditions, and geometric improvements.

The state legislature has supported traffic safety goals by passing various laws. These include:

- In 2000, graduated driver license requirements to give new drivers a safer start to their driving careers.
- In 2001, the state's "move over" law to help safeguard law enforcement,

emergency responders, maintenance workers, and others who work on the side of highways.

- In 2003, adoption of a 0.08 percent blood alcohol content standard for drunken driving and a law that prohibits motorists from driving if they have any detectable amount of a controlled substance in their system.
- In 2009, a primary enforcement seat belt law.
- In 2010, a ban on texting and driving for all drivers
- In 2012, a law that makes using a cell phone while driving against the law for any driver with a probationary license or instruction permit.

Wisconsin is making progress in reaching the ultimate goal of zero traffic deaths. Seat belt use in Wisconsin is about 82 percent—the highest level recorded—and traffic fatalities in the year 2013 were at the lowest level in nearly 70 years.

Customer Service

With more than 4 million licensed drivers and nearly 5.5 million registered vehicles, customer service is a top focus for WisDOT's Division of Motor Vehicles (DMV). The past 25 years has seen a multitude of changes in how DMV serves its many customers—including those with commercial driver licenses.

Customer service centers provide in-person service, with a center now available in each of the state's 72 counties. DMV is also making it easier for customers to conduct service online, offering a wide range of online service options that eliminate the need to travel to a service center.

In 2013, Wisconsin began issuing federal REAL ID compliant driver licenses and ID cards and also began offering driver licenses and ID cards with a veteran designation as an enhanced customer service to military veterans.

With new service demands, DMV is using data and analytics to continually improve. It has established goals to serve customers at DMV service centers within 20 minutes and answer phone calls within two minutes. Recent reports show DMV is trending in the right direction on these performance goals.

Measuring Performance

In 2012, the department launched its MAPSS Performance Improvement Program. MAPSS is helping to create a culture of performance improvement centered around the five core goals of mobility, accountability, preservation, safety, and service. Establishing goals and measuring results is essential to running a successful and efficient organization and meeting public expectations.

The department is committed to making quarterly progress reports available for review. The MAPSS Scorecard provides a snapshot of the State of Wisconsin's transportation system and interactive web pages provide a way for the public to "drill down" into more detail on each performance measure.

MAPSS is closely aligned with the state's Lean government initiative to become more efficient and continuously improve government services and control costs. WisDOT's first *Lean Annual Report* in 2013 showed significant results, with a savings of 12,500 FTE hours and $814,000. Staff training in Lean Six Sigma tools is making Lean thinking and performance improvement a part of the WisDOT organizational culture that will be sustained for many years to come.

Future Challenges

The past century has witnessed many changes in transportation including major improvements in how motor vehicles and pavements are designed and built.

The future is on the cusp of far more dramatic changes as connected vehicle technologies advance.

The increased use of hybrid and electric vehicles is already creating new challenges related to transportation financing. Wisconsin is among many states that are exploring options for transportation revenue that is adequate, sustainable, and equitable.

Several core transportation concepts will remain the same as state's work to develop a vision for transportation in the future. Our efforts to provide a safe and efficient transportation system will always rely on the close working relationship the department has with many public and private partners. Our programs and services will need to embrace innovation and technology in order to continually improve and evolve. The investments we make in the transportation network will always play a key role in the economic growth of our communities, our states, and our country.

WYOMING

Wyoming Department of Transportation

John F. Cox
Director

YEAR FORMED **1917**

FTE **Approx. 2,000**

KEY FACTS:
TOTAL STATE ROAD MILES
(OWNED BY STATE HIGHWAY
AGENCY) **6,751**

STATE-OWNED BRIDGES **1,954**

TRANSIT TRIPS PER YEAR
453,000

The Wyoming Highway Department began in 1917 after establishment by the state legislature in accordance with the 1916 Federal Aid Road Act. Wyoming's initial federal aid appropriation was $61,200.

From these rather humble beginnings, the department has grown into Wyoming's largest state agency, serving a half-million residents with more than 6,800 state highway system miles, over 2,500 bridges, and 10 commercial airports. Director John Cox leads the department and carries out the policies of the Transportation Commission and Aeronautics Commission of Wyoming.

The Wyoming Department of Transportation (WYDOT), while being one of the nation's smaller departments of transportation, includes the Wyoming Highway Patrol, Aeronautics, and all Department of Motor Vehicles functions for the state. The efficiencies gained by these divisions being components of WYDOT are many; the executive staff and personnel work together daily, with strong working relations over a wide range of transportation disciplines.

The Transportation Commission consists of seven members appointed to six-year terms by the governor with

approval by the state senate. One commissioner is chosen from each of seven commission districts and represents three or four counties. Within districts, each county will in turn have a commissioner appointed by the governor, ensuring fair representation.

State government was reorganized in 1991, producing the WYDOT. This brought Aeronautics and other sections into the department. To provide finances for the agency, the state legislature earmarked user fees as the primary source of revenue. Motor fuel taxes, commercial vehicle fees, and motor vehicle registration fees remain contributors to the highway fund, along with state contributions. Wyoming energy and mineral industries also play a role, as legislators provide a portion of severance tax revenues and a share of federal mineral royalties to fund some agency functions.

Wyoming's highway fund is administered solely by the Transportation Commission of Wyoming. While the legislature determines the sources and their relative amounts for the highway fund, the commission (with rare exception) determines how the money will be spent, on what projects, and the priority of those projects. These

projects occur in five WYDOT operational districts based in Laramie, Casper, Rock Springs, Sheridan, and Basin, with agency headquarters located in Cheyenne. This arrangement began in 1953 and still serves the citizens of Wyoming and their transportation needs.

About two-thirds of WYDOT's annual budget finances highway improvements and maintenance. The remaining third of the budget pays for each of the following: law enforcement, aeronautics, planning, and other functions.

Wyoming opened the last link in its 914-mile share of the Interstate System in October 1985 and became the first state in the Rocky Mountain region to complete its portion of that network. Interstate 80 runs parallel to the old Lincoln Highway corridor as the major east–west truck route across southern Wyoming, while Interstate 25 connects Cheyenne to Casper and then continues north. Interstate 90 slices across Wyoming's northeastern corner.

Wyoming consistently leads the nation in vehicle miles traveled. Recently, Wyoming recorded an average of 16,039 miles per capita (the national average hovers around 9,000 miles). With vast open spaces, small cities, and smaller

towns, and the lowest state population, Wyoming roads remain the critical lifeblood to families, ranches and farms, jobs, medical facilities, recreational areas, and commerce centers in this rural state. Of the total 25 million miles traveled in Wyoming each year, over 17 million miles occur on the state highway system. Wyoming interstates operate as a bridge between coastal ports and inland markets, as the primary system to move energy industry equipment and agricultural products, as the gateway to enormous swaths of public land, and as a crucial part of our nation's missile defense network. The challenges and rewards of working on Wyoming's system are as great as the mountains, plains, and rapidly changing weather defining the state.

Having one of the nation's finest road systems, the WYDOT leads the field in many areas of highway research. Blowing snow control innovations and technology including wooden snow fences and "living" snow fences of trees and shrubbery developed in Wyoming have been used throughout the world; the department utilizes a sophisticated road information reporting system and a needs analysis and priority rating process emulated by many other states; and computer programs to analyze struc-

tures for load carrying capacities and for design purposes have been widely used by others. WYDOT exports a bridge computer-aided drafting program developed in-house to countries around the globe.

Wyoming leads in other fields also, such as geothermal heating for pavements and bridge decks; hydraulics research and application; recognition and response to rutting problems and addressing a host of possible solutions using a variety of pavement mixes and techniques; using wood chips for fill material in slide areas to reduce loading on slopes; using lime for moisture resistance in pavements; and developing a culvert design system now used by many other transportation departments.

WYDOT recently incorporated advancements in de-icing agents and snow and ice control during weather events, along with technological notification initiatives and remotely controlled variable speed limits along the interstates. These advancements have saved resources and provided greater safety and mobility for the motoring public (through public information options, travel authorizations, and limited access programs). The department employs a modern travel management center staffed 24 hours a day to keep travelers up-to-date on the latest highway conditions, including very popular and successful text messaging and e-mail alerts, and a continually updated travel information web-site. Additionally, WYDOT actively participated with local, state, and federal emergency service providers in the creation and continuance of a dedicated and secure crisis communication system now in use statewide.

The department maintains multiple levels of accountability, with internal appraisals and reviews, frequent surveys targeting the public or agency employees, outside audits, and clearly defined benchmarks for success. These frank assessments shape strategic discussions and policy directions toward the dedicated mission and values of the agency. WYDOT's vision statement echoes the perpetual emphasis on true "Excellence in Transportation."

WYDOT actively promotes wildlife habitat connectivity structures and crossings. These wildlife crossings have received acclaimed nationwide notice and place Wyoming among the states taking steps to ensure wildlife have reliable and safe access to habitat. Connectivity is critical to maintaining species diversity, movement, health, and viable gene pools. These vital corridors protect historic migratory routes, increase highway safety by decreasing animal-vehicle collisions, and preserve wildlife numbers, but they also provide safer and more careful access to the natural resources critical to America's energy production and infrastructure. Wyoming is leading by example and demonstrating that economic growth and wildlife health and security are not mutually exclusive. To this end, essential wildlife habitat

connectivity serves the needs of animals and humans alike, without fostering the negative spirit bred by excluding either wildlife or economic concerns.

Recently, WYDOT completed a couple of long-term construction initiatives. One, multi-year reconstruction of the Togwotee Trail Highway in northwest Wyoming, refurbished a 38-mile corridor of US 26/287 through mountainous, national forest terrain in an aesthetically pleasing and environmentally sensitive manner. This route provides one of the main access points to Yellowstone and Grand Teton National Parks. The second initiative required reconstruction of 17-mile Road on the Wind River Reservation. This project occurred over six different construction seasons and improved a vital reservation road through cooperation with several tribal, county, state, and federal agencies. The rebuilt road improves capacity and safety.

The Wyoming Highway Patrol (WHP) operates division offices across the state. Their duties include highway law enforcement and emergency response, drug and tactical operations, executive branch protection, and commercial carrier oversight. Under the direction of WHP, the ports-of-entry operate at 14 locations around Wyoming. They monitor the size, weight, materials, and hours of service of commercial carriers and permit accordingly. Ports-of-entry personnel guard Wyoming's highway investments and enforce compliance for public safety and system health.

In 2012, Wyoming accounted for about 40 percent of all U.S. coal production. Approximately 80 train loads of coal depart from Wyoming's Powder River Basin each day en route to domestic and

international markets. Each train hauls between 125-150 cars of raw materials. Almost 2,000 miles of track are used by five railroads. WYDOT works with the railroads, local citizens, and federal authorities in promoting rail safety and efficiency.

The state's 10 commercial airports carry people and freight across the state and to regional hubs. Currently, Jackson Hole Airport remains the busiest in Wyoming and perhaps the most picturesque, with striking vistas of the Grand Teton mountain range.

The department recently completed the first diverging diamond interchange in Wyoming at a previously congested overpass in Cheyenne. This design provides for 20 years of expected growth and trucking increases. It was built using the existing bridge for a considerable cost savings.

Transit growth in Wyoming remains steady. In many communities, local transit by bus or van increases in popularity each year. The rural nature of the state, economic realities, and changes in demographics have contributed to the demand. Transit service is currently available in all 23 Wyoming counties through 44 local transit providers.

Recognizing the importance of surface transportation to the state, the Wyoming Legislature in 2013 raised the motor fuel tax 10 cents, to 24 cents a gallon. This brought Wyoming into a comparable range with surrounding states and will provide some funding for the agency, cities, counties, and other contributors to the fuel tax. Nevertheless, operating in an uncertain financial environment, especially at the federal level, WYDOT now focuses on pavement preservation, along with seasonal maintenance. This, coupled with several notable streamlining and efficiency changes, allows the department to deliver the finest transportation system the funding permits. WYDOT is also proud of its state-of-the-art asset management system, permitting efficient fleet and facilities stewardship, short- and long-term planning, and comprehensive project programming to maximize system performance with the financial resources available.

Wyoming cooperates with regional partners, AASHTO, and those in government and industry to seek answers to complex transportation and infrastructure questions and to present the unique needs, challenges, and achievements of our nation's least populous state, albeit one with some of the most wide-open and wild country in the lower 48.

Challenges and opportunities abound, and WYDOT looks forward to fulfilling its mission by providing a safe, high-quality, and efficient transportation system for the people of Wyoming and all those just passing through.

By Matthew White and John Davis